JOHN MURRAY

E

teaching secondary
BIOLOGY

JOHN MURRAY SCIENCE PRACTICE

teaching secondary
BIOLOGY

Editor: Michael Reiss

HODDER
EDUCATION
AN HACHETTE UK COMPANY

To Richard Price

Titles in this series:

Teaching Secondary Biology	978 0 7195 7637 9
Teaching Secondary Chemistry	978 0 7195 7638 6
Teaching Secondary Physics	978 0 7195 7636 2
Teaching Secondary Scientific Enquiry	978 0 7195 8618 7
Teaching Secondary Science Using ICT	978 0 7195 8071 0

© Association for Science Education 1999

First published in 1999
by Hodder Education,
an Hachette UK Company,
338 Euston Road
London NW1 3BH

Impression number 10 9 8
Year 2009

Illustrations by Tony Jones
Layouts by Amanda Easter
Cover design by John Townson/Creation
Cover photo © BSIP V&L/SPL

Typeset in 12/13pt Garamond by Wearset, Boldon, Tyne and Wear
Printed and bound in Malta

A catalogue entry for this title is available from the British Library

ISBN 978 0 7195 7637 9

Contents

Contributors

Susan Barker is a lecturer in Ecology and Science Education at the University of Warwick. She is Honorary Secretary of the Teaching Ecology Group of the British Ecological Society.

David Baylis taught Biology for 31 years in grammar and comprehensive schools. He was a Chief Examiner for Biology at CSE, CSE/GCE and GCSE from 1974–1997 and has written questions for GCE A level Modular Biology papers for one of the English examination boards. Since 1995 he has been a freelance writer and has written textbooks, examination papers, training material and support material for secondary school pupils and teachers.

Chris Brown lectures in Science Education at the University of Hull, where he also directs the Secondary PGCE programme. He moved to his present post after extensive teaching experience in state schools in England and Wales, including spending 11 years as a Head of Science. He also works as a Principal Examiner at A level for one of the English examination boards.

Jackie Callaghan is a practising teacher. She has taught Biology in high schools for the past 15 years and has been Head of Science for the past 4 years. She was previously Chief Examiner for Environmental Science and is now Principal Examiner for Biology. She has been involved in the writing of several books, mainly concerned with revision practice, examination practice and study guides.

Ann Fullick has many years experience as a Biology teacher, Head of Science and A level examiner. She has written a number of Biology and Chemistry textbooks for secondary schools and also acts as an education consultant, working to establish links between industry and education.

Jennifer Harrison was formerly a Biology and Health Science teacher at a Leicestershire Upper School and is now Head of Secondary Initial Teacher Training and a Biology/Science tutor for the Secondary PGCE at the University of Leicester

School of Education. Her particular curriculum interests are in sex education and health education in secondary schools and she has run courses and produced written material in these areas for both trainee and practising teachers.

Jenny Lewis is a member of the Learning in Science Research Group at the Centre for Studies in Science and Mathematics Education, University of Leeds. She is a Biology tutor for the Secondary PGCE and has recently completed a 3-year study of young peoples' understanding of, and attitudes towards, gene technology.

Roger Lock taught Science and Biology at state schools in Kilmarnock, Birmingham and Leamington Spa before moving into teacher education. He is currently a lecturer in Science Education at the University of Birmingham.

Michael Reiss is Reader in Education and Bioethics at Homerton College, Cambridge. His research, writing and teaching interests are in the fields of science education, bioethics and sex education.

Nigel Skinner taught Biology at secondary schools in Wiltshire for 10 years. In 1989 he became a lecturer in Science Education at the University of Exeter where he works with student teachers on undergraduate and postgraduate courses.

David Slingsby is Head of Biology at Wakefield Girls' High School and Chair of Education, Careers and Training Committee of the British Ecological Society.

Stephen Tomkins is Director of Studies for Biological Sciences at Homerton College, Cambridge and is the University of Cambridge Faculty of Education PGCE methods lecturer in Biology. He has written widely for sixth form students and Biology teachers.

Sheila Turner is Head of the Science and Technology Group at the Institute of Education, University of London, and a Reader in Education. Her teaching and research interests focus on nutrition education and science education in a multicultural society.

Acknowledgements

The authors and editor are very grateful to the following for their advice during the preparation of this book:

Jo-anne Atkinson
Ian Carter
John Dimambro
Roger Frost
Chris Gayford
Marcus Grace
Richard Heppell
Philip Hyde
Ian Kinchin
Christine Knight
George Marshall
Geoff Mines

Susan Mitchell
Len Newton
Andrew Potts
Carol Radcliffe
Julian Rouse
Neil Rowbottom
Andrew Rowell
David Sang
Graham Simons
Garry Skinner
Colin Stoneman
Toby Tufton

The Association for Science Education acknowledges the generous financial support of ESSO and the Institution of Electrical Engineers (IEE) in this project. Both ESSO and IEE provide a range of resources for science teaching at primary and secondary levels. Full details of these resources are available from:

ESSO Information Service
PO Box 94
Aldershot
GU12 4GJ
tel: 01252 669663

IEE Educational Activities
Michael Faraday House
Six Hills Way
Stevenage
SG1 2AY
e-mail: nsaunders@iee.org.uk
website: www.iee.org.uk/Schools

A consultant to CLEAPSS has read this text and confirms that, in the draft checked, the identification of hazards and the precautions given either conform with published general risk assessments or, if these are not available, are judged to be satisfactory.

Introduction

Michael Reiss

This book is one of a series of three ASE handbooks, the others being parallel volumes on chemistry and physics. It adopts a pragmatic yet enthusiastic approach to the teaching of biology to 11–16 year olds. The author team has kept in mind a teacher confronted with the task of teaching a specific topic, e.g. respiration, in the near future. What does such a teacher need to produce a series of effective lessons?

Who is this book for?

In writing their chapters, authors have identified a range of likely readers:

- new or less experienced biology teachers – though almost every biology teacher should find much of value
- chemists, physicists and science generalists who find themselves teaching parts of the biology curriculum
- student teachers and their tutors/mentors
- heads of department who need a resource to which to direct their colleagues.

While we have taken into account the current UK syllabus requirements, we have not stuck closely to any one curriculum. We expect that this book will be appropriate to secondary biology teachers in every country.

What should you find in this book?

We expect you, the reader, to find:

- good, sensible, stimulating ideas for teaching biology to 11–16 year olds
- suggestions for extending the range of approaches and strategies that you can use in your teaching
- things to which pupils respond well; things that fascinate them
- confirmation that a lot of what you are already doing is fine. There often isn't a single correct way of doing things.

How can you find what you want?

After careful discussion, the author team divided secondary biology up into ten areas. These correspond to Chapters 1 to 10. It should be clear from the Contents page (page v) what each chapter roughly consists of. A more detailed indication is given by the content boxes at the beginning of each chapter. This divides each chapter up into relevant sections. For specific topics, consult the index. This contains the terms you might want to look up; e.g. blood, heart, circulation, blood vessels and oxygen are included rather than the name of every possible component of the circulatory system.

What is in each chapter?

Each chapter contains:

- content boxes, which divide up the chapter into shorter sections
- a set of possible teaching routes through the chapter
- a brief section on what pupils may have learnt or experienced about the topic in their primary science lessons
- an outline teaching sequence showing how concepts can be developed throughout the 11–16 phase
- warnings about pitfalls
- information about likely pupil misconceptions
- helpful information about practical work and apparatus, e.g. how to prevent things from going wrong

- issues to do with safety (highlighted by the use of icons in the margin)
- suggestions for the use of ICT (highlighted by the use of icons in the margin)
- suggestions about the use of books, videos and other resources
- opportunities for the teaching of applied or ethical aspects of biology
- opportunities for investigative work
- links with other areas of biology or science.

Finally, if you have any comments that you would like to make about this book please send them to me:

Michael Reiss
Homerton College
Cambridge CB2 2PH
UK

e-mail: mjr1000@cam.ac.uk

1 *Cells and life processes*

Nigel Skinner

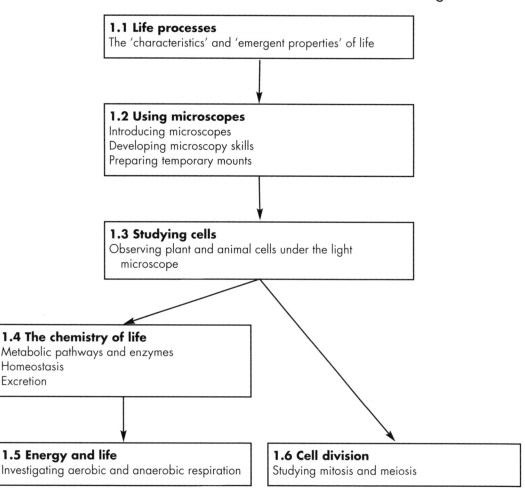

1.1 Life processes
The 'characteristics' and 'emergent properties' of life

1.2 Using microscopes
Introducing microscopes
Developing microscopy skills
Preparing temporary mounts

1.3 Studying cells
Observing plant and animal cells under the light
  microscope

1.4 The chemistry of life
Metabolic pathways and enzymes
Homeostasis
Excretion

1.5 Energy and life
Investigating aerobic and anaerobic respiration

1.6 Cell division
Studying mitosis and meiosis

◆ *Choosing a route*

Life can be thought of as the result of the various interactions between the many different chemical substances that make up an organism. Biology involves the study of life at various levels of organisation. In ascending order of size and complexity these levels are:

molecular cellular tissue organ
organ system whole organism population
community ecosystem biosphere

Studying biology at the molecular level involves dismantling organisms into their chemical components to investigate the structure and behaviour of the molecules that form them. At the cellular level biology involves finding out how these 'molecules of life' are organised and the ways in which they interact with each other. Defining what we mean by 'life' is not easy but it is at this level, in the transition from molecules to cells, that we begin to recognise the things that differentiate life from the absence of life. This chapter begins with a discussion of some of the characteristics of life that are displayed by whole organisms. The remainder of the chapter is mainly concerned with life processes at the molecular and cellular level. An understanding of these underpins the study of the many other aspects of biological science that are addressed in other chapters.

The activities suggested in the first three sections are aimed in the main at pupils aged between 11 and 14 years old and are best taught in the sequence in which they are presented. 'Life processes' outlines some of the differences between living and non-living things and the suggested approach is intended to help pupils gain an overview of what biology is all about. Microscopes are essential tools in biology and, in the second section, activities that could be used to familiarise pupils with their use are outlined. A topic that clearly requires the use of microscopes is the study of cells, and the third section includes approaches to cell biology suitable for both younger and older pupils.

The topics covered in the remaining sections are conceptually more demanding and are intended for use with older pupils. They can be taught as separate topics as set out below, or could be integrated into larger topics. For example, study of the molecules found in living organisms is often initially addressed in the context of human diet and digestion, respiration is often first taught in the context of gas exchange, and cell division in connection with growth and reproduction. Whatever approach is used when teaching these topics it is very important to emphasise the links that pupils need to make with related topics to help them achieve a deeper understanding of the nature of life and living things.

1.1 Life processes

In introducing biology as the study of life and living processes, teachers have for many years taught their pupils about the seven 'characteristics of life' – reproduction, growth, movement, responsiveness, respiration, nutrition and excretion. Some aspects of these are relatively easy for pupils to understand but it is not easy to convince pupils that these characteristics are common to all living things. For example, persuading pupils that plants can move and need oxygen for respiration can be problematic. American textbooks often refer to the 'emergent properties of living things' (see Table 1.1) and you may find it useful to refer to these when teaching the 'characteristics of life'.

Table 1.1 *The emergent properties of living things.*

Living things:
• are highly organised and more complex in structure than non-living things
• take energy from their environment and transform it from one form to another
• regulate their 'internal environment' (the technical term for this is homeostasis)
• respond to stimuli
• grow, develop and reproduce
• through evolutionary pressures become adapted to their mode of life
• contain within themselves the information by which they carry out the other functions characteristic of living things

♦ *Previous knowledge and experience*

Pupils will naturally know about many life processes, but their understanding of the difference between living and non-living things tends to be very human- or animal-centred. For example, children sometimes think that if something moves or makes noises then it must be alive. Clearly, many living things can do neither and many non-living things can do both. Many of the words we use when talking about different types of living thing have a different meaning in everyday language from their scientific meaning. The word 'animal' is often used by children when referring only to the living things that have four legs, are furry and live on land. In a biological classification these are all terrestrial mammals, a subset of the whole animal kingdom, which includes humans (a concept that many children find difficult). Similarly the word 'plant' is often used in a very restricted way to mean only those types of plant grown in 'plant pots' or the smaller plants ('flowers' and 'weeds') found in gardens. Mosses, grasses, trees and shrubs are often not considered to be plants by children, although to a biologist they clearly are.

◆ *A teaching sequence*

When teaching 11 to 14-year-old pupils about life processes it is not appropriate to include detailed discussion of respiration or excretion: this will be covered later. It is better to focus on the life processes of reproduction, growth, nutrition, movement and responsiveness, and to stress that all living things display these processes although in some cases they may not show them in an obvious way.

Recognising life

To introduce the idea that all living things display certain characteristics, pupils can examine a range of easily obtainable organisms and try to explain what features they have that enable us to recognise them as living. The organisms chosen for this study should include some that pupils will regard as obviously living and some, such as lichens, yeast and dormant plant seeds, that pupils may not at first consider to be living. The 'sensitive plant' (*Mimosa pudica*) is a useful specimen to include because when its leaves are touched they rapidly droop downwards, illustrating very clearly that plants can respond to stimuli and also move. Pupils could also compare the characteristics of living organisms with some non-living things that do things that might initially suggest that they are living, e.g. battery-powered toys or models that move and appear to be responsive, burning candles, cars, a fast-flowing river or clouds moving across the sky.

Studying life cycles

Many living processes can be discussed in connection with the sequence of events that take place from the start of life in a new individual through to the stage when the new individual is itself capable of reproduction. Animals such as stick insects are easily maintained in school laboratories and pupils can study their growth and development from the egg to the adult stage. This could include a consideration of their food preferences and patterns of movement. Plants that complete their life cycle in a relatively short space of time can also be studied. For example, pea or bean seeds planted in early spring will become mature and produce seeds before the end of the summer term. 'Fast plants' (more correctly called rapid-cycling *Brassicas*) complete their life cycle in about 35 days if kept in continuous light. Because they require little space pupils can grow their own individual plants and these can be used to study a range of different life processes including growth, development, plant responses and nutrition. Details of how to grow and use these exciting plants in schools can be obtained from Science and Plants for Schools (SAPS) whose address is given at the end of the chapter.

◆ *Further activities*

- ◆ Living things that do not show any obvious signs of life, e.g. frog-spawn, seeds and lichens, could be brought into lessons and pupils asked to explain how they would try to find out whether they are actually alive.

◆ *Enhancement ideas*

- ◆ Pupils are often intrigued by the possibility that life exists on other planets and they could be asked to devise a series of investigations that could be carried out to find out whether life exists elsewhere in the Universe.
- ◆ Pupils could design an imaginary living thing that displays the characteristics of life and is adapted to living in particular conditions, e.g. very hot or very cold climates. Their designs and ideas could be displayed as posters.

1.2 Using microscopes

Light microscopes are essential tools in biology and, if used appropriately, can play a vital role in developing pupils' knowledge and understanding of many aspects of living processes and organisms. In order to capitalise on the learning opportunities that light microscopes offer it is important for pupils to be motivated by the experience of using a microscope. To achieve this they should be taught how to use a microscope correctly and be provided with material to study that will instil in them a sense of wonder at the intricacies of the microscopic world.

◆ *Previous knowledge and experience*

All pupils will have seen magnified images in books, magazines and on the television. Many will have used magnifying glasses to study small things and some will have used (and may even own) a simple microscope. Very few pupils will have received systematic instruction in the use of microscopes.

◆ *A teaching sequence*

The importance of microscopes in biology

Before using microscopes it is worth showing pupils some images (using transparencies, video or CD ROMs) that have been gained with light or scanning electron microscopes. These should be of objects that are likely to engender interest and the images should be of a high quality. This can lead to discussion of how these images were obtained and the value of being able to magnify things when trying to find out more about them.

The functions of each part of a microscope

Having whetted pupils' appetites for studying small things the microscopes can be got out! Younger pupils will usually use microscopes with mirrors beneath the stage for reflecting light from a bench lamp or the sky (not direct sunlight) towards the object being viewed. Eyepiece lenses usually magnify ×10 and there are often three objective lenses with magnifying powers of ×4, ×10 and ×40. When first using microscopes it is sensible to use only the low and medium power objective lenses. You should stress to the pupils that microscopes are complicated and delicate pieces of equipment. It is a good idea to spend a whole lesson helping pupils become familiar with the particular type of microscope that they will be using. A useful exercise is to ask the pupils to look for similarities and differences between their microscope and a diagram of one from a textbook. The functions of each part should be explained and a set of 'rules for using microscopes' formulated jointly with the pupils. Table 1.2 shows the sort of thing you should be aiming for.

Table 1.2 *A set of rules for looking after microscopes.*

Microscopes are expensive and delicate instruments. To look after them properly we must:

- carry them carefully with one hand beneath and the other supporting the body of the microscope

- place them away from the edge of benches and sinks

- never touch the lenses with our fingers or try to take the microscope apart

- remove slides only when the tip of the objective lens is well away from the coverslip

- use the fine adjustment control when the high power lens is in use and rack away from the object when focusing

- leave the microscope set on the lowest power objective lens and the body (or stage) racked fully down so that no strain is put on the cogs that move these parts

- pick up microscope slides and coverslips (very carefully) by their edges so as to keep them clean. Broken slides and coverslips should be put into the bin for broken glass

- always cover the microscope when it is not in use

- ask the teacher for help if we think there is something wrong with our microscope or the lenses need cleaning

Using microscopes for the first time

Initial studies should be of specimens that can be seen with the unaided eye and do not require mounting under a coverslip. This will help to ensure that pupils achieve success straight away. Suitable things to use include small crystals such as salt or sugar, strands of their own hair or fibres from their clothes, prepared slides of small animals such as fleas, or parts of animals such as insect mouth parts or wings. Before viewing these objects with a microscope, pupils could make observations with the unaided eye, hand lenses, mounted magnifiers and low power binocular microscopes. The best way to use a hand lens is to hold the lens about 3 cm from one eye and bring the specimen into focus close to the lens. This technique enables pupils to concentrate their attention on the specimen being observed.

An important aim when using microscopes for the first time is to impress on pupils the usefulness of microscopes for extending the power of our sense of sight. To help develop this idea pupils could write descriptions of what the objects look like when viewed without being magnified and then when magnified using the hand lens and microscope.

Instructions produced for using the microscopes must relate specifically to the particular microscopes that are being used. Table 1.3 lists some general teaching points that could be used to help pupils get clear images.

Table 1.3 *Teaching points when using microscopes.*

- With the lowest power objective lens in place adjust the angle of the mirror (or the built-in lamp) to obtain a uniformly bright (but not too bright) field of view.

- Place the microscope slide on the stage with the object to be viewed directly beneath the lowest power objective.

- Clip the slide to the stage. Doing this will help to keep the slide firmly in position and means that when it is slid over the stage to centre the object in the field of view (see below) it will not move too quickly.

- Looking from the side, use the coarse focus control to rack the low power objective downwards (or the stage upwards) until the lens is as close as it will get to the slide. On modern microscopes there is a stopping mechanism that prevents the lenses from touching the slide.

- Looking through the eyepiece lens, slowly rack the lens away from the slide until the object is in focus. It is good practice to try to keep both eyes open when looking through a monocular microscope.

- Slowly move the slide across the stage until the object being viewed is in the centre of the field of view. The image will move the opposite way to the object – this takes pupils a little while to get used to.

- Adjust the illumination to gain a better image. With either too little or too much light little detail will be seen. This is particularly important with very thin specimens, which will not be seen at all if the illumination is too bright.

- Rotate the nosepiece to bring the middle power objective lens into position. Most microscopes used in schools are parfocal, which means that if the object is in focus when viewed under one objective lens it will remain in focus when a different lens is used. If the object does not appear in the field of view when a higher power objective lens is moved into position this is usually because the object was not accurately centred in the field of view with the lower power lens. Pupils have a tendency to immediately adjust the focus if the object is not visible. They should be told not to do this. Instead, they should carefully move the slide to search for the object. When it appears it should again be centred and if necessary the fine focus control used to sharpen the image and illumination adjusted to improve the image contrast.

Making temporary mounts

When viewing biological material with a microscope it is usual practice to mount the specimen in water (or a stain) and place a coverslip on top. Temporary mounts that are prepared properly have just enough fluid to fill the space between the slide and coverslip. If too much fluid is used the coverslip floats on top of it and moves around. If too little fluid is used the air bubbles that are left are easily mistaken for the specimen. The technique for making a temporary mount is illustrated in Figure 1.1.

Figure 1.1
a *Technique for lowering a coverslip on to a slide. The tip of a mounted needle is placed on to a slide next to the specimen. One edge of the coverslip is placed on the slide with the opposite edge supported by the mounted needle. Slowly moving the needle in the direction shown by the arrow will lower the coverslip on to the specimen without trapping air bubbles.*
b *Tissue paper can be used to soak up any excess water, as shown below. A stain (e.g. iodine in potassium iodide) placed next to the coverslip can also be drawn under the coverslip using this technique.*

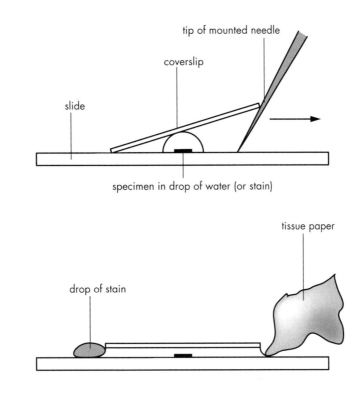

a

tip of mounted needle

coverslip

slide

specimen in drop of water (or stain)

b

tissue paper

drop of stain

Helping pupils to see what you want them to see

When pupils begin to use microscopes they will need help in finding what you want them to see and in making appropriate observations. If they are not given help you will find that they mistake such things as dirt, air bubbles, the interesting patterns left when water or a stain evaporates and even the edges of the coverslip or slide for the things that you want them to look at. Actually drawing attention to the appearance of these artefacts is a useful way of helping pupils to avoid making this mistake. Diagrams drawn on to a board, transparencies and pictures in books can be used to help pupils find those things that you are hoping they will see.

◆ *Further activities*

◆ It is a good idea to put clear plastic rulers on to the stage of a microscope and measure the width of the field of view at different magnifications using the millimetre divisions. The size of structures being viewed can then be estimated by judging how much of the field of view they occupy and doing some simple arithmetic.

♦ A huge variety of interesting microscopic organisms live in ponds or containers of water that have been left standing for some time (e.g. cattle troughs). Study of these organisms can motivate pupils, develop their microscope techniques and demonstrate the usefulness of the microscope in biological studies. Pupils will be able to identify some of the micro-organisms that they find but this is not of central importance. Such studies can be used as a stimulus for some imaginative creative writing (e.g. poems, short stories, scripts for television or radio programmes) about the lifestyle of very small organisms.

! *Good hygiene is needed.*

♦ A useful teaching aid for introductory lessons on microscope use is the Philip Harris *Microdot Kit*. This contains a variety of small images designed for mounting on slides.

♦ *Enhancement ideas*

♦ Projects in which pupils have to use microscopic analysis of specimens such as hairs, fibres and powders to help solve a fictional crime can be very motivating. Pupils could work together as teams of investigators to produce an illustrated scientific report that could be used in the trial of a suspect.

♦ Microscopic studies provide many opportunities for making posters. For example, these could include drawings and descriptions of microscopic organisms or could illustrate the development of light microscopes and their importance in many aspects of science.

♦ A video camera attached to a microscope is an invaluable aid when teaching microscope techniques. There are two video-microscopy systems available. One uses a small, traditional style camera that can be fitted on to a microscope that has a vertical eyepiece 'tutor-tube'. The other has a very small camera on the end of a flexible 'gooseneck' arm. The camera can be inserted into an eyepiece tube and can also be used independently of a microscope. Both systems can be used with pupils of all ages and abilities to demonstrate different techniques and to show images to a group of pupils. They can also be used to create a record of the images that pupils have looked at. These can be used as a starting point in the next lesson and a sequence of images can provide a valuable revision aid. Pupils could combine such images with video footage gained using a hand-held video camera to produce short documentary-type films featuring their microscope studies.

1.3 Studying cells

Cell theory is an important unifying concept in biology. Briefly it states that all living organisms are made up of cells and that all cells are derived from other cells. Many different organisms exist as single cells but most are made up of many cells. These multicellular organisms are composed of a variety of different types of cell that work together to maintain the life processes of the organism. You will find many references to cells in subsequent chapters of this book. This section suggests some teaching approaches that will help pupils to understand the structure of plant and animal cells.

Most cells are too small to be seen with the unaided eye so the use of microscopes is essential when studying cells. It is a good idea to wait until pupils are proficient at using microscopes before beginning practical work that is aimed at developing their understanding of the structure of cells. It is best to begin with plant cells because they are generally larger and have a more distinct structure than animal cells. Many sources of living plant material are easy to obtain and the techniques for handling them and mounting them on slides are relatively straightforward. Using living material will help pupils to relate the structures they look at under the microscope to the organism from which they came. In addition, preparing slides for themselves will help develop their manipulative skills.

♦ *Previous knowledge and experience*

Some pupils will know that living things are made up of cells but they are unlikely to have studied this topic in any depth. Research has shown that younger pupils sometimes think the words molecule and cell have the same meaning and that this can give rise to a generalised concept of living things being made up of 'very small units' that can be molecules or cells. In addition, pupils sometimes think that many of the non-cellular things studied in the context of biology lessons (e.g. proteins, carbohydrates and water) are actually made of cells.

Some of the terms used in cell biology may be more familiar in other contexts. For example, cells in a honeycomb or a prison. The word 'cell' is also used in the context of a battery of electrical cells and when using spreadsheets on a computer.

The difference between the nucleus of an atom and the nucleus in a cell will also need to be explained.

◆ *A teaching sequence*

Studying plant cells

The easiest plant cells to study are those that form single layers. It is relatively easy to interpret the details of each cell because they all lie in one plane and are not obscured by other overlapping cells. The technical term for these is epidermal cells and the layer that they form is called the epidermis. The bulbs of onions and related species (e.g. shallots and leeks) are a good source of epidermal cells. Red onions are particularly useful because the cells in the outer epidermis layers contain a red cell sap that makes them easier to see. The technique of obtaining the epidermal cells, mounting them and viewing them under a microscope is described in textbooks. Essentially it involves obtaining the epidermis layer by cutting an onion or leek in half and separating out the swollen leaf bases. The epidermal layer is peeled away using a pair of forceps, and a small pair of scissors is then used to cut off a piece measuring about 5 × 5 mm. If too large a piece of epidermis is used it is liable to become folded when placed on to a slide and, instead of being one cell thick, it will be two or more cells thick. To prevent tiny air bubbles being trapped next to the cells it is a good idea to wet the specimen by dipping it into some water before placing it on to a microscope slide. Two or three drops of water are put on the specimen and a coverslip placed on top using the technique illustrated in Figure 1.1.

Plant cells with chloroplasts

One disadvantage of using onion epidermis as an example of plant cells is that these cells do not possess chloroplasts. The epidermis of privet, iris or lettuce leaves are a good source of cells that do possess chloroplasts. Whole leaves can be viewed under the microscope provided they are not too thick. Leaves of Canadian pondweed (*Elodea canadensis*), ivy-leaved toadflax and young moss leaves are also particularly suitable.

Studying animal cells

Animal cells are not easy to see under the microscope so it is sensible to use transparencies, videos or CD ROMs to illustrate the structure of animal cells with younger pupils. Studying human cheek cells is an interesting and motivating activity to use with older pupils who are skilled at using microscopes. A cotton bud from a newly opened packet is used to collect the cells by gently swabbing the inside of the mouth around the gums. The saliva (which will contain the cells) is smeared on to a slide, a few drops of suitable stain (e.g. iodine in potassium iodide solution) are added and a coverslip placed on top. After use, the cotton buds, slides and coverslip must be put into a disinfectant such as 1% sodium chlorate(I) (hypochlorite). The cells are very small and pupils will need to magnify them at least 100 times in order to see them clearly.

! *There is a very small risk of transmission of the viruses that cause AIDS and hepatitis B associated with this practical but most employers allow pupils to carry it out provided they follow a strict safety procedure.*

! *Eye protection is needed when handling iodine solution.*

Drawing and interpreting microscope images of cells

The drawing of images viewed using microscopes is an important skill in biology since it encourages careful observation and thus helps pupils to understand the images they are looking at. When drawing from the microscope pupils should be taught to follow these procedures.

- Write a clear heading.
- Use a sharp HB pencil.
- Draw firm, continuous lines and avoid using too much shading.
- Include the magnification or a scale line.
- Draw label lines with a ruler. These must touch the structure they are labelling and should not cross each other.
- Write labels horizontally on the page (pupils often write along the same angle as the label lines) and arrange them neatly around (not over) the drawing.

Examples of good and bad drawings are given in Figure 1.2.

Figure 1.2
a *Good and* **b** *bad drawings of a human cheek cell.*

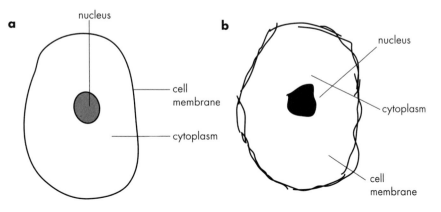

When they attempt to draw cells for the first time pupils often tend to draw too many cells. Instead they must be encouraged to draw a few cells in detail. To help interpret images of cells it is a good idea for pupils to draw what they can see starting with the low power objective lens, then use the middle and high power lenses. When using high power lenses pupils can investigate the three-dimensional nature of larger cells (e.g. plant epidermal cells) by carefully focusing on different planes of the cell. Drawing diagrams on to a board and using transparencies, video microscopy and models will help the pupils to interpret the structure of the cells they are viewing.

Cell structure and function

You will want pupils to learn the names and functions of the main parts of cells. These are described in pupil texts. Some of the technical terms are difficult to spell and pronounce so it is worth going over them carefully.

◆ *Further activities*

◆ Making three-dimensional models of cells using easily obtainable items such as shoe boxes, polythene bags and small balls to represent structures like cell walls, membranes and nuclei is a very useful way of illustrating the structure of simple cells. Different types of model can be constructed to illustrate the way in which cells become specialised (differentiated) for different functions.

◆ *Enhancement ideas*

◆ Pictures taken with scanning electron microscopes illustrate the external appearance, shape and three-dimensional nature of cells very clearly. Show pupils scanning electron microscope pictures of a selection of cells, e.g. red blood cells, unicellular organisms and the xylem cells that form wood, to demonstrate the variation shown by cells. Showing more able pupils the sort of images that can be gained using transmission electron microscopes (these show details of structures found inside cells) will help them to understand that cells are more complex structures than they appear to be when looked at using light microscopes.
◆ Simple micrometry ideas can be used to indicate to pupils the actual size of the cells.

1.4 The chemistry of life

In the first section of this chapter, life was described as arising from interactions between the chemical substances that make up organisms. Chemical reactions inside cells occur in sequences called metabolic pathways. These pathways involve either making or breaking down the large molecules that are found in living things. The steps along the pathway are catalysed by biological catalysts (enzymes) and the structure of each enzyme enables it to catalyse a particular chemical change. Enzymes are proteins, so the temperature and pH of their surroundings affect their structure. If these vary outside certain limits then the shape of enzymes changes so much (i.e. the enzyme becomes 'denatured') that they are unable to perform their functions and metabolic pathways are disrupted. This is one reason why it is important for organisms to maintain relatively constant conditions inside their bodies and cells (i.e. show homeostasis). As well as producing products that are needed by organisms, metabolic reactions produce by-products that need to be removed. The removal of the waste products of metabolism is called excretion.

◆ *Previous knowledge and experience*

The activities suggested below assume that pupils will have some knowledge of elements, molecules, compounds and the conservation of matter. Research has shown that pupils often think that 'large' molecules (e.g. proteins) are bigger than cells, which they have been taught are very 'small'. Careful use of these relative terms is therefore needed. The names of some of the types of molecule found in living things will be familiar from adverts associated with food and cosmetics while enzymes will often be associated with washing powders. Such advertising often contains somewhat questionable 'pseudo-science' that can give rise to many misconceptions.

◆ *A teaching sequence*

Examination syllabuses and pupil texts often include many details concerning the complex molecules that are needed by all living things, and enzyme action in the context of the human diet and digestion. However, before covering diet and digestion in detail, it is a good idea to go over some more general ideas about the chemistry of living things. The activities suggested below could be used in a variety of contexts and are not set out as a teaching sequence. It is hoped that the ideas suggested will enable you to help your pupils make links between many of the other topics discussed in this book and gain an overview of some of the overarching concepts of biological science.

Using models to develop ideas about metabolic pathways and the building up and breaking down of molecules inside cells

The idea that the complex molecules found in cells are assembled from smaller molecules is important in many contexts. For example, carbohydrates such as starch and cellulose are built up from simple sugars such as glucose, proteins are built up from amino acids, and nucleic acids are made up of sugars, phosphates and bases. The steps involved in the formation or breakdown of molecules in cells can be illustrated using models. This could be done using either physical models or a molecular-modelling package for use with computers. Models are also useful when relating the structure of a particular type of molecule to the functions that they perform in cells.

The role of enzymes

Pupil texts usually include a variety of investigations involving enzymes. Many of these are set in the context of digestion (see Chapter 2). Digestive enzymes are not typical enzymes since most enzymes are involved in reactions that take place inside cells, whereas digestive enzymes have their effect outside cells in the alimentary canal. Studying enzymes in the context of digestion can also give rise to the misconception that enzymes are primarily involved in the breakdown of large molecules into smaller ones, whereas far more enzymes are involved in catalysing the reactions that build up molecules. For these reasons it is important for pupils to carry out practical work that illustrates the role of enzymes in other contexts. For example, a useful demonstration is to show that an enzyme found in potato will catalyse the formation of starch from glucose. The enzyme is obtained by grinding up a small piece of potato with water. The mixture is then centrifuged and a drop of the supernatant tested with iodine in potassium iodide (commonly called 'iodine') to ensure that it does not contain any starch. When the enzyme extract is mixed with glucose monophosphate the iodine test can be used again to show that starch is produced.

 Eye protection is needed when handling iodine solution.

Homeostasis and enzyme function

The importance of living organisms being able to maintain relatively constant conditions inside their cells (see Chapter 5) can be illustrated by carrying out practical work that illustrates how the rates of enzyme-controlled reactions are affected by pH and temperature. A variety of suitable investigations can be found in pupil texts.

Metabolic pathways and excretion

Excretion is often defined as being the release of waste products from living things. Two important ideas to emphasise when discussing excretion are, firstly, that the waste products released are made inside body cells and, secondly, that they will disrupt metabolism (i.e. are poisonous) if they accumulate inside the cells. A very common misconception is that undigested food material (faeces) is one of the excretory products of animals. Faecal material is not an excretory product because it is not made inside body cells. The undigested food that makes up faeces remains in the alimentary canal and the correct term for the removal of faeces is 'defaecation' although there are of course various alternatives!

Many metabolic waste products are molecules that can be used by the organism that produces them and it is therefore a good idea to discuss excretion in the context of homeostasis. For example, the build up of carbon dioxide in cells disrupts metabolism because it forms carbonic acid, which reduces the pH inside the cells. In plants the carbon dioxide produced by respiration can be utilised in photosynthesis and only at night is there a net release of carbon dioxide. Similarly, most of the oxygen produced by photosynthesis is used by plants for respiration. However, when the rate of photosynthesis is high, excess oxygen must be released.

In contrast to plants, animals need to get rid of excess carbon dioxide all the time. Animals usually ingest more nitrogen than they need and so the other main metabolic waste products produced by animals are nitrogenous compounds, such as ammonia, that are formed by the breakdown of amino acids. Ammonia is very poisonous and in many animals is converted to urea, which is less toxic than ammonia, and filtered out of the bloodstream by the kidneys.

1.5 Energy and life

The energy needed for all living processes is made available inside cells by a metabolic pathway called respiration. This process takes place inside all living cells. Many pupils have difficulty understanding what is meant by the term 'respiration' and research has shown that they often retain many misconceptions after it has been taught, e.g. that 'respiration' and 'breathing' are synonymous, that plants do not respire or only respire when in darkness, and that respiration 'creates' energy for living processes.

There are two forms of respiration. Aerobic respiration occurs when sufficient oxygen is available and can be summarised by the equation:

food + oxygen → carbon dioxide + water + energy released

If there is insufficient oxygen available, anaerobic respiration occurs. For example, during strenuous exercise the blood system cannot supply oxygen to the muscles fast enough for aerobic respiration to be maintained. When this happens the muscle cells begin to respire anaerobically. This releases less energy than aerobic respiration and, in animals and some bacteria, can be summarised as:

food → lactic acid (strictly lactate) + energy released

The lactic acid produced in muscles is broken down into carbon dioxide and water when enough oxygen is available to repay the 'oxygen debt' that results from anaerobic respiration.

In fungi (e.g. yeast) and some bacteria anaerobic respiration produces ethanol and carbon dioxide and can be summarised as:

food → ethanol + carbon dioxide + energy released

This is the fermentation process that is used in baking and brewing.

◆ *Previous knowledge and experience*

Prior to being taught about respiration pupils are most likely to
have studied energy in the context of physics. They may have
developed some understanding of the idea that energy is always
conserved but a very common misconception in a biological
context is that energy is a physical substance that can be 'used
up' (e.g. when we 'run out of energy').

The word 'respiration' itself is most likely to have been met
in the phrase 'artificial respiration'. Artificial respiration should
really be called 'artificial ventilation' because it actually involves
the 'artificial' ventilation of a person's lungs. There is nothing
'artificial' about the respiration that one hopes will then ensue.
One of the difficulties in teaching about respiration is that
although living organisms are respiring all the time, they do
not show any obvious physical signs that this is occurring.
Something that some animals obviously do is 'breathe', which
is perhaps why respiration and breathing are often thought of
as being the same thing.

◆ *A teaching sequence*

The metabolic processes involved in respiration are invisible
reactions that occur inside cells and cannot be studied at first
hand in the school situation. However, many practical
investigations concerning the reactants and products of
respiration can be used to help pupils understand the process.
The fundamental importance of respiration to all living things
can be emphasised by using a variety of different types of
organisms in such investigations. Some possibilities are
included in the teaching sequence set out below. Further ideas
and more detailed explanations of the procedures that are
suggested can be found in many pupil texts.

Energy flow in living and non-living systems

Before teaching respiration it is important to review pupils'
knowledge of what is meant by the word 'energy'. We cannot see
or feel energy – the physical experiences that we associate with it
occur only when an energy transfer takes place. An 'energy circus'
is a useful way of helping pupils appreciate that the concept of
'energy' can be applied in many situations. Pupils can be asked the
question, 'Where is the energy now?' when presented with
examples of living and non-living systems in which energy
transformations are occurring. Examples of the ways in which

living things utilise energy could include the production of movement, growth, sound, heat, light (in luminescent organisms) and electricity (as in nerve impulses or, more spectacularly, by electric eels). After considering situations in which a few energy transfers occur, pupils could then trace the many energy transfers that occur from the Sun to their food to their own life processes.

Food as a source of energy

Many foods and drinks are advertised as being 'high in energy' and studying a variety of food labels is a useful way of illustrating the point that food is needed to provide us with energy. Making the link between the high glucose content of 'high energy' foods and the photosynthesis that produces the glucose will help pupils to appreciate the idea of energy flow.

The idea that respiration involves food being 'burnt' inside the body to release energy is often used when introducing respiration. When doing this it should be made clear that respiration involves a series of small steps that transfer energy slowly, whereas burning is a much more rapid reaction. Chapter 2 includes some ideas for measuring the energy content of different types of food.

Demonstrating that oxygen is used in aerobic respiration

A simple demonstration to show that oxygen is used in respiration can be done by measuring how long a candle will burn in a gas jar of atmospheric air as compared with expired air. The composition of atmospheric and expired air can be demonstrated more accurately using a gas syringe to measure the reduction in volume that occurs when potassium hydroxide (which absorbs carbon dioxide) and then alkaline pyrogallol (which absorbs oxygen) are added to the sample.

! *Traditional recipes for these reagents produce very corrosive solutions. Less concentrated potassium hydroxide will still absorb carbon dioxide and the pyrogallol can be made alkaline by using sodium hydrogencarbonate, which is safer.*

Demonstrating that carbon dioxide is produced in aerobic respiration

The well known lime water test for carbon dioxide can be used when the amount of carbon dioxide being produced is relatively large, e.g. in air expired from the lungs. Carbon dioxide production by respiring plants and small animals occurs too slowly for the lime water test to give positive results. Instead, hydrogencarbonate indicator can be used to demonstrate that these organisms do produce carbon dioxide.

Hydrogencarbonate indicator has an orange/red colour when in equilibrium with the carbon dioxide levels of atmospheric air. When the carbon dioxide levels rise slightly it changes to a yellow colour. This happens because the extra carbon dioxide that becomes dissolved in the indicator solution forms a very weak acid called carbonic acid. Placing Canadian pondweed (*Elodea*) into a boiling tube containing the indicator and excluding light to prevent photosynthesis will produce a colour change in about 1 hour. Pond snails are not harmed by the indicator and will cause a significant colour change in about 30 minutes. Leaves of terrestrial plants (e.g. privet) or small invertebrates (e.g. woodlice) can be suspended above the indicator solution, producing a colour change after a few hours.

Data-logging equipment connected to pH probes is a very good alternative method of illustrating the pH changes associated with carbon dioxide production, especially if the respiration rate is very slow.

Measuring heat production in germinating seeds
Germinating seeds convert energy from their food stores into the energy that they need for the metabolic reactions giving rise to growth. As in most energy conversion processes, heat is also produced. The temperature rise that occurs can be measured by placing a thermometer or a temperature probe (attached to a digital meter and if possible a data-logger) into a thermos flask containing germinating seeds.

Anaerobic respiration in bacteria
Pupils are likely to be familiar with the taste of milk that has 'gone off'. The sour taste results from bacteria in the milk respiring anaerobically and producing lactic acid. The fall in pH can be easily monitored over a number of days using a pH probe connected to a meter with a digital readout, which can be connected to a data-logger. Comparing results obtained using pasteurised and long-life milk will illustrate the role of bacteria in this process.

Anaerobic respiration in yeast
Chapter 10 discusses some of the many practical possibilities for investigating anaerobic respiration (fermentation) in yeast.

Anaerobic respiration in muscles
The rapid exercising of muscles quickly results in a build up of lactic acid and most pupils will be familiar with the sensations of tiredness, cramp and stiffness that follow strenuous exercise.

A simple procedure that illustrates one of the reasons why these sensations occur is to clench and unclench your fists two to three times each second with one hand held above your head and the other by your side. The raised arm tires more quickly because it is harder to pump blood upwards to the raised hand.

◆ *Further activities*

◆ **Using respirometers to monitor oxygen uptake in small organisms**.
This technique for measuring oxygen uptake by small invertebrates or germinating seeds is described in many textbooks. The principles by which respirometers work are fairly straightforward – the soda lime absorbs the carbon dioxide produced by the respiring organisms, the air pressure in the sealed container drops since oxygen is being used up in respiration and the water in the attached capillary tube rises. In practice they are fiddly to set up and will not provide reliable results unless they are completely airtight and maintained at a constant temperature. Depending on the ability of your pupils and the time you have available, it may be more sensible to use a respirometer as a demonstration rather than for a class practical.

! *Soda lime is corrosive.*

◆ **A quantitative investigation of muscle fatigue**.
The following simple procedure provides quantitative data concerning fatigue induced by exercise.

Procedure
1. A 200 g mass is suspended from the subject's index finger with the hand placed horizontally with the palm up over the side of a bench.
2. The mass is raised and lowered by bending the finger up and down as quickly as possible for 3 minutes. The number of times the mass is raised in each consecutive minute is recorded.
3. After 5 minutes' rest the procedure is repeated with 30 seconds' rest after each minute of activity.
4. After a further 5 minutes' rest the procedure is repeated with a 1 minute rest after each minute of activity.

Analysing the results should show that following periods of rest the finger muscles recover from the fatigue induced by the activity and that longer rests result in better recovery. The recovery occurs because the 'oxygen debt' built up during the exercise (i.e. the amount of oxygen needed to get rid of the lactate) is repaid during the break from exercise.

♦ The appreciation that respiration is a fundamental process of life can be greatly enhanced by making explicit links between the study of respiration and many other topics. These could include movement that involves muscle contraction, movement of chromosomes during cell division, the building up of large molecules from smaller ones and the active transport of materials in and out of cells. Respiration is often studied in the context of gas exchange and ventilation, as discussed in Chapter 4. If this is the only context in which respiration is discussed the misconception that respiration does not occur in plants will not be addressed. For this reason it is particularly important to include a discussion of respiration when considering photosynthesis (see Chapter 2). The importance of respiration in the carbon cycle and in energy flow through ecosystems (Chapter 9) are other topics in which the importance of respiration should be highlighted.

♦ *Enhancement ideas*

♦ **The use of radioactive tracers in studying biochemical reactions**.
Much of our knowledge about metabolic processes such as respiration comes from experiments using radioactive tracers, e.g. following the path of a radioactively labelled carbon atom from glucose dissolved in an animal's drinking water to the carbon dioxide that the animal produces by respiring. With more able pupils some of the techniques involved and the results obtained can be discussed to help them understand the importance of such experiments in modern biology. Molecular models or 'pupil modelling' in which the pupils themselves represent different atoms (labelled and unlabelled) can be used to provide a physical representation of the process.

1.6 Cell division

Cell division is the basis of growth in multicellular organisms and of reproduction in all organisms. Pupils can be taught many things about growth and reproduction without discussing cell division in detail. However, to gain a more sophisticated understanding of these processes, pupils will need to learn more about what happens when cells divide. The type of cell division that enables multicellular organisms to grow and to repair damaged tissues is called mitotic cell division or mitosis. Mitosis is also the basis of asexual reproduction, whereas sexual reproduction involves a different type of cell division called meiosis.

Teaching cell division presents a number of problems. It involves studying structures (chromosomes) which are very difficult to see even with the aid of high-powered light microscopes. The sequences of events that occur are complex and, when describing them, pupil texts often use many technical terms. More able pupils may be able to understand and use these terms but, before introducing them, it is a good idea to ensure that they understand the basic principles involved. The approach suggested here involves the use of video footage, diagrams and models to help pupils understand these principles.

◆ *Previous knowledge and experience*

Before studying cell division pupils need to have some ideas about the relationships between chromosomes, genes and the characteristics that they determine. Some suggested approaches to this topic are given in Chapter 7.

◆ *A teaching sequence*

Mitotic cell division

Mitosis is the simpler (or less complex!) type of cell division and should be covered before introducing meiosis. Mitosis is a fascinating process and a good starting point is to show pupils a video or CD ROM of actual cells dividing and an animated sequence of this process. This can be followed by using a sequence of diagrams similar to that shown in Figure 1.3 to explain the important features of the process.

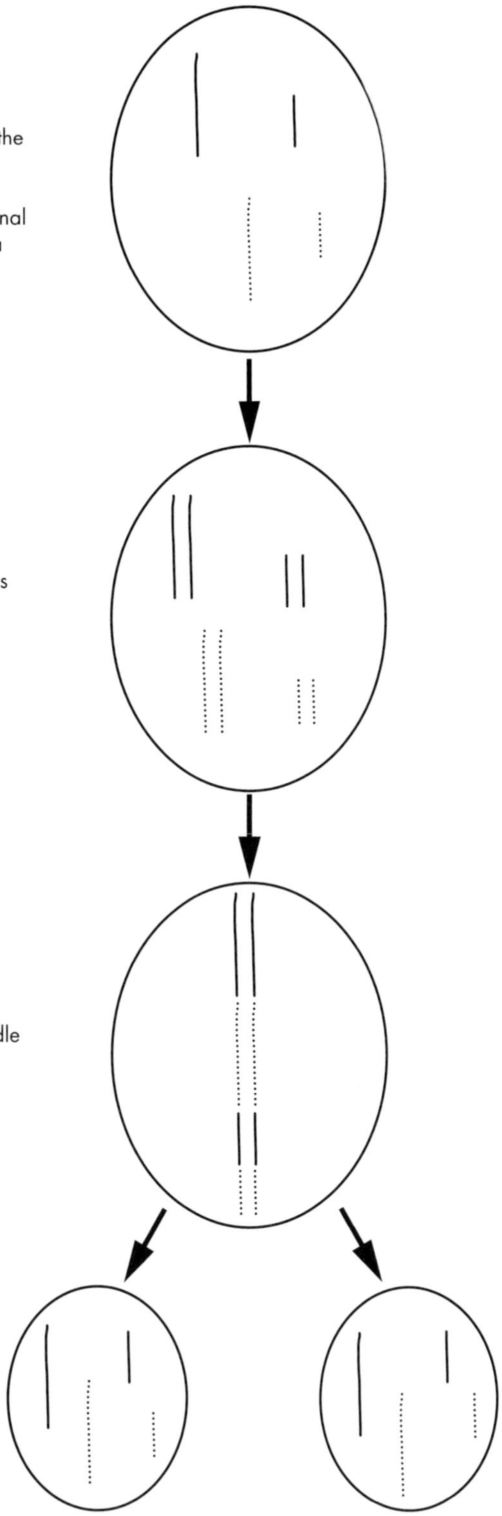

Figure 1.3
A diagram summarising the events that occur during mitosis.

1 A cell containing two pairs of (*homologous*) chromosomes. One of each pair comes from the original female parent and is shown as a continuous line. The other comes from the original male parent and is shown as a dotted line.

2 Each chromosome makes an exact copy of itself. (The copies are called *chromatids*.)

3 Chromosomes (now pairs of *chromatids*) line up in the middle (on the *equator*) of the cell.

4 The copies (*chromatids*) separate and move to opposite ends (*poles*) of the cell, which then divides to form two (*daughter*) cells. Each of these has exactly the same genetic make up as the original cell.

In order to explain the essentials of mitosis more clearly, this figure is a deliberately simplified representation of what really occurs. In all the diagrams the chromosomes are drawn as continuous or dotted lines with the circle around them representing the cell membrane (membrane and cell wall in the case of plants). In reality, when a cell is not dividing its chromosomes exist as very long, thin structures that are only just visible using electron microscopy. In the vast majority of species the chromosomes are contained within a nucleus. Stage 2 in the figure (i.e. when the chromosomes make copies of themselves) actually occurs when the chromosomes are inside the nucleus in their long, thin conformation. The nuclear envelope breaks down and the chromosomes become shorter and fatter (and visible under a light microscope) after this has taken place. Many other details have been omitted and few technical terms are used. You can find more detailed accounts of the process in advanced pupil texts. Some of the technical terms that you might want to use are included in the figure captions and are printed in italic script. You will need to judge when it is best to introduce them. For some pupils they are probably best avoided completely.

It is a good idea to draw diagrams similar to those shown in Figure 1.3 on to a board or overhead transparency using different colours (rather than continuous and dotted lines) to represent the chromosomes. An overhead is probably better since it allows more eye contact with pupils and will help you to judge an appropriate pace for your explanation. It is essential that pupils concentrate on the explanation rather than try to copy diagrams or write things down whilst you are talking. Once the sequence has been completed, pupils' understanding can be reviewed by asking them questions about each of the stages you have illustrated. A crucial point to establish is that the cells formed as a result of mitotic division contain exactly the same complement of chromosomes (and hence genes) as the original undivided cell.

A disadvantage of using diagrams to illustrate mitosis is that it is difficult to show the behaviour of the chromosomes in three dimensions. This can be illustrated by getting pupils to model the events using different coloured pipe cleaners (these are easily stained with permanent inks or fabric dyes) to represent the chromosomes.

Commercially produced models can also be used to help pupils visualise the three-dimensional nature of the process. Following these activities, the physical act of drawing diagrams similar to those in Figure 1.3 will help pupils to consolidate their understanding. A useful idea is to provide them with written descriptions of each stage that they then illustrate diagrammatically. Finally, you could return to the video or CD ROM sequence with which you began and review the whole process.

Meiosis and gamete formation

The type of cell division that produces sex cells (gametes) is called meiosis. Gametes differ from other types of cell (somatic cells) produced by organisms in two fundamental respects. First, they contain half the number (the haploid number or 'n') of chromosomes that are present in the somatic cells (the diploid number or '$2n$'). If this were not the case the zygotes (fertilised eggs) formed when sex cells combine (fuse) would contain twice as many chromosomes as the parents' cells. Secondly, the chromosomes present in gametes contain a mixture of genes derived from the male and female parents of the individual that is producing the gametes.

Figure 1.4 illustrates the important events that occur during meiosis. In common with Figure 1.3, this is a deliberately simplified illustration of what actually happens. Some of the technical terms you might wish to use with pupils are printed in the captions in italic script. Comparison with Figure 1.3 shows that the initial stages of meiosis and mitosis are essentially the same. A crucial difference occurs after the chromosomes have made copies of themselves. In mitosis, the chromosomes become arranged in a single line in the middle of the cell, and then separate. In meiosis, the chromosomes line up in pairs with equivalent (homologous) chromosomes from the male and female parent of the organism becoming aligned next to each other in the middle of the cell. These then move to opposite ends of the cell, which then divides. The cells produced by meiosis contain half the number of chromosomes found in the original cell. Another division follows in which the chromosome copies (chromatids) separate and a total of four cells is formed.

Figure 1.4
A diagram summarising the events that occur during meiosis.

1 A cell containing two pairs of (*homologous*) chromosomes. One of each pair comes from the original female parent and is shown as a continuous line. The other comes from the original male parent and is shown as a dotted line.

2 Each chromosome makes an exact copy of itself. (The copies are called *chromatids*.)

3 Equivalent (*homologous*) pairs of chromosomes (each made up of two copies or *chromatids*) line up alongside each other in the middle (on the *equator*) of the cell.

4 Equivalent (*homologous*) chromosomes move to opposite ends (*poles*) of the cell and two new cells are formed.

5 The chromosome copies (*chromatids*) now separate and move to opposite ends (*poles*) of each cell. These divide forming a total of four new cells. The number of chromosomes in each is half the number found in the original cell.

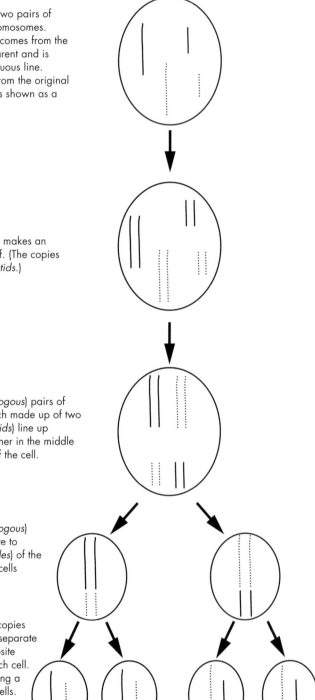

The gametes that these cells produce will be genetically different from each other because, at the stage in meiosis when the chromosomes pair up, some will have chromosomes derived from the male parent on one side of the pairing, whereas others will be the opposite way round. This is referred to as 'independent segregation' of the chromosomes and leads to independent segregation of alleles (see Chapter 7). Figure 1.4 shows one of the two possibilities that exist when there are two pairs of chromosomes in the original cell. The other possibility is for both of the chromosomes derived from the maternal parent (represented by continuous lines) to be on the same side of the pairings.

Additional variation between gametes occurs because genetic material is exchanged between chromosomes when they pair up with each other. This, together with the variation resulting from independent segregation of chromosomes, results in an almost infinite amount of genetic variation between the gametes produced by an individual (see Chapters 6 and 7). This contributes to the genetic variation that occurs in the offspring produced by sexual reproduction and this variation has important consequences for the evolution of species, as discussed in Chapter 8.

◆ *Further activities*

◆ Pupils with good microscopy skills can look at prepared microscope slides showing the different stages of mitosis and meiosis. Video microscopy is very useful to show pupils what they should be looking for. Transparencies can be used instead of (or in conjunction with) microscope work.

◆ Use computer drawing packages to produce diagrams illustrating cell division. Pupils can produce diagrams illustrating mitosis or meiosis using 'copy and paste' techniques on a computer. The procedures used model some of the events that occur during cell division, e.g. making copies of chromosomes, changing their size and shape and moving them to different positions within a cell.

Other resources

◆ *Videos*

An Introduction to Microscopy (1997) (Education Broadcasting Services Trust, 36–38 Mortimer Street, London W1N 7RB). This video is aimed at students in higher education but appropriate sequences could be used with younger pupils and the video is available in a 'master copy' format that can be edited. Sequences showing dividing living cells and animated versions of cell division often feature in videos that are concerned with cell biology in general or growth and reproduction.

Videos concerned solely with cell division (e.g. *Meiosis: The Key to Genetic Diversity* (1991), Boulton-Hawker Films, Ipswich) are often aimed at more advanced students. Relevant sequences can be selected from any of these and if necessary you can ignore the commentary provided on the video and add your own at a level suited to the age and ability range of your pupils.

◆ *Teaching aids*

Microdot Kit (1982), available from Philip Harris, Lynn Lane, Shenstone, Lichfield, Staffs WS14 DEE (tel: 01543 480077). This contains a variety of small images for mounting on slides.

Flexible arm desk-top video cameras are ideal for displaying images from a microscope on to a TV monitor. Software for capturing, analysing and logging images that are obtained with these cameras can be used in a variety of exciting ways with pupils. Details of the 'Flexcam' range of video microscopes and associated software are available from Scientific and Chemical Supplies Ltd, Carlton House, Livingstone Road, Bilston, West Midlands WV14 0QZ (e-mail: scs@scichem.co.uk).

◆ *CD ROMs*

Images of Biology for A level (1995, Stanley Thornes, Cheltenham) and *The Ultimate Human Body* (1994, Dorling-Kindersley, London) have useful material illustrating cells and cell division. *Meiosis* and *Mitosis* (both 1995, CyberEd, available from Rickitt Educational Media Ltd, Great Western House, Langport, Somerset TA10 9YU) include diagrams, photographs, animated sequences and interactive tutorials.

◆ *Models*

A variety of three-dimensional models illustrating cell structure, important biological molecules and the stages of mitosis and meiosis are available from school science suppliers.

◆ *Addresses*

Science and Plants for Schools (SAPS), Homerton College, Hills Road, Cambridge CB2 2PH (website: www-saps.plantsci.cam.ac.uk).

◆ *Further reading*

Imaginative approaches to teaching biology

Brown, C.R. (1995). *The Effective Teaching of Biology*. London, Longman.

Lester, A. & Lock, R. (1998). Flexible visual aids – sponge enzyme models. *School Science Review*, **79** (289), pp. 105–107.

Lock, R. (1991). Creative work in biology – a pot-pourri of examples. Part 1 – Expressive and poetic writing, cartoons, comics and posters. *School Science Review*, **72** (260), pp. 30–46.

Lock, R. (1991). Creative work in biology – a pot-pourri of examples. Part 2 – Drawing, drama, games and models. *School Science Review*, **72** (261), pp. 57–64.

Lock, R. (1997). Post-16 biology – some model approaches? *School Science Review*, **79** (286), pp. 33–38.

Reiss, M. (ed) (1996). *Living Biology in Schools*. London, Institute of Biology.

Pupils' ideas about the natural world

Dreyfus, A. & Jungwirth, E. (1989). The pupil and the living cell: a taxonomy of dysfunctional ideas about an abstract idea. *Journal of Biological Education*, **23**, pp. 49–55.

Driver, R., Squires, A., Rushworth, P. & Wood-Robinson, V. (1994). *Making Sense of Secondary Science: Research Into Children's Ideas*. London, Routledge. (This summarises research findings concerning the knowledge and ideas that pupils have concerning all aspects of science.)

Gayford, C.G. (1986). Some aspects of the problems of teaching about energy in school biology. *European Journal of Science Education*, **8**, pp. 443–450.

2 Nutrition, diet and photosynthesis

Stephen Tomkins and Sheila Turner

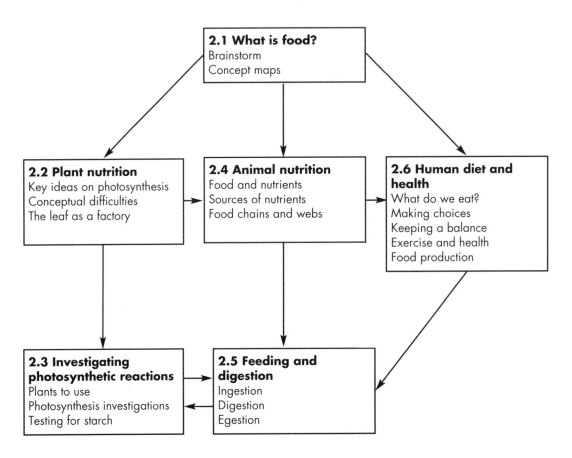

2.1 What is food?
Brainstorm
Concept maps

2.2 Plant nutrition
Key ideas on photosynthesis
Conceptual difficulties
The leaf as a factory

2.4 Animal nutrition
Food and nutrients
Sources of nutrients
Food chains and webs

2.6 Human diet and health
What do we eat?
Making choices
Keeping a balance
Exercise and health
Food production

2.3 Investigating photosynthetic reactions
Plants to use
Photosynthesis investigations
Testing for starch

2.5 Feeding and digestion
Ingestion
Digestion
Egestion

◆ Choosing a route

Planning effective lessons about nutrition, diet and photosynthesis will depend on a number of things. Establishing the previous knowledge and understanding that pupils have is a prerequisite. The content boxes show subjects to be covered and some key links and sequences for choosing a route; work with plants may be affected by the time of year. Working through the biology of nutrition requires the gradual building up of linked ideas. These concepts interconnect with topics in other chapters of this book, as shown below.

- All living things need to obtain food, containing nutrients, in order to respire, grow and reproduce (see Chapter 1).
- The nature of nutrients is the same in all organisms, e.g. animals and plants both need minerals, carbohydrates, proteins and fats.
- Plants and some other organisms, such as algae, are able to use very simple molecules, like carbon dioxide and water, to build up their complex food materials. For this process, photosynthesis, they use light energy from sunshine.
- Plants provide the food materials at the start of every food chain or web. All animals are ultimately dependent on plants (see Chapter 9).
- Energy and matter can be stored in a biological/chemical system (whether at cell/tissue/organ/organism/population level) (see Chapters 1 and 9).
- Energy is released, to do useful work, through respiration by both plants and animals (see Chapter 1).
- Ingested food matter is broken down by digestion in animals. This is both a physical/mechanical breakdown (e.g. teeth and muscle action) and a chemical breakdown (enzyme action) all demanding, not supplying, energy.
- The breakdown products of digestion are used in metabolism to build up new compounds or to provide the fuel for respiration. Only this oxidation releases the energy (see Chapter 1).
- Green plants need light, water, carbon dioxide, warmth and mineral nutrients.
- Humans need a balanced dietary intake of carbohydrates, proteins, fats, vitamins, minerals, water and fibre.
- Dietary components have specific roles and great importance for healthy living.

Of course, all these concepts and the supporting knowledge will not all be learned at once. In the curricular schemes of work it is strongly suggested that the ideas are returned to – at progressive levels – in a spiral way. It should be expected but not presumed that most of these concepts will be in place after returning to them a second time. In planning the curriculum, links should be made to ecology studies in summer months. Plant photosynthesis studies are best avoided in winter unless a 'light bank' is available in the classroom.

2.1 What is food?

◆ *Previous knowledge and experience*

The question 'What is food?' may appear to be relatively easy to answer. An obvious response that many pupils give is that food is something we eat! The fact that other animals and organisms, such as plants, also require food tends to be ignored. To some extent such responses reflect our egocentric thinking. There is some evidence that for many pupils the word 'food' can pose specific difficulties, particularly when it is used in connection with the term 'energy' in science. It has been suggested that one of the difficulties is that the word 'food' is used in different ways in different contexts, such as:

- photosynthesis – plants making food
- mineral nutrition – plants 'feeding' through their roots
- ecology – food webs and chains
- human nutrition – eating food.

Making these distinctions is important if pupils are to understand the principles of animal and plant nutrition, including the transfer of matter and energy in food chains and webs, and the important dual role of food in respiration and in metabolic processes such as digestion. Each of the topics identified above provides useful starting points for work on animal and plant nutrition, as are indicated in the suggested routes at the start of the chapter.

◆ *A teaching sequence*

Brainstorming and concept maps

A good starting point for work on food is to explore the ideas that pupils already have by brainstorming and/or by creating concept maps/diagrams that make links between the key ideas such as nutrition and photosynthesis (see Figure 2.1). Since food is a subject that features regularly in the media, newspaper cuttings, advertisements and/or television programmes also provide useful starting points for discussion.

When pupils have developed their own frame of thought, the teacher will need to steer the class's thinking towards some key biological ideas. The ways in which living organisms obtain or manufacture food substances to maintain their metabolic processes are intriguing and complex.

Figure 2.1

An example of ideas suggested by pupils aged 11 during a brainstorm on food.

Eating	Energy	Need food to make you grow
Fills you up	Some foods are grown from seeds	Survival
Different kinds of food	**FOOD**	Need food to keep you healthy
Some foods taste nicer than others	Some foods come from: • seeds • the ground • trees	
You get protein and vitamins		Don't eat too much fat
Eat different foods in different places	Some foods you have to wash or peel	Some foods are healthier than others

Plants and some other organisms, such as algae, are able to use simple materials, carbon dioxide and water, in the presence of sunlight, to build up complex molecules by the process of photosynthesis (from the Greek words for 'light' and 'putting together'). Photosynthesis takes place in plant cells, which contain minute structures, called chloroplasts. These contain chlorophyll pigments that are able to capture light energy and so power a chemical reaction. The process of photosynthesis is often represented by an (unbalanced) summary equation that indicates the beginning and end points of the reaction:

$$\text{energy (sunlight)} + \text{carbon dioxide} + \text{water} \xrightarrow{\text{chlorophyll}} \text{glucose} + \text{oxygen}$$
$$CO_2 + H_2O \qquad C_6H_{12}O_6 + O_2$$

Glucose is a simple carbohydrate that is produced during photosynthesis. It provides basic building blocks from which more complex carbohydrates, such as starch and cellulose, as well as proteins and fats can be built by plants and animals to create, for example, the materials in new cells. Glucose is also central to another vital life process, respiration. Respiration takes place in the cells of all living organisms including green plant cells. During respiration glucose is oxidised, energy is released (much of it being dissipated as heat) and carbon is returned to the atmosphere as carbon dioxide. The process of respiration is often summarised by the (unbalanced) equation shown below:

$$\text{glucose} + \text{oxygen} \rightarrow \text{carbon dioxide} + \text{water} + \text{energy yield}$$
$$C_6H_{12}O_6 + O_2 \qquad\qquad CO_2 \qquad + H_2O$$

Using pictures

Other ways of describing such reactions may involve a different teaching–learning strategy, using pictures that represent the transfer of energy and matter. Photosynthesis may be seen as a process of storing energy as hydrogen fuel in starch and, conversely, respiration as a process of unlocking that hydrogen fuel in oxidative energy release (see Figure 2.2).

Figure 2.2
Making fuel and using fuel. (Based on Boohan & Ogborn, 1996.)
a Making fuel – photosynthesis.
b Using fuel – respiration.

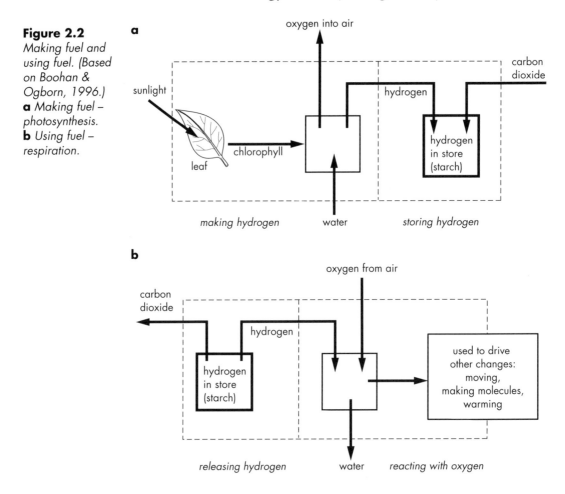

2.2 Plant nutrition

♦ *Previous knowledge and experience*

Pupils at age 11 may have some knowledge of the parts of a plant and of the life cycles of plants. They may have grown a range of plants including peas, beans and cress in varying conditions, such as in the dark and near windows. They may have grown and studied food plants from different parts of the world. They will probably have kept recorded observations over a period of time and be familiar with the need for systematic and careful recording of data. Most pupils will know that green plants require water and light if they are to grow; however, few will appreciate that plants require a range of soil-derived minerals for growth. The process of photosynthesis will not be understood (for many pupils the word 'photosynthesis' will be unfamiliar).

Green plants power almost all ecosystems and long ago photosynthesis made all the fossil fuels. Light is captured by chlorophylls (mostly green) in the chloroplasts of the leaf. The green wavelength of light unabsorbed or reflected back from the chlorophyll is the least useful wavelength: red and, especially, blue light are most useful. The role of light energy is to produce the reducing power for what is an energy-demanding synthesis reaction. Using light energy, water molecules are split leaving gaseous oxygen as a residue. This 'waste' oxygen escapes from the leaf and makes possible the aerobic respiration of living things and all oxidative burning.

Carbon dioxide is released into the air as a result of plant and animal respiration, but the carbon dioxide in the atmosphere also provides the plant with its source of carbon for making food (see Figures 2.2 and 2.3). In the light, carbon dioxide is absorbed by the leaf; as it is used, even more diffuses in from the air through the leaf stomata (microscopic holes, often on the underside). In the chloroplasts the carbon dioxide is chemically reduced by hydrogen that comes from the splitting of water. This process is called carbon fixation and is not directly light dependent. Sugars, starch and other compounds are synthesised inside the leaf cells. Pupils should appreciate that it is these compounds in crops that end up being the food for us and for farm animals.

The composition of the atmosphere reflects the balance of the relationship between the global processes of photosynthesis on the one hand and the processes of burning and respiration on the other. In the atmosphere, carbon dioxide is surprisingly scarce (0.037%, i.e. 370 ppm) but is steadily increasing by approximately one part in a million per year. The burning of fossil fuels and the destruction of forests has changed the balance. Pupils should appreciate that rising carbon dioxide levels are the major contributor to increased global warming (see Chapter 9).

Figure 2.3
Carbon dioxide output and intake by a leaf is related to light intensity. (From Nuffield Biology Book III (1966), p. 118. Harlow, Longman.)

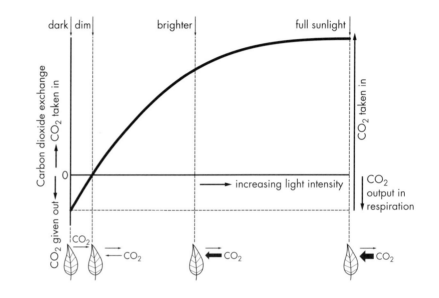

◆ *A teaching sequence*

At age 16 pupils certainly do not need more than the level of knowledge above. But they do find photosynthesis hard to get into (see Barker & Carr, 1989 and Stavy *et al.*, 1987). As Barker and Carr explain, pupils do not, at the outset, see the whole process sufficiently as being about 'producing a solid carbohydrate product' and, furthermore, the notion that plants take up an invisible gas in minute amounts through their leaves and combine it with water to produce this 'food' and oxygen seems too much of an intangible fairy story. Additionally, pupils find it hard to conceptualise how carbohydrate molecules perform their different roles in the working plant. In teaching it is important to clarify learning objectives fully, to reduce them to an achievable level and to adopt some form of constructivist approach. (The David Attenborough BBC video *The Private Life of Plants* provides an excellent introduction to this topic.)

The leaf factory

One useful and well-tried approach with younger pupils is to think initially of the leaf as a factory. Plants make wood, straw, cotton, wheat, potatoes and pineapples. How do they do it? A class might construct posters in which everyday images and language connect the science concepts. Alternatively, cards with plant shapes and products, chemical names and symbols for reactants, and process words may be used in a table-top sorting and grouping exercise.

Have plenty of real plants growing in the classroom environment. Plant anatomy will be revised in the process of learning about photosynthesis in the leaf factory. Green leaves will be seen to face the Sun and are supported by the stem and roots, which bring up water from the soil. In the leaf the light energy of sunshine is captured by chlorophyll molecules becoming excited. This excitation produces the leaf factory's power. Sugars are built in the factory from carbon dioxide and water. Sugar is the factory product; some of it is locally stored as starch and some is exported out of the leaf as a stream of sugar that is transported down the stem to make starch, fibre and wood products. The xylem and phloem are like transport motorways, for water and sugar respectively, to and from the leaf factory.

There are opportunities within all this teaching for language development, in looking at new vocabulary that may be enjoyed. Chloro-phyll is the 'green' of 'the leaf' (meso-phyll is the 'middle' of 'the leaf'). Photo-synthesis is the 'light'-'building' that goes on in the leaf factory. Carbo-hydrate is C-H_2O, its name telling you what it contains. The basic understanding from such a schema could lead straight to experimental work (see next section on *Investigating photosynthetic reactions*). This strategy should help to reinforce some central ideas.

Role play

Most children will be convinced initially that plants are 'fed' through their roots by water and minerals. This simple conceptual view is actually an historic one. An interesting approach to our present understanding might therefore be to take an historical discovery approach. Joannes Baptista van Helmont (1577–1644) discovered that a regularly watered pot plant increased greatly in mass with only a tiny loss of dry mass from the soil. He concluded that plants were made partly from water but must also have taken some other substance from the air because they were made of matter other than water. Over a century and a half later, in 1779, Jan Ingenhousz found out that plants gained this added mass from the carbon dioxide in the air while the Sun shone, and that at night they gave off a little carbon dioxide. By then Joseph Priestley, in 1774, had also discovered that green mint plants in a sealed glass jar in the light would produce oxygen to support a burning candle flame or keep a mouse alive. An historical role play might be developed to tell the story of the discovery of photosynthesis. The different characters could describe their experiments.

Minerals

To most children 'minerals' will be a word with several meanings, e.g. mineral water, mineral ores from the ground, calcium minerals in milk, etc. We need to develop a further plant mineral concept here. Small amounts of soil minerals are needed for plant health (for their different uses see a textbook table). Nitrogen, phosphorus and potassium are all minerals needed by plants. Nitrogen in the form of nitrates and ammonium salts, phosphorus in the form of inorganic phosphates and potassium often as the sulphate are marketed as NPK fertilisers. These are used in farm and garden, and have added greatly to plant productivity.

◆ *Enhancement ideas*

◆ How well are we managing carbon dioxide levels on our planet? Rank order the following practices in order of the amount of carbon dioxide added to or removed from the air (answers in brackets).

- Sustainably harvested fuel wood burning. (A neutral effect, no net gain or loss in carbon dioxide if the forest regrows.)
- Completely clearing forests for fuel. (Only an increase in carbon dioxide unless there is regrowth.)
- Burning coal and oil. (Only an increase in carbon dioxide.)
- Planting forests. (Only a decrease in carbon dioxide, until the forest is mature.)

2.3 Investigating photosynthetic reactions

Extensive opportunity is afforded for investigative work by the practical study of photosynthesis. Useful plants for investigating photosynthesis should be kept in a greenhouse or on the window-sills of the sunny side of the lab (all those listed under *Equipment notes* on page 59 will also thrive under light banks). It is important that control experiments be well designed and that these do not confuse the issue. It is a sophisticated concept that the starch food stored in the leaves of most plants is an indicator of photosynthesis and so may be tested for as a product of photosynthesis. Too often this idea is not on board before leaf testing is done. A positive test for photosynthesis comes from finding starch in a previously destarched plant. Destarching involves forcing the plant to lose its starch. This is done by keeping it in the warm and dark so that it cannot photosynthesise but will respire (see details on leaf testing and *Pelargonium* on page 59). Pondweeds provide the best way of investigating both oxygen production and carbon dioxide uptake or release.

◆ *A teaching sequence*

Advice on leaf testing for starch

Getting this practical to work requires both appropriate preparation by the teacher (see *Useful plants* on page 59) and the following sequence of activities to be undertaken by pupils.

1. Pupils need to record and draw leaf details carefully before testing, e.g. pattern of the variegation.
2. Ensure that the water in the water bath is thoroughly boiling. Boil the leaf (2 minutes), then switch off the Bunsen.
3. When boiling the leaf in ethanol, immerse the leaf in the ethanol in a large test-tube and boil using only heat from a water bath. Continue until all green pigment is gone (2 minutes).

! *Fire hazard from highly flammable ethanol. A risk assessment is needed.*

4. Soften the leaf with water in the water bath (10 seconds).
5. Spread the leaf on a white tile.
6. Cover the leaf with iodine solution (1 minute). Wash off any surplus stain.

! *Eye protection is needed when handling iodine solution.*

7. Draw leaf details again. Starch in formerly green and illuminated cells will stain blue–black.

The role of light

Investigate the role of light in the photosynthetic process. A qualitative starch test with some destarched *Pelargonium* leaves kept in the light and some in the dark establishes the involvement of light. A quantitative test of the relationship between brightness of light and photosynthetic rate may be done using pondweed bubble rate (see Figure 2.5b). Light intensity, I, is related to the distance, D, of the plant from the light source by the formula:

$$I \propto \frac{1}{D^2}$$

Photosynthetic rate increases with increasing light intensity to a plateau level, when some other factor such as carbon dioxide availability becomes limiting.

The products of photosynthesis

Investigate the products of the process of photosynthesis. Food tests may be done with iodine for starch in *Pelargonium* leaves (see above), and with Benedict's reagent for sugar in onion leaves. The bubbled-off gas from pondweed may be tested to see if it is oxygen.

! *Eye protection is needed when handling iodine solution.*

The role of gases

Investigate the role of gases in the process of photosynthesis. Carbon dioxide may be shown to be essential for photosynthesis to occur in a destarched *Pelargonium* leaf trapped in a flask with soda lime to absorb the carbon dioxide (Figure 2.4).

! *Soda lime is corrosive.*

A control (a destarched leaf exposed to the air) is needed. There are many variations on this investigation and it is worth doing well if done at all (see Andrews, 1984).

Figure 2.4
Investigating carbon dioxide as an essential for making starch in a leaf.

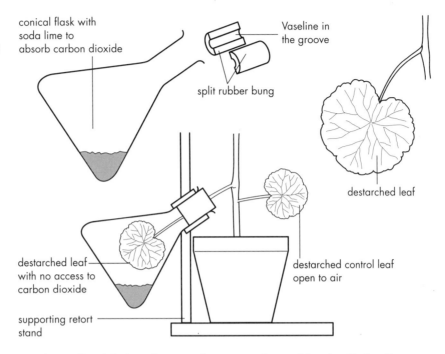

Carbon dioxide is taken up by a pondweed in the light (in water the pH may rise from 6.5 to 8.5). This is easily measured with a pH probe, nested in the rosette of the pondweed (see Figure 2.5). There are many opportunities for ICT and data-logging here; an oxygen probe can measure the level of oxygen over several days and nights (see Bowron, 1992).

Figure 2.5
a *Recording changes in dissolved carbon dioxide with a pH probe and* **b** *counting bubble rate from a pondweed. (Note the inverted weed in* **b**.)

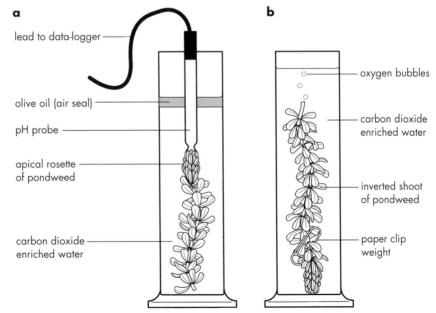

Photosynthesis and respiration

Within a balanced ecosystem photosynthesis and respiration compensate for each other in terms of gases used and produced. The light intensity at which the carbon dioxide output and uptake of a plant are in balance is termed the light compensation point. This phenomenon may be investigated with hydrogencarbonate indicator by moving a plant nearer to or further from a light source to find the balance point where the indicator goes neither yellow nor purple.

Plant growth

Investigate the production involved in plant growth. Duckweed growth may be measured by counting fronds: frond number may double in 3 days. Growing radishes under different light intensity or mineral supplies and recording their size or mass may help demonstrate some photosynthetic requirements. Growing plants from seed in a garden (peas or radishes) or under a light bank (peas or fast plants) is always instructive.

◆ *Further activities*

- ◆ What is the effect of the colour of the light on the bubble rate of a pondweed? Carry out an investigation with a slide projector and the colour filters used in physics laboratories.
- ◆ Carry out an investigation of the different pigments in chlorophyll by means of thin layer chromatography of a plant leaf extract (refer to SAPS in *Other resources*).
- ◆ Investigate the role of temperature in photosynthesis. Water plants warmed to 30 °C photosynthesise faster (bubble rate increases). A challenging extension is to investigate the significance of the thermal expansion of bubbles and changes in gas solubility with temperature, as opposed to photosynthesis alone, in bubble generation.
- ◆ Computer simulations of photosynthesis (such as that in the Logal Explorer Series, refer to *Teaching resources*) may be used to explore what happens graphically when different variables are changed.

2.4 Animal nutrition

◆ *Previous knowledge and experience*

Many pupils will have experience of looking after small mammals and observing their feeding habits. Pupils will have studied a variety of living organisms in different habitats. They will appreciate that all animals require food and that they obtain this food from plants and/or other animals. Most pupils will have some understanding of food chains and simple food webs. Many pupils will state that food is eaten to provide energy.

◆ *A teaching sequence*

It may be best to work initially from an ecological approach that builds on pupils' prior experiences. Animals are unable to produce carbohydrates from raw materials in the way that plants do. Therefore, all animals are dependent on plants for supplies of matter and energy. The way in which matter and energy is transferred between plants and animals, or from one animal to another, can be represented by food chains and webs like those shown in Chapter 9. Figure 2.6 summarises the human food web. The arrows indicate the direction of the flow of energy and matter along the chain: at each stage in the chain energy is dissipated and matter is either used or stored. (Further discussion of food chains and webs will be found in Chapter 9.)

Figure 2.6
The human food web.

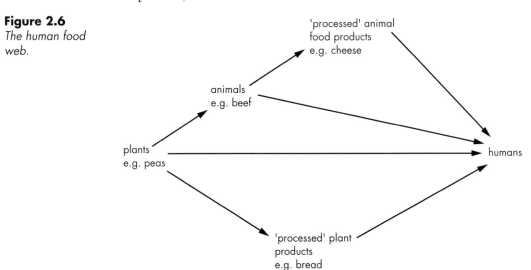

Food and nutrients

Pupils frequently find it difficult to make links between the food they eat and nutrients. When secondary pupils are asked to group foods they rarely base their groups on nutrients; more commonly they use either food groups similar to those shown in Figure 2.7 (the system currently being promoted by the UK Department of Health) or divide foods into those that are healthy and those that they believe to be unhealthy. Allowing pupils to group foods in different ways provides a good starting point for work on nutrients and for exploring the reasons for grouping foods.

Figure 2.7
The balanced diet. (Based on Department of Health, 1996.)

fruit and vegetables

bread, other cereals and potatoes

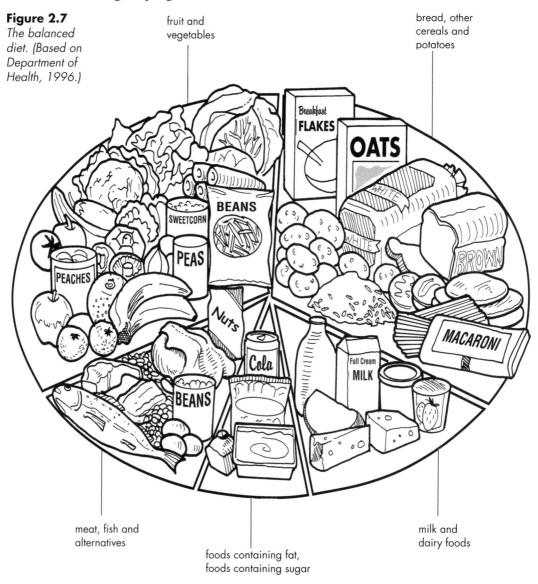

meat, fish and alternatives

foods containing fat, foods containing sugar

milk and dairy foods

Nutrient groups are based on the chemical composition of different food substances and the ways in which these chemicals are used in the body of the organism, for instance for repair of tissues. Humans, like all living organisms, require water in addition to food containing carbohydrates, proteins, fats, minerals and vitamins and fibre. Whilst all pupils can begin to identify the nutrient content of different foods, study of the chemistry of nutrients is only appropriate for pupils post-16.

The requirement for different amounts and types of nutrients by individuals as well as by different groups of humans, e.g. young children or pregnant women, can be linked to work on diet and health. The importance of specific nutrients in the maintenance of health rather than effects of deficiencies needs to be stressed. People who have access to sufficient food often eat a varied diet that contains all the nutrients required to keep them healthy. However, the importance of vitamins and mineral elements such as iron and calcium need highlighting in view of the evidence from surveys of food intakes by young people that are discussed later.

Sources of nutrients

The foods shown in Figure 2.7 could be used as the basis for developing a table that indicates which nutrients are contained by a sample of foods on the plate (an example is shown in Table 2.1 overpage). Pupils can use food composition tables in books, computer programs or information on food labels to undertake the analysis; the level of detail will depend on the age of the pupils. Such analyses will indicate that foods that are eaten contain a range of nutrients and that the proportion of nutrients in different foods varies. Comparisons can be made also of the 'energy content' of different foods and, with older pupils, different types of fat (saturated animal fat and unsaturated fat in vegetable oil).

Sample foods from a packed lunch provide an appropriate context for investigating the nutrient content of different foods. Foods can be tested to indicate the presence of different nutrients such as starch, sugars, protein, fats and specific vitamins. Pupils can also investigate the relative amounts of vitamin C in different fruit juices and fruit drinks. These tests can be linked to comparisons based on data from food labels and computer analyses.

Table 2.1 *What's on the label? What do foods contain?*

		Nutrient content per 100 g												
		Energy	Carbohydrate	Protein	Fat	Fibre	Sodium	Iron	Ca	Vit A	Vit B$_6$	Vit C	Vit D	Folic acid
Fruit and vegetables	peas	250 kJ	9.7 g	6.0 g	0.9 g	5.1 g	0.1 g					12 mg	–	47 µg
	apples	208 kJ	11.6 g	0.4 g	0.1 g	1.8 g	0.1 g							
	new potatoes*	321 kJ	17.8 g	1.5 g	0.3 g	1.1 g	0.1 g				0.3 µg			
Bread, other cereals	bread, brown (whole grain)	847 kJ	34.8 g	10.0 g	2.3 g	7.0 g	0.7 g							
	bread, white	1093 kJ	52.7 g	7.7 g	1.8 g	2.3 g	0.5 g							
Milk and dairy foods	crème fraîche	685 kJ	5.8 g	2.7 g	14.6 g	nil	trace							
Meat, fish and alternatives	eggs	612 kJ	less than 0.1 g	12.5 g	10.8 g	nil	0.1 g				B$_{12}$ 1.3 µg		1.5 µg	
Foods containing fat	butter	3017 kJ	0.7 g	10.5 g	81.1 g	–	0.8 g			1000 µg				
Foods containing sugar	Danish pastry	1653 kJ	50.0 g	6.5 g	21.7 g	1.7 g	0.4 g							

*Potatoes are often grouped with bread and other cereals.

Pupils will be familiar with the energy content of different foods from looking at food packets. The way in which the energy content of foods is determined by food scientists and manufacturers can be demonstrated using a calorimeter. As an alternative pupils can burn small quantities of food, such as nuts, below a test-tube containing a small quantity of water (this is a simple calorimeter) and measure the increase in temperature of the water. This investigation is well covered by most texts. This activity can also be used to show that carbon dioxide and water vapour are produced when the nut burns. Pupils need to be encouraged to identify the similarities and differences between the burning nut and what happens in the body during respiration. This investigation also lends itself admirably to the discussion of accuracy in experiments.

! *Peanut burning requires a risk assessment because of the possibility of pupil allergy. It may be wise to use pasta or savoury snack foods instead.*

Food chains and webs

The ideal starting point for this topic is first hand observation, e.g. observing organisms in a pond or in leaf litter. However, it is rare to be able to observe the organisms involved in an entire food chain feeding at any one time. An alternative approach is to start the topic by brainstorming on what pupils already know and following this by the type of activities described in Chapter 9, which build on pupils' prior experiences. Observation of, and discussion about, human eating behaviours and food consumption can provide insights into the human food chain, which includes consumption of processed plant and animal foods. The similarities and differences between the human food web, illustrated in Figure 2.6 on page 45, and other food webs are worth exploring; links can also be made here to food production and food processing.

♦ *Enhancement ideas*

- ♦ Although cats are carnivores they also chew plants – what substances might they need in their diet that can only be supplied by plants?

2.5 Feeding and digestion

◆ *Previous knowledge and experience*

The majority of pupils will recognise that when food is eaten it is changed in some way in the body. They can explain what happens to food in the mouth in terms of the physical composition of the food; but the nature of the chemical changes in the mouth and other parts of the alimentary canal ('gut') will not be understood. Pupils will have little understanding of the nature of the alimentary canal or the functions and structure of different parts of the digestive system. Many 11 year olds will not appreciate that the 'gut' is a tube; they may not make connections between food being swallowed and the production of faeces.

Pupils often find it difficult to recognise that the principles of feeding and digestion and egestion of waste are the same in all animals:

- most animals have a gut, i.e. a tube along which food passes from the mouth to the anus; this is through the body but not a part of it
- many animals break the food down mechanically either before it is ingested (taken into the body) or soon after, e.g. in the mouth or first part of the gut
- as food passes along the gut it is acted upon by chemicals that help to break down complex molecules into simpler molecules
- the breakdown of food substances is speeded up by biological catalysts called enzymes
- foods contain chemically different food substances that are acted upon by different enzymes in the gut
- the smaller molecules pass into the body proper of the animals and are used for maintenance, growth and development of the organism
- any food that cannot be broken down and/or utilised is egested.

◆ *A teaching sequence*

It is logical to follow a journey through the gut.

Ingestion

The ingestion of food by different organisms can provide insights into the range of different mechanisms used, including the 'engulfing' of food by amoebae; anemones ensnaring organisms with their tentacles; snails grinding away at plants;

aphids sucking up sap from leaves; and water fleas or brine shrimps filter feeding on algae. Analogies can be used to help pupils to identify the mechanical actions used, e.g. the 'syringe' used by mosquitoes and the scissor-like action by which leaf-eating ants cut up leaves. First hand observations can be augmented by video, CD ROMs and slides.

Many schools have a selection of skulls and teeth from different mammals, including:

- herbivores, e.g. cows and sheep
- carnivores, e.g. cats and dogs
- insectivores, e.g. shrews
- omnivores, e.g. humans.

Teeth from different animals can be placed in a cloth bag (the 'feely' bags used by darkroom photographers are ideal). One pupil then places both hands in the bag and describes the shape of the teeth to others in the group, who then match the description to the relevant skull. The activity increases observation – and language – skills. Such work can lead on to further observations of other characteristics of the skulls and teeth, including the articulation of the jaw, the position of the eyes on the head, and the type of teeth displayed in herbivores, carnivores and omnivores. Pupils can also study their own teeth and create dental records as shown in Figure 2.8.

Figure 2.8
Developing a dental record form.

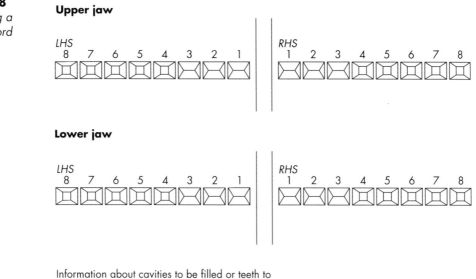

Although the outer enamel layer of the tooth is one of the hardest substances in the body it can be destroyed by the action of acids. Pupils can investigate the effects of different acids and fizzy drinks on teeth (the labels provide information about the components of the drink). Sterilised human teeth may sometimes be obtainable from a dentist.

Digestion

The principles of digestion, by which large molecules are broken down into smaller ones before being absorbed by the body in the intestine, can be demonstrated to younger pupils. They can be introduced to the importance of enzymes (biological catalysts) in the process of digestion through:

- first hand experience of the action of salivary amylase on starch through chewing a piece of bread for a minute and noting what happens to the bread (pupils should be able to note changes in taste as well as the consistency of the bread)
- investigation of the effect of salivary amylase on starch (or foods containing starch, such as bread); iodine can be used to demonstrate the presence of starch before and after the amylase is added. Commercially available amylase might be used as it is very occasionally not permissible to use human saliva as a reagent in the laboratory. Check with the school authorities/LEA, etc. (DfEE, 1996).

! *If human saliva is used, pupils should produce their own samples, rinse out glassware and place used glassware in a washing-up bowl of dilute bleach before normal washing-up.*

! *Eye protection is needed when handling iodine solution.*

Older pupils can investigate the breakdown of starch to sugars by amylase. Benedict's solution can be used to test for the presence of sugars before and after adding amylase to the starch solution.

! *Eye protection is needed when handling Benedict's solution.*

Models, including that of the human torso, can be used with pupils of all ages to demonstrate the structure and functioning of different parts of the mammalian gut. Links can be made to work on teeth by demonstrating that the structure of the gut is related to the diet; for instance the guts of carnivores, such as cats, are much shorter than those of herbivores. Pupils can be encouraged to make their own models of the gut using 'junk' material, such as plastic containers and egg boxes. As an extension activity pupils could be asked to create a simple 'dynamic' model to show how, for example, a cheese sandwich is digested. Such activities provide opportunities for pupils to clarify their ideas and are particularly valuable for pupils with special educational needs. Describing their models to others allows pupils to demonstrate their understanding of the process of digestion. Discussion of the limitations of models provides opportunities to explore how the efficiency of the digestive process can be increased, e.g. by increasing the surface area of the gut.

Figure 2.9
Modelling absorption from the gut. (From Nuffield Biology Book III (1966), p. 96. Harlow, Longman.)

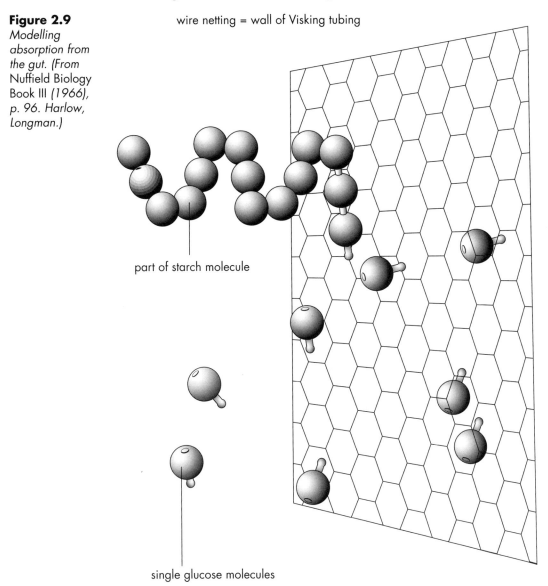

wire netting = wall of Visking tubing

part of starch molecule

single glucose molecules

Pupils often find it difficult to envisage the length of the human gut and a piece of string is an inexpensive but effective way of demonstrating this length. Inventive teachers have been known to knit a model gut (Healey, 1987) to illustrate the different parts and the overall length! Most teachers prefer not to use dissection, but this may occasionally have its place in good teaching. The structure and function of different parts of the alimentary canal in humans and other mammals can be linked to investigations of how different nutrients, such as fat or carbohydrate, are digested. Such studies link also to Chapter 10 where the action of microbes in the gut is discussed.

Peristaltic action can be easily demonstrated using a tennis ball pushed along a sock or nylon stocking. Lego building blocks provide a useful resource for illustrating how large complex molecules can be broken down, e.g. starch to sucrose or glucose.

The passage of molecules across the wall of the gut can be simulated by means of simple models; Lego or poppit beads and netting or chicken wire can be used to show how small molecules can pass through a model membrane when larger molecules cannot (see Figure 2.9). With older pupils dialysis tubing can be used to demonstrate how starch molecules are unable to pass through the cellulose membrane whereas smaller sugar molecules can.

Egestion

Pupils often find it difficult to distinguish between excretion and egestion. Excretion is the process by which waste substances produced by the body are eliminated. Egestion describes the process by which food substances which cannot be broken down or absorbed during digestion are eliminated.

♦ *Further activities*

- ♦ Investigate the action of proteases on foods such as solid egg white, and of lipase on full cream milk.
- ♦ Investigate whether the digestion of starch by amylase is affected by factors such as different pH, temperature and salinity.
- ♦ Find out from the school library/resource centre exactly what happens to food in the stomach.

2.6 Human diet and health

◆ *Previous knowledge and experience*

The majority of 11 year olds will recognise nutrient terms like fat, salt, sugar and vitamins, and some will have heard of iron and calcium. However, fewer will recognise words like carbohydrate, protein or mineral (other than in the context of 'mineral water'). Most pupils will be able to list foods that contain salt, sugar and vitamin C; other vitamins are more problematic. The function of nutrients and fibre in the body is not likely to be understood, other than in general terms such as 'sugar gives you energy'. Many pupils have some understanding of the need for 'balance', i.e. variety and correct proportion, in the diet and can distinguish between foods perceived as healthy and/or unhealthy (see Turner, 1997 and Banet & Nunez, 1997).

◆ *A teaching sequence*

What do we eat?

The reasons for individual food choices are complex. Asking pupils to complete a 24-hour recall diary (see Table 2.2) can provide a starting point for work in this area. What is written is best kept confidential as young people can be very sensitive about what they eat, particularly those who may be suffering from eating disorders (the incidence of anorexia is rising amongst teenagers, both girls and boys). It is worth emphasising that the diet for any one day may not be typical of dietary intake as a whole.

Table 2.2 *Food diary: what did you eat yesterday?*

Time of day	What did you eat/drink?	Where did you eat?	Who was with you?	Why did you eat/drink these things?
7.30 am	Cereal with milk; cup of tea with milk and sugar	At home	No-one today; sometimes with my sister	I always have this for breakfast
8.30 am	*Kit-kat*	On the way to school	My friend	We go past the shop on the way to school; I like chocolate
10.30 am	Orange juice; bun and crisps	At school	Friends	It was break and I was hungry, etc.

Making choices; keeping a balance

Food diaries can be used as a basis for discussion about why food choices are made (see Figure 2.10) and even why we may not be truthful in reporting what we eat. Such discussion should be linked to current government advice on diet and health (Coles & Turner, 1995) and illustrated by the 'plate' shown in Figure 2.7 on page 46 that stresses the importance of a varied diet containing plenty of fruit and vegetables.

Figure 2.10
Factors that influence food choice.

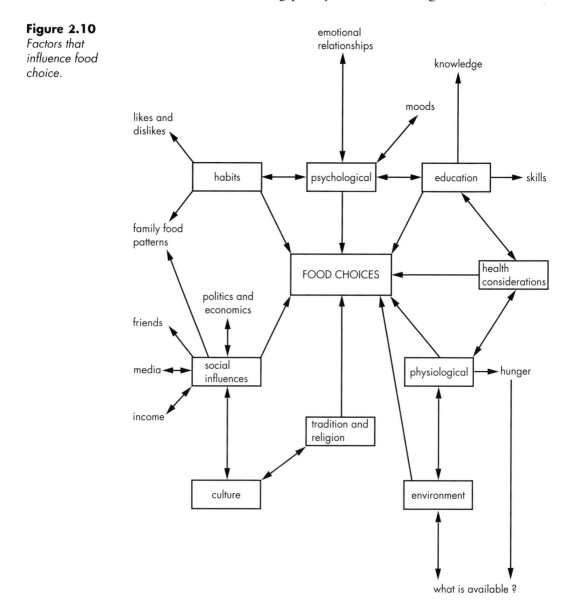

Pupils can investigate and monitor their intakes of specific nutrients and estimate energy intakes, using computer programs (e.g. *Eatmeter* produced by the British Nutrition Foundation) or food composition tables. Data on individual food intakes need to be treated with caution; careful weighing and accurate recording of what is eaten is required over a period of some days. Surveys investigating nutrient intakes among 5 to 16 year olds (e.g. Department of Health, 1989) have indicated that:

- on average children were consuming 90% of the recommended energy (see overpage on *Exercise and health*)
- the main sources of dietary energy were bread, chips, milk, biscuits, meat products, cake and puddings
- at the time of the study about 75% of children were eating more fat than the 35% of food energy recommended
- average intakes of protein and vitamins, including thiamin, nicotinic acid and vitamin C, for both girls and boys were above the recommended amounts
- intakes of riboflavin (vitamin B_2) among older girls (14–15 years) were below recommended levels
- average intakes of iron among girls were below the recommended levels
- about 60% of girls in the surveys consumed less than the recommended daily amount of calcium; the mean intake for boys was above the recommended daily amount.

Although the surveys suggested that some young people had intakes of iron below the recommended levels they may still have had an adequate intake to meet their own individual requirements. However, some of the findings are cause for concern, particularly the low level of iron intakes in one in three girls. Low iron intakes may be the result of dieting to lose weight involving the exclusion of certain foods thought to be fattening, such as potatoes, that contain ample vitamins and minerals. Survey data of this type can be used as a basis for older pupils to develop advice on diets for different groups of people, such as young athletes.

There is some suggestion that an increasing number of young people are becoming vegetarian for non-religious reasons. Vegetarian diets can be satisfactory if they are not too high in fat. Vegan diets are much more restrictive and the intake of some nutrients (most commonly vitamin B_{12} and, typically, iodine and riboflavin) may be inadequate, as they depend on the effect of the rest of the diet for their absorption.

Young people who become vegans require professional advice and support.

Analysis of nutrient intakes can be linked to practical work that investigates the nutrient and energy composition of different foods as well as sources of specific nutrients.

Exercise and health

A key factor in maintaining health appears to be the frequency and type of exercise taken by individuals. In recording dietary intakes pupils could also include information on the type and amount of exercise they have taken. Work in this area links to Chapter 4 (page 79) and to physical education programmes. Although energy intakes in the UK have been falling during the past two decades the incidence of obesity and lack of fitness in young people is a cause for concern. The reduction in the amount of exercise taken by young people has been identified as one reason for the increasing number of overweight pupils. Low exercise, and low calcium intake, in young people is also linked to low bone density in adults, which is a contributing factor in the development of osteoporosis in later life.

Some young people who engage in competitive sports adopt rigorous diets in an attempt to improve their performance. Where minimal body fat is desirable, as in gymnastics or distance running, weight control may become compulsive, leading to undernutrition.

Food production

The economics of food production and distribution are important factors in the availability of food that contributes to a healthy diet. Work on food production links to the study of plant growth described in this chapter, to food preservation and making food products using biotechnology, as discussed in Chapter 10, as well as to work in geography and technology. Pupils can investigate the parts of plants that are eaten by humans and other animals – which links to the study of food webs and chains in Chapter 9 – and the nutrient content of different parts of plants.

◆ *Further activities*

◆ Devise an experimental method or find out by library/ multimedia research what proportion of a cabbage is fibre.
◆ Use DCPIP to investigate the vitamin C content of fresh apple juice from a carton, apple juice from an apple (use a blender) and carton apple juice after standing for a day at room temperature and for a day in a refrigerator. Control experiments with solutions of known strength may be made from vitamin C tablets.

◆ *Enhancement ideas*

◆ Could the population of the UK maintain a healthy diet without any food imports?
◆ Wasting food. What proportion of food plants, such as wheat, tomatoes or peas, is eaten by humans? What happens to the parts not eaten by humans?

Equipment notes

◆ *Useful plants*

Get to know these plants well.

The *Pelargonium* plant is often incorrectly called a geranium. These are subtropical (South African) plants, tolerant of drought and classroom neglect! Variegated plants are useful to show the significance of chlorophyll. Dark green plants are best for high starch yields. Destarching should be done in a warm, dark place (cupboard) with a well-watered plant for 2 full days. At a pinch, a plant will destarch overnight in an airing cupboard. After 4 days in the dark a plant will begin to suffer and its leaves go yellow!

Elodea and *Lagarosiphon* species are pondweeds that bubble oxygen well and demonstrably absorb carbon dioxide from surrounding water (see Figure 2.5 on page 43). To photosynthesise well these need to be actively growing and warm, with carbon dioxide enriched water. The plant is naturally buoyed up by the gas produced. If cut, inverted and weighed down with a paper clip in a measuring cylinder or large test-tube the cut stems will bubble freely. The plants seal these 'wounds', sometimes quite quickly, so you may need to recut them to ensure that they bubble freely. Although oxygen is liberated, gaseous diffusion will occur from the water into the bubble so that the collected 'oxygen' may be partly nitrogen and carbon dioxide. If the gas is collected quickly, the gas will relight a glowing splint, or at least show it glowing more brightly.

Lemna minor, the common (lesser) duckweed, is useful for production studies. Leaves (strictly speaking they are fronds) may easily be counted and leaf 'doubling time' may be less than 4 days. *Raphanus sativa*, the radish, is a very fast-growing plant in warm and well lit conditions. It is ideal for plant growth (production) studies or for investigating the effects of fertilisers at different concentrations on growth. Seedlings form a substantial plant in 4 weeks. Rapid-cycling *Brassicas*, the so-called 'fast plants', are useful for many aspects of plant science (see *Other resources*).

Other useful materials, equipment and procedures

Hydrogencarbonate indicator is a cheap and readily available reagent for the teaching of photosynthesis and respiration and may be purchased as a stock solution or made up directly. (The indicator contains the dyes thymol blue and cresol red and is buffered in sodium hydrogencarbonate.) Diluted, the solution is an orange–red colour at equilibrium with atmospheric air, yellower with more carbon dioxide and more red–purple with less carbon dioxide.

Indicator colour	Yellow	Orange–red	Red–purple
Carbon dioxide concentration	High: >500 ppm	As in air: 370 ppm	<300 ppm

Hydrogencarbonate indicator is relatively non-toxic to plants and animals. Some of the solution in a test-tube just covering a piece of pondweed (and sealed to the air) will, in the light, go more purple in half an hour (CO_2 used up) or, in the dark, go more yellow (CO_2 produced). The pondweed will be unaffected by the indicator over a period of days.

Many school experiments with plants fail because of lack of light and warmth for growth. One simple solution is to build a light bank (see under SAPS in *Other resources*). This consists of four to six parallel strip light tubes supported above the laboratory bench. Many plants will grow well under such conditions.

Other resources

- The SAPS programme is a charity set up to promote the teaching of plant science and molecular biology in schools and colleges. It provides advice on the construction of light banks. Further information can be obtained from Science and Plants for Schools (SAPS), Homerton College, Hills Road, Cambridge CB2 2PH (tel: 01223 507168).

    SAPS has developed a moderated and interactive plant science site for schools on the internet (website: www-saps.plantsci.cam.ac.uk).

- The rapid-cycling *Brassica* kits are available from Philip Harris Ltd, Lynn Lane, Shenstone, Lichfield, Staffs. WS14 0EE (tel: 01543 480077; fax: 01543 480068). Each kit contains a comprehensive set of documentation written by the SAPS team with advice on growing the plants, ideas for investigations and student sheets. Seeds of the rapid-cycling *Brassicas* and replacement growing materials are also available from Blades Biological, Cowden, Edenbridge, Kent TN8 7DX (tel: 01342 850242).

◆ *Teaching resources*

- Attenborough, David. *The Private Life of Plants* (video). London, BBC Publications. Provides an excellent introduction to photosynthesis.
- *Photosynthesis*, Logal Explorer Series (for PC or Mac) is available from Philip Harris Ltd.
- *Food: a Fact of Life* (1996). British Nutrition Foundation/Ministry of Agriculture, Fisheries and Food.
- *Energy and Nutrients (for pupils aged 11–16 years)*. The *Eatmeter* computer program is available from British Nutrition Foundation, High Holborn House, 52–54 High Holborn, London WC1V 6RQ.
- The nutrition section of Microsoft's *Encarta* CD ROM. Using this a pupil's food intake can be matched to a large database of foods and their nutrients. It is available from AVP, School Hill Centre, Chepstow, Gwent NP6 5PH (tel: 01291 625439; website: www.avp.com).

◆ *Useful addresses*

British Dietetic Association, Elizabeth House, 22 Suffolk Street, Queensway, Birmingham B1 1LS (tel: 0121 643 5483).

British Heart Foundation, 14 Fitzhardinge Street, London W1H 4DH (tel: 0171 935 0185).

The British Nutrition Foundation, High Holborn House, 52–54 High Holborn, London WC1V 6RQ (tel: 0171 404 6504).

The Health Education Authority, Health Promotion and Information Centre, Trevelyan House, Great Peter Street, London SW1P 2HW (tel: 0171 222 5300).

◆ *Background reading*

Department of Health (1991). *Dietary Reference Values for Food Energy and Nutrients for the United Kingdom. Reports of the Panel on Dietary Reference Values of the Committee on Medical Aspects of Food Policy.* Report on Health and Social Subjects No. 41. London, HMSO.

Osborne, J., Wadsworth, P. & Black, P. (1992). *Processes of Life – Primary SPACE Research Report.* Liverpool, Liverpool University Press.

World Health Organisation (1993). *Health for All Targets: the Health Policy for Europe.* European Health for All Series, No. 4. Geneva, WHO.

References

Andrews, I. (1984). A simple way to show that carbon dioxide is needed for photosynthesis. *School Science Review*, **65** (232), pp. 499–501.

Banet, E. & Nunez, F. (1997). Teaching and learning about human nutrition: a constructivist approach. *International Journal of Science Education*, **19**, pp. 1169–1194.

Barker, M. & Carr, M. (1989). Photosynthesis – can our pupils see the wood for the trees? *Journal of Biological Education*, **23**, pp. 41–44.

Boohan, R. & Ogborn, J. (1996). *Energy and Change.* Hatfield, Association for Science Education.

Bowron, G. (1992). Measuring photosynthesis in the classroom. *School Science Review*, **73** (265), pp. 85–87.

Coles, A. & Turner, S.A. (1995). *Diet and Health in School Age Children*. London, Health Education Authority.

Department of Health (1989). *The Diets of British Schoolchildren*. Report on Health and Social Subjects No. 36. Sub-committee on Nutritional Surveillance Committee on Medical Aspects of Food Policy. London, HMSO.

Department of Health (1996). *Guidelines On Educational Materials Concerned With Nutrition*. London, Department of Health.

Department for Employment and Education (1996). *Safety in Science Education*. London, HMSO.

Healey, J. (1987). 'Knit yourself a gut'. *Journal of Biological Education*, **21**, p. 85.

Stavy, R., Eisen, Y. & Yaakobi, D. (1987). How students aged 13–15 understand photosynthesis. *International Journal of Science Education*, **9**, pp. 105–115.

Turner, S.A. (1997). Children's understanding of food and health in primary classrooms. *International Journal of Science Education*, **19**, pp. 491–508.

3 *Transport within organisms*

David Baylis

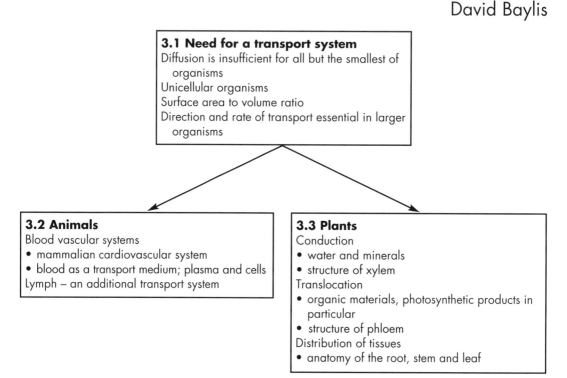

3.1 Need for a transport system
Diffusion is insufficient for all but the smallest of
  organisms
Unicellular organisms
Surface area to volume ratio
Direction and rate of transport essential in larger
  organisms

3.2 Animals
Blood vascular systems
• mammalian cardiovascular system
• blood as a transport medium; plasma and cells
Lymph – an additional transport system

3.3 Plants
Conduction
• water and minerals
• structure of xylem
Translocation
• organic materials, photosynthetic products in
  particular
• structure of phloem
Distribution of tissues
• anatomy of the root, stem and leaf

◆ *Choosing a route*

It is helpful to get the pupils to identify the factors, at a very
simple level, that may have 'pressured' the evolution of
transport systems.

Secondary school pupils seem to have an innate aversion to
the study of plants. Most pupils respond better to animal-
related topics than to plant-related topics. Perhaps they find
animals easier to relate to. Many will have or have had pets. In
their words animals 'look alive' and 'do things' whereas 'plants
simply exist' and 'nothing appears to be going on at all in
plants'. The very easy demonstration of chloroplastic cyclosis in
Elodea is a dramatic demonstration that plants are 'doing
things' – even at the cellular level.

As a result, once the ideas behind the evolution of transport
systems have been discussed it is probably advisable to
concentrate in the first instance on transport in humans.

3.1 Need for a transport system

◆ *Previous knowledge and experience*

Pupils are likely to have met the idea that organisms need food and oxygen, and produce and get rid of wastes. What they are unlikely to have done is to have considered the common principles involved in the transport systems of different organisms.

◆ *A teaching sequence*

Diffusion as a means of transport

A good way to start this series of lessons is to get the pupils to look at some pond water or cultures of unicellular organisms or simple filamentous algae. Ask the pupils to consider the following questions while they are looking at the organisms and to write down their thoughts as they go along. Less able pupils might benefit from a clear, structured worksheet to help them organise their thinking.

- How do these organisms interact with their environment?
- What do organisms take from their environment?
- What wastes do organisms release into their immediate surroundings?
- How do materials move into and out of the cells?

Most pupils find looking at these organisms with a low power microscope fascinating and get quite excited by the experience. Often the problem is getting them to stop!

Pupils will understand that the organisms they have been looking at are very small, and that the maximum distance over which exchanges take place is extremely small. More able pupils are likely to suggest that diffusion is involved in the exchanges between cells and their immediate environment; others may need more help getting there. A simple demonstration of diffusion of a solution like potassium manganate(VII) in water will help to establish or reinforce the idea of diffusion as a likely process, but a random and relatively slow one.

Surface area to volume ratios

The concept of decreasing relative surface area with increasing volume is always tricky for pupils. Plasticine models, which can be rolled out into different shapes, are a nice way of getting over the problem: while mass and volume do not change, the surface area can be altered quickly and substantially. The changes that take place in the surface area to volume ratio, as organisms of increasing mass and volume are considered, can also be demonstrated quickly using model animals represented by cubes – where doubling the linear dimension increases the surface area by a factor of four but the volume by eight. The area of surface available for exchange and diffusion alone is enough to supply the needs of a unicellular organism. The increasing volume and distance from deeply seated cells to the relatively smaller exchange surface make diffusion alone too slow and haphazard as the sole means of exchange for larger organisms. The evolution of transport systems that give faster delivery, and delivery with direction, has overcome both these inadequacies.

Pupils might carry out an investigation into the effect of decreasing surface area to volume ratios on surface exchange using agar or gelatine cubes and an aqueous solution of a food dye or, for example, 1% aqueous methylene blue. Cubes of differing sizes immersed in the dye could be sectioned after a fixed time to see the extent of 'delivery' by diffusion alone. You will need to have tested this earlier to find out when to section the cubes to give a clear difference.

It is important to get pupils to appreciate that common principles are involved in transport systems in larger animals and plants: only the details differ.

◆ *Further activities*

- ◆ Pupils might be encouraged to think about other problems for living organisms that may be associated with an increase in size. Examples could include a review of the way gases are exchanged in larger organisms, how temperature control is achieved and the way physical support is maintained.
- ◆ Pupils could do some individual research on the size of different living organisms. They could find out which are the biggest organisms, plants as well as animals, in different types of habitat. If they have access to appropriate data they might compare the maximum size shown by terrestrial and aquatic organisms from the same phylum.

3.2 Animals

◆ *Previous knowledge and experience*

Pupils are likely to have met little specific information about circulatory systems. They will probably have met the heart as an organ and perhaps blood as a tissue. Most pupils will recognise that the food they take in through their mouths and the oxygen in the air they breathe must get around their body somehow. They are likely to know that a pump is required to circulate blood to all parts of the body and that the heart functions as a muscular pump. They will have met the idea that blood flows around the body in blood vessels. Some pupils will appreciate that arteries carry blood away from the heart and that veins carry blood back towards the heart, irrespective of their relative oxygen content. A common misconception here is that arteries always carry oxygen and veins always carry carbon dioxide. It is worth correcting this misconception as soon as possible by establishing direction of flow relative to the heart as the distinguishing feature. It is likely that you will have to remind some pupils of this on several occasions.

Pupils are also likely to have some idea about the effects of different lifestyles on the health of the heart, if not from classroom teaching then from the media. They will certainly have been exposed to information about the possible harmful effects of tobacco and alcohol on the circulatory system.

◆ *A teaching sequence*

By the end of this section of work pupils should be able to offer answers to some or all of the following questions:

- What are the basic components of the blood circulatory system?
- Where do materials get into and out of the transport system?
- How do materials get into and out of the transport system?
- What acts as the transport media?
- How does blood function as a transport medium?
- What part does the lymph system play in transport?

As always at the start of a new topic, you will need to establish how much the pupils already know from their previous work on their science course and their general background knowledge. The way you do this will depend on your own preference but could involve:

- your posing simple questions during a 'scene-setting' session when you outline the learning objectives for the section
- using a simple worksheet, in the form of a questionnaire
- setting up a quiz, with small groups writing questions about the topic based on what they 'know' already, followed by a short, structured, question-and-answer session
- getting the pupils to list as many human organ systems as they can with a brief description of their functions
- when time is limiting, simply asking them to identify where food gets into the body, where oxygen gets in and how they think these substances get to where they are needed.

Group feedback, however obtained, will give you a feel for where the pupils are with respect to the topic.

Mammalian cardiovascular system

The class could observe a demonstration dissection of a small mammal but there are now plenty of video programmes to get the teaching points across just as well and often much better. These will show the circulatory system as an organ system.

The pupils could be provided with an exploded human diagram, perhaps asking them to colour in the arterial/venous blood red/blue, respectively. They can refer to standard biology textbooks to help them with this.

Figure 3.1
Blank flow chart of blood circulatory system.

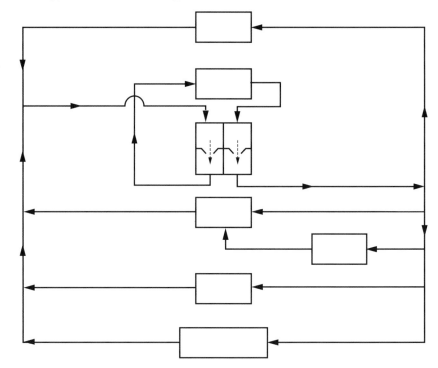

In addition, a flow chart (Figure 3.1) could be built up either on an OHP or on a prepared worksheet. Most standard biology textbooks will have a diagram similar to Figure 3.1 to help the pupils with this task.

It can be difficult to decide whether to involve dissection in a teaching programme or not. Dissection is often an emotive subject and one that a school science/biology department may have a policy statement about.

 Good hygiene is essential during dissection.

The heart

If it were desirable and acceptable and you felt able and happy to do so, it would be appropriate to get the pupils to dissect something like a sheep's heart at this point. However, the dissection is relatively complicated and can take up a lot of time, if the pupils are to get more from it than simply the opportunity to cut something up. A lot will depend on the general attitude of the class. Many pupils may object to dissection and so a valid alternative would need to be provided for them. Whether it is justifiable to use potential food in this way or not could provide a question for class discussion or homework. Also, if time and cost are limiting, as is likely, it might be more economical in both senses to resort once more to a video presentation of the dissection.

Figure 3.2
Dissected heart.

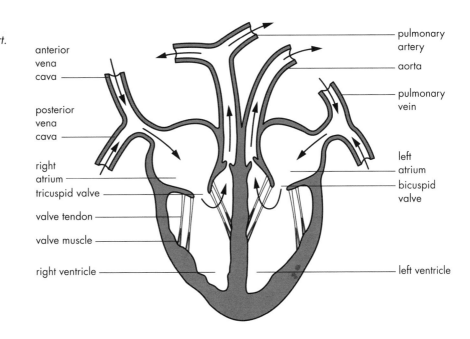

The dissection/video should establish the features shown in Figure 3.2, unlabelled copies of which could be supplied to the pupils. Most standard biology textbooks will have a diagram similar to this.

A video programme showing the sequence of contractions and blood flow through the heart could be used at this stage. Many CD ROMs about the human body include animated sequences of the beating heart that may be useful too.

The following suggestion might be useful for those pupils who have been working with a video. Pupils, working individually or in small groups, could be asked to unscramble the following statements, delivered by OHP and hard copy (see Table 3.1), into a sequence describing the cardiac cycle they have just seen. A second viewing could be paused at appropriate points in the cycle for the pupils to review their original decisions. Feedback from the class can then be used to establish the correct sequence.

Table 3.1 *Suggestion for an OHP master 'Statements summarising the cardiac cycle'.*

Rearrange the letters to show the correct sequence of events taking place during the cardiac cycle. The first and the last have been done for you.

A	Blood passes from the atria into the ventricles.
B	Pressure continues to increase, opening pocket valves at the base of the pulmonary artery and the aorta.
C	Blood enters the atria. Their walls stretch to accommodate the blood.
D	Blood leaves the heart via the pulmonary artery for the lungs and via the aorta for the rest of the body.
E	Pressure increases in the ventricles closing the tricuspid and bicuspid valves, so preventing backflow of blood into the atria.
F	Blood collects in the atria until pressure forces the cuspid valves open.
G	Muscles in the ventricular walls contract.
H	Blood returns to the heart in the vena cavae.

Arteries and veins

It would be appropriate at this point for pupils to use a microscope to look at prepared transverse sections of an artery and a vein. Projected images of the same sections using photomicrographs would be helpful to make sure that pupils are actually focused on what you want them to see. A table, similar to the one shown in Table 3.2, could be supplied if necessary, to direct the pupils' examination of the slides. They could draw and label diagrams of their own if time permits, or be provided with unlabelled diagrams if not. Most standard biology textbooks will have diagrams of transverse sections, or more likely stereo-diagrams, to help the pupils with this task.

Table 3.2 *Table to show differences between arteries and veins.*

Feature	Artery	Vein
Relative thickness of wall		
Amount of elastic tissue, including muscle		
Relative size of lumen		
Valves	No valves present except at the base of the aorta and pulmonary artery	Pocket valves present

Hopefully, after an exercise like the one outlined above, the pupils will recognise that blood vessels bringing blood to the heart (veins) differ in structure from those taking blood away from the heart (arteries) and that the differences reflect the differences in pressures that they have to accommodate.

There are now quite a number of good three-dimensional models of arteries and veins showing the differential thickness of the walls, valves etc. that the pupils could examine at this stage to reinforce their own findings.

Having identified the pulmonary artery and vein, pupils are also more likely to understand more fully why using 'carry oxygenated versus deoxygenated blood' to distinguish between arteries and veins is not always satisfactory.

Capillaries

Having established how blood is moved around the system, and in a particular direction, the next idea to sort out is how things 'get on and off' the transport system. Pupils know that arteries and veins work as tubes carrying blood from one place to another, and to do so efficiently presumably must not leak. Pupils are now introduced to a third type of vessel, a capillary, which has a structure that allows leakage, and re-entry, to take place (Figure 3.3).

It is possible, depending on availability, to demonstrate a capillary bed in action using the tail of a tadpole viewed under a low power microscope. Note that stress must not be caused to a vertebrate; it is illegal to restrain movement by means of an anaesthetic. As an alternative to using a tadpole pupils could place a drop of cedarwood oil on the skin of one finger, just in front of the nail base. If they look at this under a stereo-microscope, they will see very clearly the tiny threads of the surface capillaries. This is a good demonstration and easy to do. It means that this can be done at any time of the year and avoids the need to use a live animal. There are videos available that include sequences on this topic.

Discussion about the way materials enter and leave the transport system in capillary beds provides a natural progression to the nature of blood and the way it functions as a transport medium.

Figure 3.3
The site of exchange – the capillary.

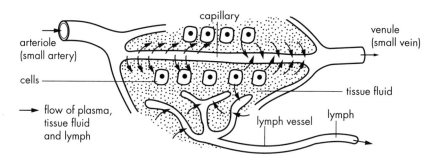

Blood as a transport medium

It is worth mentioning, briefly, the problems associated with a practical study of this topic in terms of blood-borne disease. Some practicals that were possible only a few years ago are now rarely permissible for pupils under the age of 16 years. Pupils must rely on photomicrographs and permanent, prepared microscope slides of blood to establish the cellular nature of human blood. Observation of prepared slides will establish that blood contains red blood cells, white blood cells and platelets. Pupils will need to be told that the cells are suspended in a fluid component known as plasma.

What is transported?

At this point pupils could be asked to work in groups, listing the things that must be transported around the body in blood. They could be invited to record where these things come from, where they are going to, how they travel and perhaps what for. Feedbacks could be written up in the form of a table (Table 3.3).

Table 3.3 *Functions of blood.*

Material	From	To	How	For
Oxygen	Lungs	All cells	In red blood cells	Respiration

Lymph as a transport medium

Pupils may have covered work on the digestion of food and have been made aware of the involvement of lymph in the transport of digested fat. Alternatively, the lymph system might be introduced via pupils' awareness of 'swollen glands' at times of illness. (See also Figure 3.3.)

◆ *Further activities*

- ◆ One novel way of demonstrating the pulse is to attach a drawing pin to the base of a safety match. If the drawing pin is delicately balanced over the radial pulse with the arm resting firmly on a flat surface, it is possible to actually see the pulsating action of the left ventricle.
- ◆ If time permits, or perhaps as an individual project, pupils might investigate the effect of additives on heart rate in the water flea, *Daphnia*, provided this is not in conflict with the school/department policy on the use of animals. They might investigate the effect of soluble aspirin or perhaps ethanol. Pupils might also investigate the effect of coffee (which contains caffeine) on their own heart rate.

◆ *Enhancement ideas*

- ◆ There are numerous opportunities to link social, moral and ethical issues to pupils' work in this topic. Newspapers and magazine articles often explore these issues. Pupils could be encouraged to watch particular television programmes or use materials based on them either in their lessons or for homework. Focused discussions, involving recording and feedback, could be employed on any of the following subjects. Perhaps pupils could be put into small groups, each of which could give a mini-presentation to the rest of the class on a particular topic. Alternatively, they might provide topics for individual research. The following list is offered only as a guide:

  - diet, smoking, exercise and coronary disease
  - valve by-pass operations
  - heart transplants
  - use of pigs' hearts as a means of treating cardiac disease in humans
  - the ethics of developing transgenic organisms to provide organ banks
  - blood donation/transfusion
  - blood transfusion and HIV.

3.3 Plants

◆ *Previous knowledge and experience*

Pupils are likely to have met the idea that plants absorb water from soil via roots and that water passes up the stem to the leaves. They are also likely to be aware that leaves need water to produce food by photosynthesis.

◆ *A teaching sequence*

Once more it is important to start by deciding what you want the learning outcomes to be for the section. Having established those, find out what the pupils know already. Use whatever method suits your style of teaching and one that you have found successful with the group involved.

Conduction

Pupils could start this section with some simple demonstrations and investigations. The following list gives a few examples.

- They might examine the root hairs produced by cress seedlings, germinated in advance of the lesson, using a hand lens or a low power microscope.
- Flowers with white petals will take up stains if their stalks are left in water containing coloured ink overnight. It is possible to take the thick stems of white carnations and split them down the middle, putting each half into different coloured inks. The following day this gives a flower head that is exactly twin-coloured and quite spectacular.
- A shoot taken from a plant such as Busy Lizzy or a celery petiole (stick of celery) will take up the stain and can be used to provide material for sectioning.

    Pupils can cut thin sections of the stained stem or petiole and prepare their own temporary slides. These will demonstrate that the ink is confined to particular regions of the section.
- Sugar cubes dipped into coloured ink could be used to demonstrate that some of the water might be taken up by the porous root hair cell walls passively by capillarity.

It should become obvious to pupils that water appears to be transported in specific regions within the stem, in a particular tissue, namely the xylem.

Root hairs

There are some difficult concepts to get across in teaching the transport of water in plants. Your approach will depend, as always, on the ability and expectations of the pupils being taught. It may be sufficient simply to refer to the special features shown by root hair cells in terms of thin wall and large surface area – features that enable efficient uptake of water and mineral salts. Work with more able groups is likely to include an explanation involving osmosis and active transport.

Transpiration

The fact that plants lose water from their shoot systems can be demonstrated by placing a clear polythene bag over the shoot, but not the soil, of a potted plant for a few hours in advance of a lesson.

Pupils might investigate the way leaf structure affects water loss by weighing detached leaves where the upper, lower or both surfaces have been coated with petroleum jelly. This leads conveniently into an investigation of the distribution and involvement of stomata in transpiration. Microscopic examination of nail varnish replicas of upper and lower epidermal tissue, produced by the pupils, might be useful here. Practical details for these investigations are found in most standard biology textbooks.

Transpiration can be demonstrated in a variety of ways. Most involve a potometer of some description. A simple bubble potometer is shown in Figure 3.4.

Figure 3.4
Simple bubble potometer.

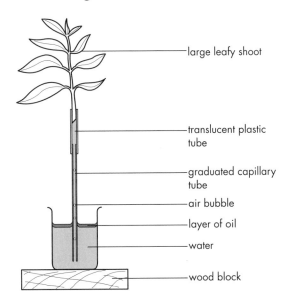

large leafy shoot

translucent plastic tube

graduated capillary tube

air bubble

layer of oil

water

wood block

Pupils can be introduced to the way transpiration is affected by changes in the plant's immediate environment using a detached shoot system and a bubble potometer at different ambient temperatures or humidity. The effect of air movement can be demonstrated using an electric fan or hair drier. Pupils might have the opportunity here to employ data-logging devices linked to computers to obtain continuous readings of water loss from a whole plant (see Figure 3.5). Continuous readings of the mass of a plant on a balance experiencing known changes in environmental variables can produce some interesting graphs for interpretation.

Figure 3.5
'Mass' potometer.

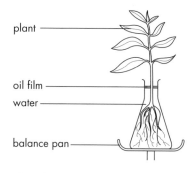

Once more the depth of treatment of the forces and processes involved in getting water from the roots to the leaves and out into the atmosphere will depend on the ability of the pupils involved. It may be sufficient to describe the transport in terms of 'a pressure generated in the root system pushing' and 'a suction force in the shoot system pulling' water to the leaves and its 'evaporation from the leaves through the stomata'. On the other hand it may be possible to structure an explanation in terms of the three stages of 'getting water into the root', 'getting it out of the leaves' and as a result of the two processes, 'getting the water up the stem'. The extent to which osmotic uptake of water by the root hair cells, movement across the root cortex along an osmotic gradient, and the negative pressure resulting from the evaporation of water to the atmosphere, etc. is explained will be conditioned by your expectations of the pupils involved.

Xylem and support

It might be appropriate at this stage to consider the way in which xylem is important as a tissue in terms of support in woody plants, and its significance in providing an adequate supply of water to explain the support of non-woody plants in terms of turgor, wilting, etc.

Pupils could prepare temporary mounts of macerated woody stem tissue to discover a variety of lignified cells. They can be supplied with a diagram showing different types of xylem cells and asked to see how many different types they can find.

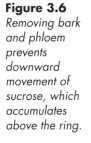

Tissue samples provided to pupils should not still contain the corrosive macerating fluids.

Translocation

Getting first-hand evidence of the involvement of phloem in transport is difficult at this level. However, pupils may be aware of the damage to trees and shrubs that occurs if their bark is 'ringed' (see Figure 3.6). They may well have seen young trees in woods or parks with protective sleeves around them to prevent their bark being damaged.

Figure 3.6
Removing bark and phloem prevents downward movement of sucrose, which accumulates above the ring.

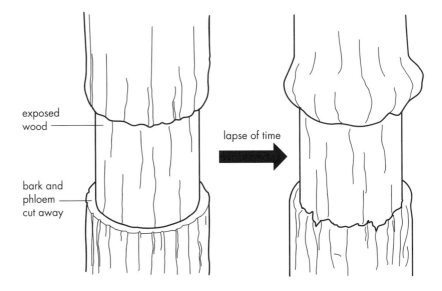

One possible approach to get round the difficulty might be via a comprehension exercise. Provide the group with a piece of continuous prose about translocation, written to suit their reading level and learning expectation, and set some specifically targeted questions to extract the desired information. At this level it is probably sufficient to bring out the following points:

- phloem cells are alive
- their walls are permeable
- phloem is involved in the transport of sucrose, formed from photosynthetic glucose, and other organic molecules
- transport in phloem occurs both up and down the plant.

Distribution of tissues involved in transport

Transverse sections of a root, a stem and a leaf using prepared microscope slides or photomicrographs might be used to establish the distribution of xylem and phloem. Most standard biology textbooks will have diagrams of transverse sections to help pupils with this task.

◆ *Enhancement ideas*

◆ Pupils could be encouraged to consider the use of systemic pesticides, comparing their desirability and effectiveness with other methods of pest control.

Other resources

◆ *Background reading*

Baker, E. (1997). Blood pressure. *Biological Sciences Review*, 9 (5), pp. 14–17. Too much detail for direct use at this level but good background information.

Foster, R. (1997). A stroboscopic method to investigate the effect of caffeine on *Daphnia* heart rate. *Journal of Biological Education*, **31**, pp. 253–255. Interesting account of an investigation carried out by a sixth form pupil. Contains recipes for dilutions that might be useful in the investigation referred to in the text of this chapter.

Griffths, H. & Howard, A. (1997). Roger the red blood cell. *School Science Review*, 79 (286), pp. 101–103.

Lester, A. & Lock, R. (1998). Sponges as visual aids – bath time fun for biologists. *Journal of Biological Education*, **32**, pp. 87–89. This article describes teaching aids using synthetic sponges: models of red blood cell and the heart.

Marshall, H. (1997). ECGs – getting to the heart of the matter. *Biological Sciences Review*, **10** (1), pp. 21–24. Too much detail for direct use at this level but good background information on heart disease.

Pacini, D.J. (1997). An aspirin a day . . . ? *Biological Sciences Review*, **10** (1), pp. 25–29. Too much detail for direct use at this level but good background information on heart disease.

School Science Review (1997). Volume **97** (287). Several very useful articles in ICT.

Tanner, M. (1997). Blood group antigens. *Biological Sciences Review*, **9** (5), pp. 10–13. Too much detail for direct use at this level but good background information.

4 Gas exchange, movement and fitness

Ann Fullick

4.1 Gas exchange
Knowledge and understanding of the thorax and breathing system
How breathing and gas exchange take place, relating structure to function
Effect of tobacco smoke/pollution/allergens on the breathing system

4.2 Respiration
Need of all living cells for usable energy source
Aerobic respiration
Anaerobic respiration

4.3 Skeleton and muscle
The roles of the skeleton and associated tissues – bone, cartilage, tendons, ligaments and muscle – in joints and in movement

4.4 Exercise and fitness
Fitness as an example of the way different body systems work together
Anaerobic exercise and oxygen debt
The changes in heart, lungs, skeleton and muscles in response to increased exercise

◆ Choosing a route

These topics can be taught as part of a linked and integrated whole. This can work very well, giving a good example of integration of organ systems and purpose behind learning – doing a practical on exercise which makes a pupil puff makes it very clear why breathing matters and also what fitness is all about! On the other hand, the topics can be taught in smaller linked groups – you might choose to link gas exchange and respiration, or skeletons and fitness, or respiration and fitness, or gas exchange, respiration and fitness – or as independent topics. The route you choose will depend on a variety of things including:

- the order in which other topics are to be introduced
- personal preference
- departmental policy
- syllabus content

and any combination will be effective if presented in a lively and enthusiastic way!

Pupils often get confused between breathing, gas exchange and respiration. Whilst teaching these topics it is helpful to be constantly aware of this and to try to keep the different concepts separate in their minds. Some people prefer to do this by dealing with breathing and gas exchange at a different time to respiration. Others prefer to help pupils recognise with great clarity the way the different processes are dependent on each other. If a pupil really understands that breathing movements get air into the lungs so that gas exchange can take place, and that the oxygen brought into the body in this way is needed in the cells for respiration, then the likelihood of confusion is much reduced. Examination syllabuses often place the two in the same section, so it may be that you deal with the topics separately for younger pupils and together when teaching exam groups.

One of the joys of teaching these parts of the curriculum is that pupils can use their own bodies as an experimental system. As long as teachers are aware of safety concerns and of the need to control any unhelpful and competitive comparisons of performance, this is an area of biology that can be full of interest for pupils because it is so easily related to themselves, their families, their peers and sporting personalities.

> ! *Be aware of medical conditions that affect the ability of certain pupils to perform exercise, e.g. asthmatics may need to use their inhalers first. Exclusions from practical work need to be handled carefully to avoid 'labelling' pupils with disabilities.*

One final point is that as teachers we need to keep remembering the demands of a spiral curriculum. Pupils are often revisiting a topic when we introduce it to them, or we in turn may be revisiting it later in their school careers. Thus when planning these topics for younger pupils it can be helpful if we also think about what they will be taught later. Tempting as it can be to tell all our best anecdotes and introduce all the really fascinating ideas to our pupils lower down the school, if we ration them and keep some things fresh for later we – and our pupils – will reap the benefit.

4.1 Gas exchange

◆ *Previous knowledge and experience*

Pupils will have met relatively little material specifically linked to breathing and gas exchange in primary schools. They will probably have studied the lungs as one of the organs of the body, and will know that living things need oxygen and produce carbon dioxide as a waste product. A common misconception at this level is that we breathe in oxygen and breathe out carbon dioxide – this can be cleared up quite easily by asking pupils what makes up the air. When that has been established you can demonstrate that air is what we breathe in and breathe out – the balance of the gases in it has just been changed slightly!

◆ *A teaching sequence*

Before beginning to teach this topic it can be a valuable exercise to decide what your desired learning outcomes are – in other words, where you hope your pupils will be by the end of the topic. These will tend to vary depending on the age and ability of the pupils you are working with, but if you have a list to start off with it gives you a tool for evaluating the success of what you do. For example, with younger pupils you might be quite happy if they know and can label the main parts of the breathing system, but with older pupils you might be hoping that you will also have given them an insight into the physical effects of exercise, smoking and altitude on that system and why the body reacts as it does. It is always worth having high expectations of what your pupils will be able to take away from this topic. It has lots of intrinsic interest, and if you expect a lot from them you may be surprised at what they can achieve!

Background knowledge

It is a good idea to start off with some questions that will give you a feel for what the pupils have met before – Do they know that people need to get oxygen into their bodies and get rid of waste carbon dioxide? Do they know that other animals and even plants have the same requirements? Do they have a feel for the idea of the gases being exchanged in a specific organ? Where do they think breathing comes into all of this? etc. By planning your questions carefully you can find out quite a bit – and if you can structure things so you get a feel for the knowledge of the whole class rather than one or two individuals, so much the better ('Hands up everyone who thinks plants don't need to bother with getting oxygen and getting rid of carbon dioxide.' 'Who thinks breathing helps us get rid of carbon dioxide?').

It is often particularly useful to go into the first lesson with plenty of material prepared. If your feeder schools or colleagues lower down the school have covered this topic in great detail and the pupils have a really good grasp of the basics you were planning to deal with, it is always helpful if you know that you have more than enough prepared to keep them occupied and interested! If the first lesson of the topic interests the pupils, they are much more likely to view the coming lessons in a positive light. It can be useful in the first session to give them an overview of what they will be looking at in the topic, and why it is exciting and relevant to them. This can help pupils to see a purpose to what they are learning and give them a sense of how the parts of the topic interlink and support each other.

Social, moral and ethical issues

When possible, everyday examples can help pupils grasp ideas – you'll find some examples in the different areas of the topic covered below. They often love the stimulus and challenge of social, moral and ethical issues associated with a syllabus area – they will wrestle to understand the science to help them argue a case for or against an idea – and if you read a daily paper or a magazine it is useful to cut out articles linked to topic areas like this when you see them. Material on asthma, cystic fibrosis, health risks from air pollution and smoking often appear in the press. You can then use them in teaching as a basis for a discussion, a class exercise, a homework exercise or a starting point for individual research.

Physical principles

There are four physical principles that must be grasped for complete understanding of gas exchange:

- diffusion
- surface area
- surface area:volume ratios
- air movement in response to pressure changes.

It is worth checking with colleagues to find out if you can reasonably expect some understanding of these areas from work done in other subjects. However, it is a good idea to run a quick experiment or demonstration of each when you reach the appropriate place in the teaching sequence to make sure pupils really do have a clear picture of what is going on.

There are lots of easy demonstrations of diffusion, from potassium manganate(VII) crystals dropped in water to a perfumed spray squirted in one corner of the lab. It is useful to emphasise that diffusion takes place along a concentration gradient from where there are a lot of particles of the diffusing substance to where there are relatively few. This is also a useful opportunity to point out that diffusion 'just happens' – that it is due to the random motion of particles and is not an active, energy-consuming process.

To help pupils grasp the idea of the alveoli providing the lungs with a large surface area for gas exchange (and indeed for showing the problems that result in emphysema when the alveoli break down to form big air sacs) the following exercise is useful. Provide groups with one large potato and several little ones which weigh approximately the same as the large one. Ask the pupils to peel the potatoes and use graph paper to work out the approximate surface area of the peel of each group of potatoes. The small ones should demonstrate a larger surface area – like alveoli.

! *Pupils must be reminded not to eat any of the raw potato because of the risk of contamination in the lab.*

Surface area:volume ratio can be demonstrated with cubes (either drawn on the board or real) with sides of different lengths.

For demonstrating the movement of air in response to pressure changes use either a bicycle pump or a model chest (many labs have one of these made up) (Figure 4.1). It can be useful to have a single balloon and present this simply as a model of the way air moves in and out as the pressure changes, rather than to have two balloons set up as model lungs. This is because many pupils already have the misconception that their lungs are like a pair of balloons inflating and deflating in their chest, and the traditional 'model chest' reinforces that misconception. By having a single balloon it can be presented as a single air sac, one of millions within your lungs, whereas pupils have a marked tendency to interpret two balloons as two lungs! A cut open pink bathroom sponge is useful too – show them the spongy structure and then explain that the balloon represents one sac.

Figure 4.1

An artificial chest with diaphragm in different positions and air moving into or out of the balloon. (Try the apparatus out beforehand. All too often the seals are leaky, the balloon has perished and it will not work! Well put together, it can be good.)

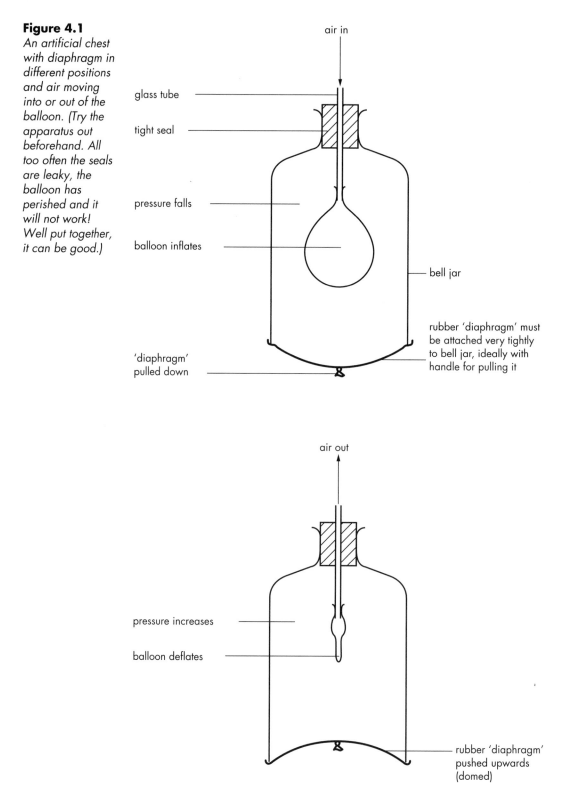

air in

glass tube

tight seal

pressure falls

balloon inflates

bell jar

rubber 'diaphragm' must be attached very tightly to bell jar, ideally with handle for pulling it

'diaphragm' pulled down

air out

pressure increases

balloon deflates

rubber 'diaphragm' pushed upwards (domed)

The need for gas exchange

Living things need energy to carry out all the reactions of life. To release the energy from their food and transfer it to a usable form requires oxygen in respiration. During the release of energy from food carbon dioxide builds up in the cells and must be removed from them because it is poisonous. Living organisms need oxygen and need to get rid of carbon dioxide, so they need to do a gas exchange. Tell pupils this is the same principle as changing an empty gas cylinder for a full one when they are camping, or returning a book they have read and finished with to the library and exchanging it for a new one they want to read. It is useful and important to emphasise here that gas exchange takes place in all living organisms, whether or not they breathe. This is a point at which you might choose to bring in the idea that gas exchange takes place as a result of diffusion, and clarify diffusion as described above.

Organs for gas exchange

The idea that some organisms need specialised organs to bring about successful gas exchange is an important one. Plants have low energy requirements, make their own oxygen in photosynthesis, and use up the carbon dioxide they produce, so do not require special ventilated organs. Very small animals can obtain sufficient oxygen to supply their needs by simple diffusion. As animals get bigger the diffusion pathways get too long to supply all the oxygen they need to support their much more active lifestyles. The concept of surface area:volume ratio (see *Physical principles* on page 82) and its implications for breathing systems as animals get bigger and more active is an important one to get over.

Gas exchange in humans

The three important aspects of the process of gas exchange in humans are as follows.

1. Structure of breathing system

A model chest with removable parts can be used to make it easier to understand how the breathing system and thorax fit together. Get across the spongy structure of the lung tissue. Particularly with older pupils it might be worth either letting them use microscopes themselves to look at slides of lung tissue, having slides projected on to screens to make this clear or using an appropriate CD ROM. The cartilage rings of the trachea and the way food is swallowed past them often generates interest, and the protection mechanism of the body to prevent food going down the windpipe into the lungs is one most people have experienced even if they have not understood what is going on. A brief explanation of why food in the lungs is damaging, and why choking can cause death, can lead to a brief but valuable description of how to help someone who is seriously choking.

With older pupils the beating of the cilia of the ciliated epithelium in the trachea, etc. can usefully be mentioned, not least because it will be referred to later when talking about smoking.

2. Method of ventilation

This involves looking at the principle of air moving in response to changes in external pressure. There are a number of ways of approaching this. If you start off by simply asking the pupils how they breathe in and out, you will know what their misconceptions are. You can then describe what happens in your body when you breathe in and out. Putting their hands on their own rib cages and taking a deep breath in and out usually enables pupils to work out how the ribs move. Envisaging the intercostal muscles that move the ribs is helped if they think of barbecued spare ribs or rib of beef and realise that what is eaten are the muscles that move the ribs (although these examples might not be appropriate when teaching in a multicultural environment, where many pupils would not eat these foods for religious reasons).

The movement of the diaphragm as it flattens will usually need describing. The effect these movements have on the volume of the chest and so on the air pressure in the chest can then be explained. Then, using the demonstration in Figure 4.1, the passive movement of air into and out of the lungs can be discussed. Pupils should recognise that in normal quiet breathing, breathing in is active but breathing out is passive as the intercostal and diaphragm muscles simply relax, reducing the volume of the chest cavity and so increasing the pressure of air in the lungs and forcing it out of the system. They will need to know that breathing out can be active too.

3. Exchange process in the alveoli/adaptations to function

This is where the concept of diffusion becomes very important (see *Physical principles* on page 82). Pupils need to know the structure of an individual alveolus and its close association with blood vessels. If they have not yet looked at the circulatory system, here is a good place to flag the fact that having got oxygen into the body it is important to be able to carry it to the cells where it is needed – hence the blood supply as a transport system.

It is difficult to talk about the structure of the alveolus and its capillaries without dealing with the issues of adaptation to function. Looking at the single cell layers and the close proximity of the blood vessels makes it easy to point out how this system is so well adapted to the movement of oxygen out of the air in the lungs into the blood, and the movement of waste carbon dioxide from the blood into the lungs:

- large surface area for gas exchange to take place (see *Physical principles*)
- thin alveolar walls (single cell thick) so short diffusion pathway
- rich blood supply to carry carbon dioxide to the lungs and oxygen away from the lungs – maintaining a concentration gradient to aid diffusion in both directions.

The concentration gradient that is maintained by blood flowing through the vessels and the changing of the air in the lungs can be explained to older and more able pupils. You can let pupils observe the effect of gas exchange in their own breathing using the apparatus shown in Figure 4.2. Either lime water (clear liquid that turns cloudy when carbon dioxide reacts with it) or hydrogencarbonate indicator solution (red liquid that turns yellow when carbon dioxide dissolves in it) can be used as indicators. Because this involves pupils putting their mouths in contact with the apparatus, care must be taken to make sure that each child uses an individual straw and that they are told very clearly to avoid getting liquid into their mouths. (As long as the experiment is not continued for too long, the lime water in the exhaled tube goes cloudy and the lime water in the tube they have inhaled through does not. Stop once this has happened because eventually the carbon dioxide in the inhaled air makes the lime water go cloudy and too much carbon dioxide causes the clouding in the exhaled tube to disappear.)

Eye protection is needed when handling lime water.

Some schools suggest doing this with the apparatus joined together so children breathe in and out, squeezing various bits of tubing to direct the flow of air. The apparatus shown here is simpler, avoids confusion and also helps to prevent much spluttering and lime water everywhere!

Figure 4.2
Apparatus to show testing of inhaled and exhaled air for carbon dioxide.

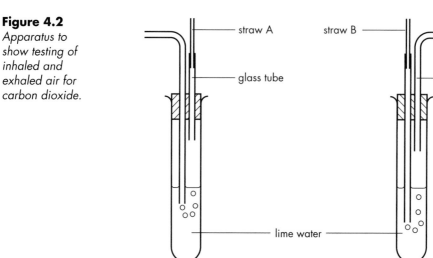

straw A

straw B

glass tube

glass tube

lime water

Breathe in through straw A – inhaled air bubbles through lime water.

Breathe out through straw B – exhaled air bubbles through lime water (can be just a straw into lime water).

Effects of smoking/pollutants/allergens on the functioning of the breathing system

The effects of smoking on the lungs and the way they work can be dealt with very effectively here as part of the work on gas exchange, or they may be covered when dealing with the effect of drugs on the body as a separate topic. One advantage of looking at the effects of smoking at this point is that it can be tied in with the effects of other air pollutants and of allergens in causing asthma.

The main effects of smoking on the breathing system are as follows.

- Smoke anaesthetises the cilia in the trachea and bronchioles, allowing mucus, bacteria and dirt to accumulate in the lungs and so making smokers more open to infection.
- Smoke contains a number of known carcinogens that can trigger changes in the cells of the lungs turning them cancerous. Because the lungs are a large space with few sensory nerve endings, cancers can grow until they almost fill one of the lungs and have spread widely about the body before they make the individual so ill that they go to a doctor and are diagnosed. Because of this lung cancer is often fatal.
- Tar and other chemicals that are part of cigarette smoke build up in the lungs on the surface of the alveoli and make gas exchange less effective.

- Many alveoli break down in response to the irritant chemicals in the smoke, leading to fewer, bigger air spaces. There is less surface area for gas exchange to take place and the large spaces may fill with fluid – the person is suffering from emphysema.
- Cancer of the mouth and upper respiratory tract are much more common in smokers.

The smoke from a cigarette can be drawn through a simple filter of glass wool – pupils are often appalled at the level of muck collected from even mild cigarettes.

Care is needed when handling glass wool.

Many of the problems caused to the breathing system by tobacco smoke are also seen as a response to air pollution of various other types. Breathing in dust from industrial processes used to be a common cause of lung cancer and emphysema.

Industrial pollution and more everyday allergens such as grass pollen, the faeces of house dust mites and pet hairs can affect the breathing system in more immediate ways. In sensitive individuals they trigger a release of histamine from the cells lining the respiratory tract, causing the tissue to swell and narrowing the tubes leading down to and into the lungs. This in turn increases the resistance to air flow, making it very difficult to move air into and out of the lungs and giving the symptoms of asthma. This can be treated in a number of ways, most commonly by inhalers, which deliver a small dose of adrenergic drugs to the lining cells, causing an almost immediate dilation of the tubes and easing of the breathing.

Treat your pupils sensitively

When dealing with health aspects like these it is important to be very sensitive and non-condemnatory. Many pupils will have parents who smoke, and they may feel great concern for their health. When dealing with asthma, a number of pupils in most classes will carry asthma inhalers and will suffer from the problem to a greater or lesser degree. If the pupils are confident and outgoing, and you have a good relationship with the class, some of your asthmatic pupils may be prepared to explain to their class mates what it feels like and how they use their inhaler. However, it is never a good idea to spring a request to share personal information on a pupil in the middle of a lesson. The end of the preceding lesson is an ideal time to have a quiet word, explaining that you will be covering asthma in the next lesson and asking if the pupils are happy to make some input.

Data research

This part of the course offers many opportunities for pupils to research and discuss the implications of scientific knowledge. The internet, libraries and doctors' surgeries are all places where pupils can find out for themselves about the effects of smoking, or asthma and air pollution. There are a lot of data available on the Net about mortality and morbidity of smokers, which you could present to pupils for analysis and comment. Questions such as: 'Why is air quality and the pollen count now a regular feature of weather forecasts in the summer months?', 'Why do people think that the number of people with asthma has gone up and up at a time when most diseases have been getting less and less common?' can be posed for research, thought or discussion.

Articles or data on smoking obtained from the media can be looked at, and reasons why young – and older – people continue to smoke in spite of widespread awareness of the health risks can be discussed. Issues such as the damage to the health of non-smokers by passive smoking (breathing in smoke-filled air from smokers) can be raised, or the rights of smokers to smoke against the rights of non-smokers to clean air. Should cigarette advertising be allowed? Are people sometimes diagnosed as asthmatic and given inhalers now when in the past they would have managed without them, simply because the drugs are there and drug companies encourage doctors to prescribe them?

This area of biology really is an excellent opportunity to set up discussion, role plays and other forms of interactive involvement for the pupils. As long as the activities are focused and there is an element of reporting back findings or ideas within a set time, this is often a remarkably fruitful experience for pupils across a wide range of ages and abilities.

A common misconception amongst pupils is that exercise/sport will undo the effects of smoking. This is not true. Exercise will make the very immediate effects of breathlessness less noticeable by increasing the size of the heart and lungs. However, smoking means that the benefits from this will not be as great as they should be – so your sporting performance will not be at its maximum – and the problems of addiction, smoke damage to the lungs and carcinogens are exactly the same whether you exercise or not.

Gas exchange in other living organisms

Gas exchange is vital to living organisms. It is important that pupils recognise how and where it takes place in plants (spongy mesophyll) and how the use of carbon dioxide and release of oxygen by plant cells as a result of photosynthesis reduces the need for specific gas exchange systems. For completeness and interest a lightning tour of some of the ways a variety of animals other than mammals manage gas exchange can also be stimulating and fun. Fish (gills), insects (tracheae), frogs (skin, simple lungs) etc. are obvious examples and more exotic creatures – such as those insect larvae that breathe through their bottoms – are always popular! A useful exercise is to look at each of the gas exchange systems with reference to the way they are adapted for their function, so that as well as broadening the pupils' knowledge of a function common to all living things it reinforces the 'large surface area, thin walls, concentration gradient' ideas that are so fundamental to an understanding of gas exchange.

◆ *Further activities*

- ◆ The response of the breathing system to exercise and increased oxygen demand.
- ◆ Adaptations of the gas exchange system in response to regular exercise, living at high altitude, etc.

These topics can be brought in and dealt with here, or in a separate section looking at the concept of fitness, which might lead on from this work on gas exchange, or might be used to link and reinforce work both on gas exchange and respiration.

◆ *Enhancement ideas*

- ◆ Work can be done on diseases of the breathing system: looking at ways in which diseases are spread and the role of social improvement, drugs and vaccination in the reduction of many such diseases.
- ◆ There are great opportunities both for data handling and developing an awareness of how selective use of data can slant a picture. A good example of this are the figures for the incidence of tuberculosis in the UK, where the decline can appear to be almost entirely due to the introduction of a vaccination programme and antibiotic treatment if only the latter part of the 20th century is considered, but the decline was in fact already occurring as living and working conditions improved over the whole of the century.

4.2 Respiration

◆ *Previous knowledge and experience*

Different people will choose to teach respiration in different places in their courses. In this book it is dealt with in detail in Chapter 1 as one of the fundamental processes taking place in cells. If, in your school, respiration has been dealt with before you tackle it here, a quick résumé as suggested below is very useful to support the next section of work. This looks at the demands of the body during exercise, when levels of gas exchange and breathing change to supply the changing demands of cellular respiration. However, if respiration has been dealt with only in passing earlier in the course, you may choose this point to cover the material fully.

◆ *A teaching sequence*

Crucial ideas about respiration that the pupils need to have grasped to make sense of the work on exercise and fitness are as follows.

- Food taken into the body contains stored chemical energy that needs to be transferred into a form that can be used by the cells of the body during respiration. This aerobic respiration needs oxygen, which is supplied by breathing and gas exchange.
- Sugar + oxygen → carbon dioxide + water + *usable energy*.
- At rest and during quiet activity, normal breathing supplies enough oxygen for respiration to take place.

Ideas on respiration that you might wish to revisit briefly with more able pupils before embarking on work on fitness include the following.

- Respiration occurs all the time in all living organisms.
- Aerobic respiration takes place in special cell organelles called mitochondria. They contain all the enzymes needed to produce usable energy from sugar using oxygen.
- If there is insufficient oxygen reaching the cells, then the enzymes of the mitochondria cannot function properly and *anaerobic* respiration takes over.

4.3 Skeleton and muscle

◆ *Previous knowledge and experience*

Pupils will have met the idea that humans need food to survive and move around and that humans have skeletons and muscles to support their bodies and to help them move. They may well have done projects on skeletons, made moving models of skeletons etc., depending on the enthusiasm of their primary teachers – be prepared to value and use ready-made 'experts'!

◆ *A teaching sequence*

Before dealing with issues of exercise and health it is important for pupils to have an understanding of how the body moves. The skeleton and how it is moved by the muscles makes an interesting topic in its own right, and if this work is then used immediately alongside knowledge from their work on gas exchange and respiration to look at anaerobic respiration, exercise and fitness, a well-rounded and integrated picture of real bodies working, rather than just theoretical systems, can be developed.

Background knowledge

As before, at the beginning of each unit of teaching it is useful to have developed your own desired learning outcomes for the pupils. Giving a broad overview of the work to come and asking questions to find out the level of prior knowledge of the group you are teaching – maybe in the form of a quiz, or a questionnaire, or simple questions as you talk – will set the scene for the topic to come and enable you to pitch in at the right level. Again this topic has lots of opportunity for individuals to use themselves as experimental organisms, and lots of intrinsic interest.

Structure and function of the skeleton

There are a number of ways to move into this topic. One is to imagine people without a skeleton – as large pink blobs – and then work out what a skeleton makes possible. Perhaps the most direct – and certainly very effective – way is to go straight in with a full-sized human skeleton (real or plastic). Put yourself and the skeleton at the front of a circle of pupils and talk through the different bits of the skeleton and what they do. The more this is sprinkled with anecdotes and explanations the more effective it will be – and don't forget to ask pupils to let you know if they have broken any of the bones you are looking at!

Pupils are often quite fascinated by this part of the course and have many interesting observations and contributions to make, so it is worth keeping an eye on the clock so that you manage to cover the whole skeleton in the time available. Some of the information snippets that help things to stick in pupils' memories include:

- the idea of the skull protecting the brain – but with joints that allow the head to be squashed during birth so the baby can be squeezed through the pelvis, and to allow the brain to grow after birth
- the fact that the joints of the skull only close up slowly to allow brain growth – the soft spot or fontanelle of babies – ageing ancient skeletons by looking at the skull joints, etc.
- orbits – deep and strong to protect the eyes
- no nose bone – nose made of cartilage
- only the lower jaw moves
- the different type of movement at the shoulder and elbow
- ribs – stick your hand into the rib cage to show how effectively the lungs, heart, etc. are protected; remind them of the position of the intercostal muscles and the diaphragm
- vertebrae – where the nerves come out, trapped nerves, cartilage discs and how they become compressed during the day so people 'shrink' by about 1 cm between the morning and the evening, and permanently compressed with increasing age
- why a broken neck or spine is so dangerous
- pelvis – the way the bones are fused; the coccyx as the tail remnant with all the nerves intact, which is why it hurts so much to fall on it; sexing skeletons by the shape of the pelvis, the gap through which a baby is delivered and why it is important that all the ligaments holding the pelvis tightly together relax in late pregnancy; protective role of pelvis for reproductive organs, etc.
- hip joints – where replacement surgery takes place
- femur – size and weight, how the length of a long bone from an ancient skeleton can be used to calculate the height of a long-dead individual
- ankles and feet/wrists and hands – the number of small bones needed for them to function properly.

There are many other special aspects of the skeleton, of course, and the pupils generally find it very rewarding to be told these 'added extras'. Throughout you can usefully and repeatedly point out examples of the main roles of the skeleton: support, protection and movement. It is usually more effective in both time and effort to provide pupils with ready-drawn skeletons to label rather than getting them to draw their own. However, they may appreciate the opportunity to handle a particular bone – skull, vertebra, long bone or pelvis – look for special features on it and then draw and label it. This type of activity often works best if a time limit is set.

Physical principles

When dealing with skeletons and movement the most important physical principle for pupils to get to grips with is the payoff for living things between load-bearing capacity, strength of materials and mass. They can make models to show that hollow cylinders support almost as much weight as solid ones but are much less massive, and then look at sliced-through long bones to see how this relates to bone structure. Big bones need very big muscles to move them – this can lead to interesting discussions about what actually limits the size of terrestrial animals.

Bone is an important living tissue. It is a common misconception amongst pupils that bone is the sort of dead white material we see in a dead skeleton. It can be quite thought provoking for them to realise that their skeletons are structures that are constantly being built up and broken down. Whenever you reduce exercise levels bone density is lost – bone cells are removed – and as soon as you carry out a new or different type of movement extra bone is laid down to strengthen the existing structure. Most bone growth takes place in children and adolescents. In young people the long bones have an area of cartilage at each end (known as the epiphyses) and this is where growth in length of the bones takes place.

After the adolescent growth spurt these soft regions become hard, calcium-containing bone like the rest of the skeleton and from that point on no further growth in height is possible. If there is a period of starvation or serious illness during childhood bone growth is halted until conditions improve, and this halt in the growth remains marked forever as a pale horizontal line in the structure of the long bones. This is used in archaeological analysis to give information about diet and disease in people who died hundreds of years ago.

It is also useful to mention osteoporosis – perhaps bringing in leaflets on the problem from your local doctor's surgery – so that pupils recognise that this condition affects men and women (although women are more likely to suffer from it) and that plenty of calcium and vitamin D in the diet as well as regular load-bearing exercise can help to prevent the problem arising.

Structure and function of joints

The skeleton could perform its functions of protection and support without allowing any movement to take place at all. The joints are there so we can move, and different types of joints allow different amounts of movement. The groundwork for this topic can easily be done when looking at the skeleton, and the skeleton can be used again to remind pupils of the different types of movement the different joints make possible. The importance of cartilage and synovial fluid in ball-and-socket and hinge joints can be emphasised, and discussing sporting injuries and arthritis as these affect old and young people often catches the interest of pupils and helps them understand the importance of these tissues in healthy joints.

Muscles and movement

The texture and appearance of muscle can be demonstrated with a piece of red meat – pupils can tease it out and look at it under a low power microscope. Using chicken limbs with feet still attached you can demonstrate clearly the way muscles are attached to bones by tendons.

!

In both cases hygiene must be rigorously observed for health and safety reasons, and if you do demonstrate with raw chicken it is important that your hands, lab surfaces and all the equipment used are scrupulously cleaned afterwards to avoid contamination by Salmonella, etc.

Antagonistic pairs of muscles

It is very important to help pupils grasp the idea that muscle tissue can only pull, as the protein fibres contract. Once this is clearly understood the idea of antagonistic pairs of muscles moving parts of the skeleton makes sense. Pupils have a useful practical aid in their own muscles, particularly the biceps and triceps. This fits in well with standard textbook diagrams too.

◆ *Enhancement ideas*

- ◆ Both smooth muscle found in the gut, and cardiac muscle in the heart can be introduced here. Details of structural differences are probably not needed but some groups may find it interesting to see the differences from slides projected on a screen, and to link differences in the structure to differences in the functioning of the muscles.

4.4 Exercise and fitness

◆ *Previous knowledge and experience*

Pupils will have considered whether taking exercise helps to keep people healthy.

◆ *Teaching sequence*

Background knowledge

At the beginning of each unit of teaching it is useful to develop your own desired learning outcomes for the pupils, to give you a tool for evaluating your teaching and your pupils' learning as you move through the topic. Giving pupils a broad overview of the work to come and asking questions to find out the level of prior knowledge of the group you are teaching – maybe in the form of a quiz, or a questionnaire, or simple questions as you talk – will set the scene for the topic and enable you to pitch in at the right level. This topic has lots of opportunity for individuals to use themselves as experimental organisms, and lots of intrinsic interest.

It is useful to begin by finding out what pupils understand by the term 'fitness'. They will have met the idea before in their primary schools and it is very interesting to find out what they have taken on board. A useful working idea is that a fit body is capable of carrying out all of the exercise demands of normal life without any excessive stress, and can cope with sudden extra demands when necessary.

Depending at what point you cover the work on fitness, you can use it as a good example of integrated body systems. Dealt with fully it encompasses the cardiovascular system, the breathing system, the skeleton and muscles, even the senses and the gut can be mentioned.

The consequences of exercise

When we exercise, our muscles are working, and the more we use particular muscles the more the body will respond by building extra muscle in that area. This is why exercise of different sorts results in a more toned and muscular body. Similarly, if we are ill and in bed for a week or two (e.g. with flu) then the body breaks down muscles that are not being used and we get muscle wastage. This contributes to the weak and tired sensations we get when we try to get up and about again – we have to take time to build up our muscles again. A good example of this muscle wastage can be seen when people have had a broken leg or arm encased in plaster for several weeks.

When we exercise and our muscles work, the demand for oxygen goes up. Practical work measuring the response of pupils' own bodies to exercise is a really useful teaching tool here and there are a number of important ideas to get across. This work can be done in the lab or in a sports hall or outside, depending on the nature of the group, space available and your own choice. It is very important before children undertake exercise to check if any of the class do not do PE for health reasons, or if individuals need to use asthma inhalers before exercising. Although they will not be doing anything too strenuous, these precautions should always be taken. Also prewarn pupils to bring in PE shoes to avoid any possible injuries. If there are several pupils who cannot exercise, use them to help – they can do the timing, record the breathing rates of small groups of children, etc., so that they are included in the practical.

Procedure

1. It is necessary for each individual to have a fairly accurate picture of their own resting breathing rate. They must sit still and in silence for a few minutes, breathing normally, and then count the number of breaths they take over three 30-second periods. They must not move or talk during the measuring, but can just note down the number of breaths at each count. One breath counts as breathing in and then out again. Each of their results can then be doubled, and then the average of the three numbers found. This will give them their average breathing rate per minute. It is important to stress the need for them to be completely *at rest* when they are measuring their breathing both at this stage and after exercise. This practical may give you one of the quietest lessons on record!

2. Pupils should then undertake a minute of gentle exercise and then, staying still and quiet, record their breathing rate at the end of that exercise and at 1-minute intervals for 5 minutes, after which for most pupils it will have returned to the resting rate.

3. Pupils can then undertake a more vigorous 1-minute's exercise, or a longer period of gentle exercise, and repeat the process of measuring their breathing rate for 5 minutes afterwards.

You may choose to let pupils plan this experiment for themselves, or ask them to follow instructions, or give instructions on the basic method but give them the freedom to decide how to exercise. A clear worksheet with a results table to fill in will help less able children to cope with this, and you may need to go through the explanation of finding the average breathing rate step-by-step on the board.

One of the nice things about this sort of experiment is that it provides pupils with real raw data that they can use in a number of ways. Pupils may simply work with their own data, or the whole class might feed their results into a spreadsheet program so that every pupil can have data from the whole class to work with (obviously the value of this will depend on whether everyone undertakes similar exercise). When looking at the results and trying to draw overall conclusions, some of the problems of interpreting data, and producing reliable data, as well as the pleasures of seeing patterns emerging can be brought home to your pupils.

Anaerobic respiration

This is a good place to introduce or revisit the idea of anaerobic respiration and oxygen debt. As exercise increases, more energy is needed and so respiration levels go up in the muscle cells. Often the need for extra oxygen is not met immediately, and in vigorous exercise it is sometimes impossible for the body to supply all the oxygen needed. In these cases anaerobic respiration takes place in the muscle cells: glucose is broken down without oxygen. This is inefficient – it does not produce very much energy and lactic acid is formed as a waste product. Lactic acid build up in the muscle causes pain and eventually stops it working. When exercise stops you have built up an 'oxygen debt' during the time you have continued to work with insufficient oxygen. Although you are at rest, your body cells continue to need more oxygen than usual because oxygen is needed to get rid of the lactic acid. Only after the oxygen debt is paid off does your breathing return to normal.

Fitness

When people exercise regularly they become fitter. They have bigger muscles with a good blood supply. Their hearts are more muscular and stronger, capable of pumping more blood more rapidly than an unfit heart. Their lungs become bigger, with a better blood supply so that they are capable of breathing more air into their lungs with each breath and carrying more oxygen into the body from each breath. Increased fitness is linked with increased health – pupils can be given data both on the effects of exercise on health and on the numbers in the population who take part in regular exercise as a stimulus to discussion.

◆ *Further activities*

- ◆ Either in conjunction with the ideas below or as a free-standing exercise, pupils could design a poster/leaflet/advert for local radio aimed at informing young people of the benefits of exercise and encouraging them to get fitter.

◆ *Enhancement ideas*

- ◆ Many leisure centres now run GP referral schemes where patients with cardiovascular and respiratory problems are prescribed courses of supervised exercise instead of drugs. Either you or your pupils may be able to talk to staff and even look at some of the results achieved. It is important to make sure that leisure centre staff know that you do not want to know who is involved in these schemes, simply the data on health benefits.
- ◆ Pupils will probably have seen adverts for 'fitness assessment' in their local leisure centre. They can find out about the various measurements taken to assess fitness – and think about the accuracy of these measures. You may find your local leisure centre willing to provide someone to come along and talk to pupils and demonstrate some of the tests – it is, after all, in their interests to convince young people of the need for exercise!

Other resources

◆ *ICT resources*

There are interesting ICT resources that can be used to enhance your teaching in these areas, support weaker pupils or stretch more able ones. If your laboratory has internet access, there are sources of data – such as the World Health Organisation – that are changing and being updated all the time. The places to find these are at teacher's centres, such as www.ase.org.uk, who will have done the necessary short-listing. It is also a good idea to encourage pupils to publish the results of some of their experiments on the internet themselves. This can be very motivating for both able and less able pupils – visit *ScI-Journal* at www.soton.ac.uk/~plf/ScI-Journal to see examples.

A number of resources relevant to curriculum work are recommended by Roger Frost in his *The IT in Secondary Science Book* published by ASE Booksales, Hatfield. These resources include those encouraging pupils to carry out a survey of people's attitudes to health and fitness and then using a database program to analyse the data by sorting and graphing.

Software on the human body is useful in many areas of biology. For example, Dorling Kindersley's *The Ultimate Human Body* (Mac/PC available from AVP) shows the anatomy of the skeletal and respiratory systems, how the joints work and what happens to the heart and lungs during exercise. Pupils may enjoy referring to these in the library or the various animations can be demonstrated during teaching. There are very many CD ROM titles about the body including *Adam – The Inside Story* (Mac/PC available from AVP) while for Acorn computers Sherston offer *Bodywise*.

Sensors can be linked to computers. As a short demonstration, the air in a polythene bag can be rebreathed and the change in humidity and oxygen levels monitored. Sensors can also be used to measure the effect of exercise on pulse and breathing. Stand alone wristwatch pulse sensors and ECG monitors make inexpensive alternatives.

◆ *Addresses*

AVP, School Hill Centre, Chepstow, Gwent NP6 5PH (tel: 01291 625439; website: www.avp.com).

Dorling Kindersley, 9 Henrietta Street, Covent Garden, London WC2E 8PS (tel: 0171 836 5411; fax: 0171 836 7570; website: www.dk.com).

Mindscape (tel: 01444 246333; website: www.mindscapeuk.com).

Sherston Software, Angel House, Sherston Malmesbury, Wiltshire SN16 0LH (tel: 01666 840433; website: www.sherston.com).

5 Communication and control

Jackie Callaghan

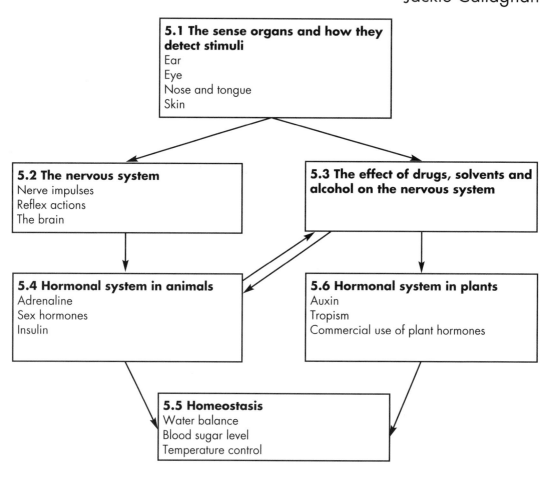

5.1 The sense organs and how they detect stimuli
Ear
Eye
Nose and tongue
Skin

5.2 The nervous system
Nerve impulses
Reflex actions
The brain

5.3 The effect of drugs, solvents and alcohol on the nervous system

5.4 Hormonal system in animals
Adrenaline
Sex hormones
Insulin

5.6 Hormonal system in plants
Auxin
Tropism
Commercial use of plant hormones

5.5 Homeostasis
Water balance
Blood sugar level
Temperature control

♦ Choosing a route

It is helpful to lead pupils from what they know and understand, e.g. the function of the eye and ear, and develop their knowledge. If the course is human biology, the section on hormonal systems in plants can be omitted.

Most secondary school pupils have difficulty relating to plant biology. However the large number of practical activities suggested here should help overcome this problem.

The issue of homeostasis will become apparent in most lessons, allowing you to bring all strands together in explaining the overall controls needed to maintain a constant internal environment.

5.1 The sense organs and how they detect stimuli

♦ *Previous knowledge and experience*

Pupils are likely to have met the name of the different sense organs and what they detect.

♦ *A teaching sequence*

An interesting way to start a lesson would be to keep the class very quiet and ask them to listen for noises outside of the classroom. Use this to lead into what sense organ the pupils were using. What was the stimulus they were detecting? Allow time for pupils to discuss the other sense organs and the different stimuli detected. Draw a basic table on the board and allow pupils to fill in sense organ and stimulus detected.

The ear
Links can be made with physics to reinforce:

• how sound travels
• the use of the terms wavelength, frequency and amplitude.

Vibrations and sound
Pupils enjoy investigating the fact that sound is caused by vibrations. Attempt the following:

• blowing across the edge of a strip of paper between your thumbs
• holding a vibrating tuning fork above water
• causing air molecules to vibrate by blowing across the top of a test-tube (if time allows, investigate change in pitch as water is added to the test-tube)
• placing an inflated balloon on to a pupil's cheek then speaking into the other end.

Develop these concepts by demonstrating a signal generator connected to a loudspeaker. Place small pieces of screwed up paper on top of the speaker. Start off within the audible range of sound and watch the pieces of paper vibrate off the speaker. Move the dial towards non-audible range. Ask pupils to indicate when they can no longer hear a sound. Introduce the oscilloscope, with a microphone connected. Repeat the signal generator experiment with the oscilloscope; demonstrate the waveforms produced in the audible range, and then continue through into the non-audible range. The oscilloscope will demonstrate that sound is still being produced, although it cannot be heard. Discuss dog whistles and the ability of other animals to detect sounds at different frequencies.

Pupils enjoy talking into the microphone to watch the different waveforms. Play different musical instruments into the microphone and watch the different waveforms. Ask a pupil to shout into the microphone. The amplitude of the wave increases. Inside the cochlea quieter sounds cause small vibrations to the sensory hairs and loud sounds cause larger vibrations.

Ear models

Use a model ear/OHT diagram/poster/diagram in book to help your explanation of what happens to the sound as it enters the ear:

- the pinna funnels sound waves into the ear canal
- the vibrations cause the eardrum to vibrate
- this moves the ear ossicles (three small bones: hammer, anvil and stirrup)
- the stirrup vibrates against the oval window, which causes the fluid inside the cochlea to move
- movement of the fluid is detected by the sensory hairs inside the cochlea
- when the sensory hairs move, they send nerve impulses to the brain.

At this point pupils may want to discuss: perforated eardrums, ear syringe, hearing aids, etc. It is useful to have a worksheet showing the structure of the ear. If sections of the ear are drawn separately, pupils can cut them out and stick them into their book in the correct order. Tell pupils which labels to include (syllabus check), as there are usually more labels printed in books than pupils will need to remember.

Noise levels

The loudness (intensity) of sound is measured in decibels (dB). The quietest sound is called the threshold of hearing and is 0 dB, normal conversation is 50–60 dB and the threshold of pain is 120 dB. Use a chart to show the decibel scale and a decibel meter to measure levels of sound in different areas of the school. Discuss noise pollution, the harmful effects of loud noise, airports, concerts, etc.

Balance

The ear is also responsible for balance. On the diagram indicate the semicircular canals. A useful model is three clear plastic tubes filled with fluid, but showing a few air bubbles. Hold the tubes next to your head as you move and tilt your body so the fluid inside the tubes moves. Inside each canal there are sensory hairs that detect the movement of the fluid and send impulses to the brain. Discuss how ear infections can sometimes cause people to lose their balance.

Alcohol and drugs can affect this process. These substances enter the bloodstream and are carried to the brain where they affect the nervous system. It takes longer to respond to a stimulus. Excess use of drugs and alcohol causes irreparable damage to the cells in the brain and the liver.

The eye

Links can be made with physics to reinforce:

- how light travels
- the use of the terms reflection and refraction
- coloured light
- the use of lenses.

The structure of the eye

Most pupils enjoy dissecting a pig's eye and a lot of understanding can be gained through this exercise. If this is a new experience you should attempt a dissection yourself before the lesson. For safety reasons, the possible BSE risk, a bull's eye must not be used. Enquire if the school has a policy about dissection experiments.

! *Good hygiene is essential during dissection.*

A worksheet showing the structure of the eye should be available for reference during the dissection. Use the pointed blade of dissection scissors to cut through the tough sclerotic layer: jelly-like fluid (vitreous humour) will seep out of the eye. Continue cutting all around the eye, leaving the optic nerve at one end and the pupil, lens, etc. at the other. Turn the eye inside out to study the retina. Extract the lens (carefully, as this is a delicate jelly-like structure); hold the lens above some print and look through it: the print will appear slightly larger. Study the iris and the pupil.

A model eye

If eye dissections are not possible a model eye might be available. Pupils could be given a worksheet showing the structure of the eye. Allow them to colour the different parts in using a key for different colours. Explain the functions of the different parts of the eye.

- The conjunctiva is a thin, delicate membrane that protects the cornea.
- The centre of the eye is the pupil and is surrounded by the coloured iris (ask pupils to look at the colour of the iris of the person sitting next to them).
- The iris controls the amount of light entering the eye (pupils could work in pairs to study the movement of the iris – close their eyes then open them whilst looking towards a bright light, not the Sun).

! *Never look directly at the Sun.*

- The lens can change shape to focus light on to the retina.
- The retina is a light-sensitive layer containing rod cells that work in dim light and cone cells that detect colour and details.
- The yellow spot (fovea) is the most sensitive part of the retina.
- The blind spot is where the optic nerve attaches to the eye, so there are no light-sensitive cells here (there are experiments in most textbooks showing how to find your blind spot).
- The optic nerve carries nerve impulses to the brain.

The formation of an image

It is important to emphasise to pupils that as light enters the eye, light rays are bent (refracted) by the cornea and then the lens to bring them together, into focus, on the retina. There are various models available that demonstrate this concept.

Ask pupils to concentrate on the sensations they feel around their eyes whilst looking at their thumb held close to their eyes then at a distant object. When focusing on a close object the ciliary muscles contract; this slackens the suspensory ligaments, so the lens goes fatter. When focusing on a distant object the reverse happens and the lens becomes thinner.

Pupils can now be introduced to the idea of the inverted image formed on the retina, due to light travelling in straight lines. Comparisons can be made between the working of a camera and the eye.

Occasionally light does not come to a focus on the retina. The focal length can be shorter than the eye (short-sighted) or longer than the eye (long-sighted). Various models are available to demonstrate this concept. These models usually contain fluorescein and lenses can be used to demonstrate correction of long-sight (converging lens) and short-sight (diverging lens). A blackout is usually necessary to carry out this demonstration successfully.

The nose and the tongue

Pupils enjoy sampling different jellies to try to determine their flavour. Add different flavourings to the jellies, e.g. a red jelly tasting of onions. This will lead to discussions about what pupils expected and that their sense of smell was more sensitive than the sense of taste. It would be more suitable to attempt this activity in a classroom or home economics room, rather than a science laboratory.

! *Eating should not be allowed within science laboratories.*

! *Avoid using nuts in the tasting experiments as some pupils have allergic reactions to nuts.*

Smells are chemicals in the air. The chemicals dissolve in the moist lining of the nose; this stimulates the sensors and impulses are sent to the brain. The brain interprets these impulses as different smells. Discuss how you cannot taste your food as much when you have a cold.

You only taste sweet, sour, bitter and salty things. Sensory cells are found in taste buds. The chemicals in food dissolve in saliva, the taste buds sense the taste and send impulses to the brain.

Pupils could copy the outline diagram of the tongue, then taste sweet, sour (lemon juice), bitter (strong coffee) and salty solutions to try to identify which area of the tongue is detecting the taste.

Figure 5.1

The taste-detecting areas of the tongue.

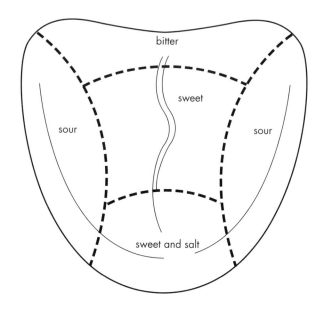

The skin

Pupils could be provided with a worksheet showing the structure of the skin, and could then label the diagram from an OHT or book. Discuss if there are the same number of sense receptors in skin over all parts of the body. Investigate this using reflex pins (see *Equipment notes* on page 121). As one pupil closes both eyes the other pupil touches the skin with one or both of the pins. The pupil states if one or two 'touch sensations' is felt. Responses are recorded. Less sensitive areas of the skin can only discriminate one sensation of touch, not two. Discussion of results should show that there seems to be the greatest number of sensors in fingertips.

Temperature detection

To investigate temperature sensors pupils could place one hand into a bucket containing hot water (approximately 45 °C) and one hand into a bucket of ice-cold water. After a couple of minutes, both hands are plunged into a bucket containing water at room temperature; each hand will seem to sense a different temperature. After discussing the role of temperature sensors, the importance of temperature control can be introduced.

 When setting up 'temperature buckets' ensure that the temperature of water is not too hot for the pupils. Place the bucket containing water at room temperature in between the other two buckets.

The brain senses a rise in blood temperature and controls the body-cooling processes. Sweat glands become active and sweat pores open, the body cools as sweat evaporates from the surface of the skin. Blood vessels near the surface of the skin dilate (vasodilatation), so that more blood flows close to the surface of the skin, allowing more heat to be lost from the blood. When the brain senses a fall in blood temperature the body-warming processes begin. Hairs stand on end and trap an insulating layer of air around the body. Sweat glands are inactive. Blood vessels near the surface of the skin become narrower (vasoconstriction), restricting the amount of blood flowing close to the surface of the skin, which reduces the amount of heat loss. It is useful to allow pupils to copy diagrams illustrating this control mechanism; ensure they emphasise the size of blood vessels and add a written description for each labelled part.

◆ *Further activities*

- ◆ Research into the laws protecting workers from noise in the workplace, causes of deafness and other hearing problems.
- ◆ Investigations:
    Which material is most suitable for soundproofing a room?
    Did the old-fashioned hearing aids really work?
- ◆ Research into eye disorders and diseases.
- ◆ Pupils can work in pairs. Blindfold one pupil, the other pupil will feed him/her various foods; without using the sense of sight try to guess what the food is.

! *Good hygiene is needed. Pupils must not share utensils.*

- ◆ Show the BBC for Schools video Scientific Eye programme *Keeping warm*.
- ◆ The Royal National Institute for the Blind (tel: 0171 388 1266) will provide samples of Braille and a key to their symbols.
- ◆ Investigations:
    Which materials are best to insulate the body?
    What factors affect the rate of heat loss from the body?

◆ *Enhancement ideas*

- ◆ Explain why there are more sensors in our fingertips.

5.2 The nervous system

◆ *Previous knowledge and experience*

Pupils will be aware of the life processes and that plants and animals respond to stimuli. However, they will not be familiar with how this process takes place.

◆ *A teaching sequence*

Discuss with pupils *how* they entered the room. Direct discussions towards why and how muscles moved the skeleton to enable them to walk into the room. The brain sent a message (a nerve impulse) along the spinal cord then along the nerve cell (neurones) to the muscles in the legs. The brain and the spinal cord are called the central nervous system.

If a full skeleton is available it is possible to show how the spinal cord passes down through the vertebrae. Pupils could examine individual vertebrae to observe the hole through which the spinal cord passes.

Reflex actions

The nervous system includes the central nervous system and all the other neurones. The nervous system also co-ordinates involuntary actions such as breathing and blinking.

All reactions follow a similar pathway:

stimulus → receptor → co-ordinator → effector → response

Ask pupils to imagine they had put one of their hands into very hot water. The hot water is the stimulus. This stimulus is detected by the receptor, the temperature sensors in the skin. The co-ordinator is the central nervous system, which causes the effector, the muscle cells, to bring about a response. The response would be for the hand to move away from the hot water.

To reinforce this pupils could produce a flow chart showing the pathway for the reaction if they sat on a drawing pin.

These are examples of reflex actions; the pathway is called a reflex arc (Figure 5.2).

Figure 5.2
A reflex arc.

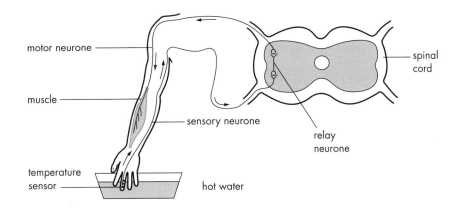

Pupils could try to test some reflexes with a partner.

- Tap the back of your partner's foot just above the heel.
- As one pupil sits on the bench with their legs relaxed, the partner taps just below the knee.
- With care, as one pupil looks straight ahead, the partner waves his/her hand in front of the pupil's eyes.

Diagram and models

Pupils could label a diagram of the reflex arc. This will introduce the differences between sensory neurone and motor neurone. Pupils could be provided with diagrams of sensory and motor neurones then asked to work in groups to produce models. These models could be used to create a large wall display showing the nervous system. From making the models, discussions can then lead towards how structure is related to function:

- neurones are long with few junctions so the electrical signals (nerve impulses) can pass very quickly along the axon
- the fatty sheath insulates the axon so impulses travel faster.

Multiple sclerosis is a disease that causes the fatty sheath to break down; this slows down or may even stop the impulses. Sufferers gradually lose the use of their muscles because impulses never reach them.

Reaction times

In between each neurone there is a small gap, called the synapse. As an impulse reaches the end of the axon a chemical diffuses across the gap. This chemical then triggers an impulse in the next neurone. The functioning of the synapse is affected by drugs (see the next section).

Pupils enjoy measuring their reaction time with a falling ruler. Working in pairs, one pupil places his/her arm on the bench. The other pupil holds the ruler with zero next to the partner's index finger; the partner's fingers should be poised ready to catch the ruler but not touching it. As the pupil drops the ruler the partner attempts to catch it, as soon as possible. Record the measurement next to the index finger. Discussion of results will show that the time taken to catch the ruler improves with practice. Links can be made here with stopping distances and the affect drinking alcohol has on driving skills.

The brain

The improvement of reaction time is part of a learning procedure, which introduces the topic of the brain. The brain contains more than 10 billion neurones. It co-ordinates incoming and outgoing impulses. Pupils need to realise that the brain is very complex and we still have a lot to discover about its workings. Use a model or a diagram to show:

- the cerebral hemispheres, the front parts of the brain, are responsible for emotions. This area also controls complex behaviour, memory, reasoning and intelligence. In this area senses of hearing and seeing respond to bring about movement of the body
- the medulla attaches the brain to the spinal cord. Automatic actions, such as breathing, are controlled by the medulla
- the cerebellum allows us to make precise movements, such as walking. It controls the sense of balance and muscular actions.

The brain can also influence some reflexes; this type of reflex is called conditioned. It is conditioning that causes your mouth to water when you smell food. Conditioning is a type of learning.

Using a microscope

This is an opportunity for microscope work. Prepared slides are readily available of sections of spinal cord, neurones and synapses.

♦ *Further activities*

- ♦ Measuring reaction time can also be carried out with an electronic timer and two switches. Make connecting wires to the switches about 2 metres long. As the operator switches the timer on, the other pupils attempt to switch it off as soon as possible.
- ♦ Research motor neurone disease.

5.3 The effect of drugs, solvents and alcohol on the nervous system

◆ *Previous knowledge and experience*

Pupils will have some knowledge of drugs from their PHSE (Personal, Health and Social Education) course, but with little understanding on how they affect the body.

◆ *A teaching sequence*

As pupils are naturally interested in this subject it lends itself well to group work. The facts about the effects of drugs on the body could be introduced, and then each group could select one topic to produce a display/board game/lecture/video. Recording their presentations on video, for a slightly younger audience, often promotes enthusiasm and interest.

Drugs
- Drugs affect the functioning of the brain and nervous system.
- Barbiturates (tranquillisers) and heroin are depressants; they slow down the nervous system.
- Amphetamines, ecstasy and cocaine are stimulants; they speed up the nervous system.
- Cannabis and similar drugs are smoked to make people feel relaxed, but it is thought that they cause respiratory diseases.
- Synapses are easily affected by drugs; some drugs, including alcohol, block the synapses making it difficult for impulses to be carried forward. Some drugs make the synapses work too quickly.
- Injecting drugs can be dangerous as it is easy to overdose and sharing needles spreads the HIV virus that causes AIDS.
- The body becomes used to drugs and increased amounts have to be taken to produce similar effects. The body develops a tolerance to the drug, the person then becomes dependent on the drug; this is called addiction.
- Once the body has become dependent on the drug, when people stop taking it they experience withdrawal symptoms.

Solvents

- Solvents contain dangerous chemicals that can kill.
- Solvent fumes are absorbed into the blood via the lungs; then soon reach the brain.
- Solvent fumes slow down the rate of heartbeat and breathing.
- Deep breathing of fumes often causes loss of control and unconsciousness. Many then choke on their own vomit.
- Some people die immediately after inhaling some solvents; this sudden death is due to heart failure.
- People die from suffocation either from inhaling from plastic bags or if aerosol sprays are squirted directly into the mouth because this freezes the air passages.

Alcohol

- Alcohol slows down the body's reactions; it is a depressant.
- People can become dependent upon alcohol, giving similar effects to other drug dependency.
- Alcohol enters the blood via the gut and is then carried to the brain; from here it affects the nervous system.
- People's judgement and reactions become affected after drinking alcohol; this is why people should not drink and drive.
- Large volumes of alcohol cause people to lose control of their muscles, speech becomes slurred and they have difficulty walking.
- Excessive drinking of alcohol over several years can lead to stomach ulcers, heart disease and brain damage.
- The liver breaks down alcohol; excessive alcohol can lead to cirrhosis of the liver. This causes liver tissue to become scarred and healthy cells become replaced with fat or fibrous tissue. The liver is then unable to function efficiently.

◆ *Further activities*

- ◆ Many leaflets are available from your local Health Centre, Healthy Lifestyle Centre or Drug Wise; see your local telephone directory.
- ◆ Caffeine is also a drug; pupils could record pulse rate before and after drinking strong coffee.

! *Coffee should not be drunk in the science laboratory.*

5.4 Hormonal system in animals

◆ *Previous knowledge and experience*

Pupils may have heard of hormones, and their connection to the contraceptive pill, as part of their PHSE (Personal, Health and Social Education) lessons.

◆ *A teaching sequence*

Recap that the body responds to changes with the nervous system sending electrical messages along nerves. The body can also respond to change by the hormonal system (Figure 5.3) sending chemical messages around the body in the blood.

The body's response to hormones may last for a few minutes or for years. Hormones can affect growth, metabolism and sexual development.

Pupils could produce a large display showing the hormonal system. Using a large piece of paper (wallpaper or several A3 sheets fixed together), draw around the outline of a pupil. Cut this out and fix to the wall. Pupils can be provided with information on each of the different glands and the role of the hormones produced. A group of pupils can select one gland and hormone, draw a picture of the gland to stick on the body outline and write about the hormone. Details of the main glands and hormones are available in most pupil textbooks.

Figure 5.3
The hormonal system.

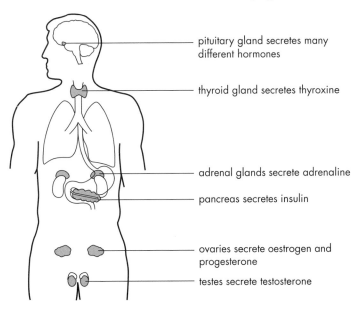

pituitary gland secretes many different hormones

thyroid gland secretes thyroxine

adrenal glands secrete adrenaline

pancreas secretes insulin

ovaries secrete oestrogen and progesterone

testes secrete testosterone

Role of specific hormones

It is now possible to develop an understanding of certain hormones in more detail.

Adrenaline prepares the body for action by increasing the breathing and heartbeat rates; blood is directed away from the gut towards the muscles, enabling respiration to take place in the muscle cells at a faster rate to ensure energy for flight or fight.

Testosterone brings about development of the male secondary sexual characteristics, such as growth of body hair and a deepening of the voice.

Oestrogen and progesterone bring about the development of the female secondary sexual characteristics, such as the development of breasts and the start of periods. During a period the uterus lining breaks down and a small amount of blood and cells are lost from the vagina. This is called menstruation. Pupils find control of the menstrual cycle a difficult concept to understand. The use of a worksheet showing a diagram is most helpful. Check the syllabus or scheme of work for how much detail is required.

Figure 5.4

The menstrual cycle.

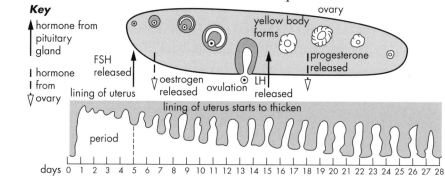

The regulation of blood sugar introduces the concept of homeostasis (see the next section).

◆ *Further activities*

- ◆ Research into medical conditions created by irregular amounts of hormone.
- ◆ Completion of a table to show glands, hormones secreted and their effects on the body.
- ◆ Completion of a flow chart showing how hormones control ovulation and menstruation.

◆ *Enhancement ideas*

- ◆ Links with PHSE with the effects of hormones in the pill.
- ◆ Changes in emotion during puberty.
- ◆ Menopause and hormone replacement therapy (HRT).

5.5 Homeostasis

♦ *Previous knowledge and experience*

Pupils are likely to have met temperature control whilst studying the skin; this is an example of homeostasis.

Links can be made with physics in electronic control systems.

♦ *A teaching sequence*

Discuss with pupils the idea of an oven set at a certain temperature to cook their dinner. If the heater creates too much heat a thermostat will turn off the heater; if the oven is too cool the thermostat will turn the heater on. Compare this with the temperature control system in the blood. Homeostasis means keeping conditions more-or-less constant inside the body.

Insulin

Remind pupils about the lesson concerning hormones, where it was mentioned that the pancreas secretes a hormone called insulin. Special cells in the pancreas detect high glucose levels in the blood. The pancreas then secretes insulin, which instructs the liver to convert glucose into glycogen. When too little glucose is in the blood, e.g. after running a race, then the pancreas secretes glucagon. This hormone instructs the liver to convert glycogen back into glucose. Pupils find it easier to learn such processes by filling in a flow chart. Discussions on diabetes can help to reinforce pupils' knowledge about insulin.

Solutions labelled urine can be prepared and tested for glucose, either using a glucose-testing strip or by using Benedict's reagent.

Kidneys

The kidneys are organs of excretion and they regulate the amount of water in our blood. A description of how the kidneys work is necessary. It is fun to demonstrate how fluid is forced out of the renal artery. Using about a 1 m length of rubber tubing, cut small holes into the tubing using scissors. Holes made with a pin are too small. Attach one end of the tubing to a tap, allow water to pass through and into the sink, then increase the pressure by holding the other end closed. Water will squirt out through the small holes. This water represents the small molecules filtering through the renal artery to be collected in the Bowman's capsule.

As this process is non-selective, useful substances need to be reabsorbed back into the blood from the nephron. Urea, waste salts and water (urine) are left behind. The urine then flows down the ureter into the bladder. This process can be easily explained with the help of a diagram. Kidney dissections are possible if time allows; this helps to explain the structure of the kidney.

Figure 5.5
How blood is filtered in the nephron.

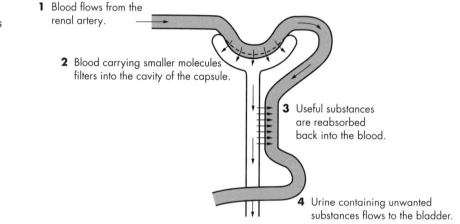

1 Blood flows from the renal artery.

2 Blood carrying smaller molecules filters into the cavity of the capsule.

3 Useful substances are reabsorbed back into the blood.

4 Urine containing unwanted substances flows to the bladder.

The amount of water present in the urine depends upon the body's requirements. If it is a hot day and a person has lost fluid through sweat the blood risks containing too little water. The brain detects this and adds ADH (antidiuretic hormone) to the blood. This hormone instructs the kidneys to reabsorb most of the water from the nephrons back into the blood. A small amount of concentrated urine is produced. The reverse happens when too much water is present in the blood.

Discussions can lead on to kidney dialysis machines and kidney transplants.

◆ *Further activities*

- ◆ Research into the problems encountered by diabetics and people suffering with kidney diseases.

◆ *Enhancement ideas*

- ◆ How the pH of the blood is kept constant at 7.4.
- ◆ How the carbon dioxide concentration of the blood is controlled by our lungs.

5.6 Hormonal system in plants

◆ *Previous knowledge and experience*

Pupils may have been taught about hormones in humans.
Some pupils will be familiar with hormone rooting powders.

◆ *A teaching sequence*

Fast plants (see *Equipment notes* on page 121) can conveniently
show how plants respond to light and gravity. Shoots of about
3 days' growth, with just the cotyledons (first pair of leaves)
having been produced, are most suitable. At the start of the
lesson cut off the shoot, leaving about 2 cm of straight stem.
Press the cotyledons on to damp filter paper positioned inside
the cap of a film case. Fix the film case on to the cap then Blue
tac on to the desk. Leave this set up during the lesson. At the
end of the lesson, open the film case to see whether the shoots
are positively geotropic or negatively geotropic. If left for over
30 minutes the shoot should have grown away from gravity; it
is negatively geotropic. Be aware that some pupils may become
confused because they think it is the 'wrong end' of the shoot
growing upwards. As this end of the shoot is close to the root,
some pupils assume that this is an action of the root and not
the stem.

Auxin passes down from the tip of plants, preventing the
growth of side shoots. If a hedge is clipped and the tips are
removed then more side shoots will be allowed to develop.

Phototropism

It should be easy to find a potted plant that has grown towards
the light. Discuss the advantage to the plant of facing its leaves
towards the light, for increased rate of photosynthesis. Explain
how a hormone (called auxin) has caused the plant to grow
towards the light. More auxin passes down the shaded side of
the shoot, making the cells elongate more on this side, causing
the shoot to bend towards the light. Experiments can be set up
with either cress seeds or fast plant seeds (from SAPS) to
demonstrate this response towards light (see *Equipment notes*).
Slow growth responses are called tropisms and the response
towards light is called phototropism.

Geotropism

Use a potted plant to show how plant roots have grown downwards. The auxin in non-vertical roots builds up on the lower side; this time auxin causes the cells to elongate less, so the roots grow downwards. This response is called geotropism. Experiments can be set up to demonstrate geotropism, using bean or pea seeds or fast plant seeds. Roots are positively geotropic: they grow towards gravity. Shoots are positively phototropic: they grow towards light.

Figure 5.6
Experiment to demonstrate geotropism.

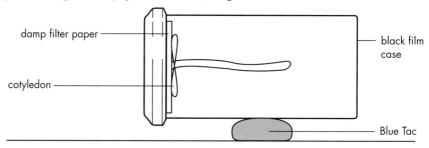

damp filter paper — black film case

cotyledon — Blue Tac

Commercial uses

Pupils could see examples of commercial uses of plant hormones, such as the use of rooting powder. Selective weed-killers contain synthetic auxins; they kill weeds by making them grow too fast. Seedless grapes are grown with the help of auxins. The auxin controls the ripening; it encourages the ovary to develop into a fruit. As fruits have formed without fertilisation there are no pips. Plant hormones are also used to regulate the ripening of fruit during transport. Many fruits produce ethene; it causes the fruit to ripen. Bananas are picked unripe then ethene is used to make them ripen during transit.

♦ *Further activities*

- ♦ The effect of different-coloured light on growing shoots.
- ♦ Use of a clinostat to show geotropism.
- ♦ Growing of shoots (carnations and chrysanthemums) using hormone rooting powders.
- ♦ Investigate selective weed-killers; narrow-leafed grasses and cereals should not be affected.
- ♦ Investigate the effect of cutting off plant stem tips and then covering the tops of the stems with foil or opaque caps.

♦ *Enhancement ideas*

- ♦ The problems caused by the use of weed-killers.

Equipment notes

The ear

You will need to spend a little time before the lesson on vibrations and sound becoming familiar with the **signal generator** and the **oscilloscope**. Ask a technician to set up the oscilloscope and microphone.

The school may have a **sound probe** that can be connected to a **data-logger**. The sensor can not only be used to measure noise levels but also the design of the device (membrane, transducer, wire to the computer brain) provides a fair model of how hearing works. A graph could then be produced to show the changes in the level of sound during the lesson.

The eye

When demonstrating the correction of sight, it is useful to have a small but strong ray of light from a **slide projector** shining into a **flask of fluorescein**. This can be achieved by cutting a card the same size as a projection slide and making a small hole in the centre. Trial this experiment before the lesson to make sure you have the correct combination of **lenses**.

If it is a dull day you may require **torches** to demonstrate the changing size of the iris.

Textbooks show 'how to find your blind spot'.

The skin

Hairpins or hairgrips make useful 'reflex pins'. The ends can be pulled apart to a distance of approximately 1 cm; this enables pupils to be able to touch the skin with one point or two.

Drugs, solvents and alcohol

Video cameras are best set up in advance on a tripod. Ensure you are familiar with the workings of the camera before the lesson. You may require an extension lead or fully charged battery packs.

Phototropism and geotropism

Fast plants are a fast-growing variety of *Brassica*. The seeds and growing kits are available from SAPS (Science and Plants for Schools), Homerton College, Cambridge (tel: 01223 507168), Philip Harris, Lynn Lane, Shenstone, Lichfield WS14 0EE (tel: 01543 480077) or Blades Biological, Cowden, Edenbridge TN8 7DX (tel: 01342 850242). Kits come with full planting instructions; worksheets providing good ideas for practical work are available termly.

To investigate **phototropism**, holes can be drilled around the base of film cases and seeds allowed to germinate on damp filter paper in the cap (film cases need to be black or a dark colour). Holes can be drilled into film cases and coloured filters placed over the holes to investigate the effects of coloured light on the growth of seedlings.

To investigate **geotropism**, use Petri dishes and a grid photocopied on to an OHP transparency, cut the transparency and some filter paper to the size of the Petri dish. Place the cut transparency into the Petri dish, with the filter paper on top. When the filter paper is wet it will become translucent and seeds will stick to it. Hold the top of the Petri dish on with an elastic band. Stand the Petri dish upright and leave for about 2 days, observe and measure root growth, turn the Petri dish through 90° before leaving for a few more days, repeat. This experiment only works this fast with SAPS seeds.

Other resources
♦ *ICT resources*

- A concept keyboard can be set up to allow pupils to label the various parts of the eye.
- Computer programs allow pupils to create ray diagrams on screen.
- Many multimedia CD ROMs about the body offer detail and animation on the eye, senses, skin and reflex actions.

♦ *Background reading*

Souter, N.T. (1998). A balanced way of teaching semi-circular canals. *School Science Review*, 79 (289), pp. 61–64.

Wellcome News, a free magazine issued by The Wellcome Trust, often contains information concerning hormones and neurological diseases. Obtainable from: The Wellcome Trust, 210 Euston Road, London NW1 2BE (tel: 0171 611 8888; fax: 0171 611 8242; e-mail: publishing@wellcome.ac.uk).

Achoo Internet Healthcare Directory for information on various issues such as: human anatomy, diseases, drugs, mental health, poisons and general health information (http://gandalf.bellamy.on.ca/achoo/directory/index.htm).

Illusionworks for a comprehensive collection of optical and sensory illusions (www.illusionworks.com).

6 *Reproduction and sex education*

Jennifer Harrison

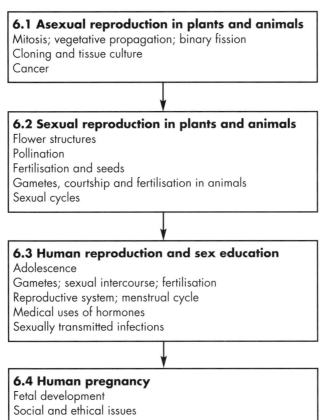

6.1 Asexual reproduction in plants and animals
Mitosis; vegetative propagation; binary fission
Cloning and tissue culture
Cancer

6.2 Sexual reproduction in plants and animals
Flower structures
Pollination
Fertilisation and seeds
Gametes, courtship and fertilisation in animals
Sexual cycles

6.3 Human reproduction and sex education
Adolescence
Gametes; sexual intercourse; fertilisation
Reproductive system; menstrual cycle
Medical uses of hormones
Sexually transmitted infections

6.4 Human pregnancy
Fetal development
Social and ethical issues

◆ *Choosing a route*

Reproduction is a crucial phase in the life cycle of any organism. It is the way in which a species is perpetuated, given that individuals must eventually die. Most pupils know that all living organisms grow and reproduce. However, they may have had little observational experience of reproduction in simpler organisms, and only limited understanding of reproductive processes in more complex ones. They may have little clear understanding of asexual reproduction – the simplest form of reproduction – which does not involve sex, or sex cells. There may be confusion between reproduction (in terms of production of new cells for a subsequent generation) and growth (in terms of increase in number of cells, and therefore of mass and possibly of size of organism, for the same generation). A key difference between asexual and sexual reproduction is that, crucially, the latter results in new variations amongst the offspring. The connection between sexual reproduction and the process of meiosis (see Chapter 1) is frequently missing in pupils' understanding of sexual reproduction.

Practical work with plant materials interspersed with animal materials may help to overcome the possible aversion by many teachers and pupils to the study of plants. Care should be taken in planning with respect to the seasons and availability of specimens. Observation of the cycles of reproduction in plants generally requires long-term planning for practical work. Find out how many of your pupils have had the opportunity of growing and propagating plants, or indeed, of examining in detail a variety of living organisms. The topic provides abundant opportunities for bringing living things into your laboratory or classroom and providing pupils with hands-on experience. A well-stocked school greenhouse provides access to a variety of seasonal species.

Animal sexual reproduction presents good opportunities for maintaining and observing a variety of organisms throughout their life cycle; some organisms need little laboratory space and may have a life cycle that can be watched over just 2 weeks and independently of the seasons (e.g. the fruit fly). Other organisms may demand more extensive maintenance, space and equipment, requiring observation over many weeks or months, and within specific breeding seasons. The whole topic links directly with 'growth and development' in plants and animals (see Chapter 1).

Basic microscopy skills are assumed, and pupils' ideas to do with microscopic size and the concept of magnification can be reinforced and extended. It is useful for pupils to know how to estimate the size of the cells they are examining (see Chapter 1).

Finally, pupils need a firm understanding of the mechanisms of the nuclear and cell divisions which lead to the formation of *either* genetically identical cells (as a result of mitosis) *or* the gametes (as a result of meiosis) (see Chapter 1). They also need a grasp of the role of the genetic material DNA in the control of the cell's activities by the nucleus (see Chapters 1 and 7).

Teaching about human reproduction presents particular challenges to all teachers. Sex education in schools includes the study of human reproduction together with sexuality. Schools vary in the delivery of this area, in some cases relying on a well-integrated whole school approach, in other cases devolving much of the area of study to the Science department. It is crucial, as a teacher of biology, that you are well informed about the precise part you are to play in this sensitive area.

6.1 Asexual reproduction in plants and animals

◆ *Previous knowledge and experience*

Pupils are likely to have met aspects of growth and reproduction in plants and animals that will have been almost entirely concerned with sexual rather than asexual reproduction.

◆ *A teaching sequence*

Using a variety of examples, teachers can show pupils that asexual reproduction has several advantages over sexual reproduction:

- no energy is wasted in finding a mate
- many offspring are produced very rapidly
- favourable circumstances can be exploited very efficiently.

Examples of asexual reproduction

A variety of organisms can be used to show that there is only one parent in asexual reproduction. In each case some part of this parent divides to produce an identical individual, which then separates from the parent. A circus of activities (suggestions are largely seasonal) can provide an overview of the range of mechanisms for asexual reproduction in plants:

- estimation of the number of plantlets associated with a spider plant or *Bryophyllum*: ask pupils why there are so many
- illustration of reproduction (fission) in bacteria or a unicellular organism, such as *Amoeba proteus*: use a sequence from a video or CD ROM
- bread mould cultures: observe the development of colonies of mould (a fungus) and the tiny black dots (sporangia) containing the spores. Ask pupils how these may be dispersed.

Some fungal spores can trigger asthmatic and other allergic responses, so keep cultures in closed plastic bags.

Mitosis

Explore with your pupils the role of this division in that it allows cells (and therefore whole organisms) to reproduce themselves to form genetically identical offspring. You can extend this to make links with the role of mitosis in allowing multicellular organisms to grow and to repair themselves. Mitosis should eventually be understood as the basis of asexual reproduction (see Chapter 1).

Cloning and tissue culture

Cloning provides a genetically identical, and stable, gene pool in which a clone (e.g. a clump of daffodils) results from a single cell. You can consider many examples from horticulture and agriculture (e.g. wheat, potatoes, tomatoes) where the advantage is that particular characteristics of the crop plant can be maintained from one generation to the next. Consider also how a change in an aspect of the environment, e.g. prolonged drought, can be a disadvantage to a species reliant on asexual reproduction. Notice also how a range of wild plants (e.g. grasses) use both methods of reproduction and the disadvantages of cloning become less significant (see Chapter 8).

The term 'clone' is also used in connection with genetic engineering. A useful example to use with your pupils is the human gene for insulin. This can be inserted into the chromosome of a bacterium; the bacterial cell is then cloned by allowing it to reproduce asexually in a culture medium. All the offspring carry the gene and therefore have the potential for making a supply of insulin for medical use.

 Tissue culture is a way of conducting asexual reproduction on a massive scale; the process is now a routine laboratory and commercial procedure, and examples can help pupils' appreciation of the extent to which this is part of everyday life. A video sequence is useful to trigger debate on the subject.

Pupils should always be encouraged to discuss cloning in a balanced way in order to clarify some of the advantages to society of these techniques. Cloning animals is not as easy as cloning plants; for further discussion see pages 149 and 179.

Cancer

Few pupils have a good understanding of what constitutes cancerous growth. You can provide help by making the link with asexual reproduction in terms of uncontrolled cell divisions (mitosis). A video sequence can demonstrate the irregular mass of cells (tumour) that may have come about as a result of a mutation in a gene that controls cell division.

Useful second-hand data can raise older pupils' awareness of the way in which scientists begin to correlate the incidence of a disease with a particular factor. This is also an opportunity to talk about different carcinogens (ionising radiation, certain chemicals) and some viruses, all of which are linked with the promotion of cancerous growths.

Remember to treat the topic with some sensitivity since a pupil may be living with a relative who has suffered from, or is being treated for, cancer.

♦ *Further activities*

- ♦ Spring: record numbers of duckweed in a particular area of a pond over several days to demonstrate the rate of increase.
- ♦ Try some common horticultural methods:
  - late spring – stem cuttings (geranium, *Coleus*); leaf cuttings such as *Begonia rex*; layering ('pinks')
  - early summer – rooting the 'buds' of runners (strawberry).
- ♦ Older pupils can research tissue culture procedures: finding out how a callus is formed and how tiny plants are grown from subdivisions of this. Introduce this activity with a  video sequence together with literature from commercial plant breeders (e.g. producers of hybrid orchids).

♦ *Enhancement ideas*

- ♦ Examine yeast cells for signs of budding. Under the microscope pupils can watch cells reach a certain size and produce outgrowths (buds), which eventually split to form new individuals. An eyepiece graticule on the eyepiece lens of the microscope allows pupils to judge the size of the cells. A large TV screen attached to a video camera on the eyepiece of the microscope provides for a whole class observation. Extend the work for investigative activities in which pupils might explore the effects of culture temperature, or the amount of sugar, on the rate of cell division. Withdraw a drop of culture from the starter flask every 15 minutes and count the number of cells in the field of view. Plot a line graph to illustrate the increase in numbers of cells over time or pool class data entered on a spreadsheet and obtain mean values and plots of rates of increase in numbers.

Figure 6.1
The growth curve for yeast.

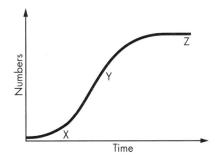

Ask pupils to explain what might be happening at X, Y, and Z. Why does the yeast stop budding eventually?

6.2 Sexual reproduction in plants and animals

♦ *Previous knowledge and experience*

Pupils will have met the idea (mainly through observation) of life cycles, for instance, in the main stages of the human life cycle, humans produce babies that grow into children and then adults; similarly, the main stages of the flowering plant include growth, pollination, seed dispersal and the germination of seeds to form new plants.

♦ *A teaching sequence*

Sexual reproduction leads to:

- an increase in numbers of individuals
- variation amongst offspring of the same species
- wide distribution of individuals.

Pupils can think about the advantages of sexual reproduction, which is technically more complex than asexual reproduction. Encourage them to deduce that it requires more energy, specialised organs that produce gametes, and also results in fewer offspring. Important advantages include individuals that are slightly different from either parent and other offspring of the same parents. In a changing environment some may be well-suited and be able to exploit new resources or colonise new areas. An organism's 'fitness' for a particular environment is a useful concept since it links environmental features and the organism's individual characteristics (see Chapter 8). Many of the advantages of sexual reproduction may be seen as the disadvantages of asexual reproduction, where only a static environment will ensure reproductive success. Pupils can summarise the advantages and disadvantages of both types of reproduction as a table.

Pupils should begin to appreciate that almost all organisms can reproduce sexually, even those that also reproduce asexually. Examples might include life in a coral reef, including invertebrates such as sea anemone, coral and jellyfish (e.g. see sequences from the BBC video *Malice In Wonderland*) as well as the more usual examples of bacteria, bluebells and strawberries. Show that sexual reproduction requires specialised sex cells (gametes), usually one from each parent or strain of the same species, which join to form the first new cell of the new individual (zygote). Examples should also show that some animals and plants are able to produce both male and female gametes and are described as hermaphroditic or bisexual (e.g. most flowering plants, earthworms, many molluscs such as snails, slugs and octopuses).

Sexual reproduction in plants

Flower structures
Pupils can examine different flower structures (e.g. tulip, wallflower, rapid-cycling *Brassica*, plantain). Exploit this to encourage pupils to observe, describe and record the structures carefully and to use a hand lens correctly.

These flowers have a similar basic set of structures. Ask younger pupils to identify the male parts: stamens, filament, anther, pollen; the female parts: carpels, stigma, style, ovary, ovules; and nectaries, sepals and petals. They should notice particular arrangements (including numbers, colour and sizes of petals, stamens, and carpels) and consider how these might enhance particular functions of the flower.

Suitable line diagrams can support this activity. Pupils can identify and dissect out the major parts of a flower, which might be stuck to card and labelled. Pupils can also 'build' a model flower, which provides a reinforcement activity to follow initial identification of parts; they could cut and paste the separate paper parts according to a series of instructions.

Older pupils will almost certainly need to refresh, or to build upon, their knowledge of these structures and their variety. Include the examination of a grass flower (e.g. rye grass) under a dissecting or binocular microscope, since pupils frequently are unaware of these insignificant-looking flowers. They can then record the special features of a wind-pollinated flower. There are also some excellent video sequences of flower structures and pollination mechanisms, which beautifully illustrate more exotic species.

Gamete formation in plants

Older pupils need to appreciate that pollen grain and ovule nuclei are formed by a special nuclear division, meiosis (see Chapter 1).

Pollination

Distinguish for older pupils those plants described as 'conifers' that do not have flowers, but do make male and female cones. They can examine a Scots pine, which produces two types of cone. Identify the pollen inside the male cone and the seeds, which are located between the woody scales of the large ripe female cone.

When a flowering plant reproduces sexually, pupils need help to appreciate that it produces male and female gametes that can be transferred between flowers, either on the same plant – self-fertilisation – or on to different plants – cross-fertilisation. Ripe pollen grains from different species can be examined microscopically. The big variation in size, shape and texture provides plenty of opportunity for improving observation, drawing and measuring skills. Ask pupils to work out a way of measuring the diameter of a pollen grain; pool the class data and calculate a mean value.

! *Great care is needed when using flowers that produce large amounts of pollen, as some pupils and teachers have allergic responses to different pollens. Ensure that flowers are not shaken so that pollen does not become airborne in significant quantities.*

Pollen tube

For older pupils the development of the pollen tube, which carries the male nucleus towards the female nucleus, can be stimulated fairly easily on a coverslip. It can be observed microscopically by using pollen from a rapid-cycling *Brassica* flower. The SAPS protocol is very reliable and can be demonstrated to pupils. There is further opportunity for investigative activity, such as designing a way of measuring the rate of growth of the pollen tubes. A significant growth can be observed within 30–45 minutes.

Ask older pupils to make a table to compare two insect-pollinated flowers and indicate differences in number, size and arrangement of sepals, petals, stamens and ovary. Ask them to explain how each adaptation makes pollination more likely. Pupils might describe the journey a visiting insect would make to approach and enter an insect-pollinated flower.

Fertilisation

Following pollination the nuclei of the gametes fuse to form a zygote. It is important to be aware that pupils of all ages frequently confuse pollination with seed dispersal mechanisms; that is, the adapted structure and related function of insect and wind-pollinated flowers, with the advantages and disadvantages of different mechanisms of seed and fruit dispersal.

Seed production

Older pupils can draw a flow diagram showing the sequence of events from pollination to seed formation. Many pupils need help in understanding the difference between a fruit and a seed, so reinforce these ideas with examples. In some instances (e.g. the apple) a false fruit is formed from the receptacle (the enlarged end of the flower stalk) rather than the carpel; the true fruit is the core of the apple; the pips are the seeds. In the strawberry the fleshy part is the false fruit (the swollen receptacle) with the surface pips as the true fruits, each containing the seed.

Avoid poisonous specimens of seeds and their pods (e.g. laburnum seeds and pods, castor oil seeds, uncooked red kidney beans and potato plant fruits). Seeds sold commercially for germination may have been treated with pesticides. Handle these with gloves or forceps, or wash hands thoroughly after handling.

Examine the dried pods and contents of rapid-cycling *Brassica*. Class data can be collated on a spreadsheet, and mean values obtained with respect to pod size and number of seeds per pod, together with observation of colour and diameter of seeds. Links can be made to illustrate the effects of growth conditions; for example, nipping out the apical tips of the flowering shoot at the 12–15-day stage can reduce the number of pods per plant, but significantly increase the size of pods. Explore with the class why this is so.

Seed dispersal

Pupils can collect seeds at suitable times of the year; many can be kept dry for subsequent examination by pupils. Aim with older pupils to refresh and broaden understandings of the variety of structures. Good quality pictures or a collection of your own photographs can provide good stimulus material. Find illustrative examples to include mechanisms that rely on:

- animal dispersal: tomato, blackberry, apple, goosegrass, hazelnut
- wind dispersal: poppy, sycamore, rosebay willow herb, dandelion
- water dispersal: coconut
- mechanical mechanisms: lupin, poppy, rapid-cycling *Brassica*.

Dissection of fruits and seeds

Pupils can examine the cross-section of a fruit containing a single seed (e.g. plum fruit with stone) to identify the embryo, food store and seed coat (testa).

The fertilised ovule grows into the embryo and you can illustrate the protective role of seeds by teasing out, from a soaked broad bean seed, the dormant embryo plant formed within the seed; explain that this has resulted from the ovule.

In a broad bean, food storage compounds are found in the two seed leaves (cotyledons). Soak a broad bean seed in water for 24 hours; identify the scar that attached the seed to the pod, and tiny hole (micropyle); then remove the coat (testa). Look for the tiny shoot (plumule), tiny root (radicle) and the position of the seed leaves (cotyledons). Drop a small amount of iodine solution on to one of the cotyledons. Ask pupils what they conclude about the food storage compound.

! *Eye protection is needed when handling iodine solution.*

The seeds of monocotyledons (such as maize or barley) also contain food storage compounds in the endosperm. Soaked maize and barley seeds provide good sources of material for further exploration of the chemical composition of storage compounds (see Chapter 2).

Seed germination

Once the testa of the seed is broken and the radicle is produced, pupils can discover that water, oxygen and warmth are essential for germination (that is, for aerobic respiration). Set up cress seeds on cottonwool in test-tubes under different environmental conditions, and ask pupils to predict which seeds will germinate. Examine the seeds a week later to check the predictions. Light is generally not needed, though some species, such as lettuce, do require light.

With older pupils aim to make links with processes of tissue respiration (Chapter 4) since the carbohydrate food reserves are broken down to simple sugars by enzymes in order for tissue respiration to occur and provide energy to the developing seedling.

Competition for important resources such as light, water and other nutrients is prevented to some extent by the effective dispersal of seeds from the parent plant. A punnet of cress seedlings provides a good stimulus for discussion in order to make links between biological understanding and commercial production methods. Try asking the following questions.

- What soil material has been used to get the cress seeds to germinate?
- How has the packaging been used to create suitable germination and growth conditions?
- How many cress seedlings are there in a single punnet? Pupils can then work out a method to calculate/estimate this figure.
- What does a punnet of cress cost in the shop?

Sexual reproduction in animals

The idea that most animals reproduce sexually as a result of the production of specialised gametes will need reinforcing for younger pupils; the male gametes are spermatozoa (singular: spermatozoon) or sperm; the female gametes are ova (singular: ovum). Meiosis is a special cell division that produces the gametes (see Chapter 1).

Always use key terminology with care: technically fertilisation refers to the fusion of the nuclei; the fertilised ovum develops into a zygote to form an embryo and subsequently the fetus.

Pupils need to gain an idea of size and number of gametes at the time of fertilisation. Generally the number depends on whether fertilisation is outside the body (external) or inside the body (internal). Older pupils can summarise the similarities and differences between the structure of an ovum and a sperm.

Video sequences can be well deployed to illustrate courtship procedures, as well as the act of copulation and fertilisation, in a variety of animals, such as amphibians, fish and birds.

◆ *Further activities*

◆ Soaked broad bean seeds provide younger pupils with independent, observational homework (over 4–5 weeks). Each pupil needs a jam jar and a roll of thick absorbent paper ensuring the seed is clamped to the side of the jar. The paper sits in 2 cm of water and acts as a wick. Ask pupils to keep written diaries, supported by drawings, for the whole life cycle.

◆ Pupils might consider how fruits are formed without seeds (e.g. seedless grapes or satsumas). These are generated by spraying with hormones that stimulate fruit production. Pupils can deduce that the crucial stage of fertilisation has been omitted, and the resulting fruit is of no use in producing another generation.

◆ *Enhancement ideas*

◆ Interesting investigations with small seeds and fruits can be carried out. How do particular seeds fall? Ask pupils to use dandelion (or sycamore) seeds in order to examine the relationship between height above ground and rate of falling. Ask them which variables (in terms of mass, size and shape, etc.) might be changed to slow down (or speed up) the rate of fall. Data can be put on a spreadsheet for further graphical analysis. Model seeds can be made to test ideas further. Ask pupils why a slower rate may be an advantage to the species.

◆ For older pupils, demonstrate the role of the enzyme amylase using halved, soaked barley seeds placed with the cut side in contact with starch agar in a Petri dish. After 24–28 hours at room temperature, flood the dish with iodine solution. The zone around each grain remains clear while the iodine on the rest of the starch agar is blackened. Ask pupils to account for the lack of starch in the clear zone.

Eye protection is needed when handling iodine solution.

6.3 Human reproduction and sex education

You are likely to be involved in teaching aspects of sex education whether or not you are a biology teacher.

Governors of maintained secondary schools and special schools with secondary-aged pupils are required to provide sex education for all registered pupils, including those over compulsory school age. However, the law does not define the purpose and content of sex education other than that it *must* include education about HIV and AIDS and other sexually transmitted infections. All such schools must have a policy on sex education with copies available for parents. The policy should take account of any representation made to the governors from the community and be up to date. The content and organisation of sex education should ensure that it is given in a manner that encourages pupils to have due regard to moral considerations and the value of family life, and can permit either parent to withdraw their child from all or part of sex education except that which is included in the National Curriculum.

Where your school has a well-formulated and clearly expressed sex education policy the ground rules for any teacher of sex education will be in place. You should be able to be supported in knowing the lines of referral within your school if a particular situation arises. You do *not* have a duty to inform the headteacher of a disclosure by a pupil (e.g. of under-age sexual activity or pregnancy) *unless* the headteacher has issued an instruction that he/she should be informed, in which case you must comply. You should always provide invited speakers and other visitors with a copy of the school sex education policy and ask them to abide by it.

Your own classroom relationships with your pupils are important in being effective in this sensitive area, and you should not be deterred from encouraging wherever possible open and frank discussion about issues, though not about particular personal circumstances. Where a pupil might approach you to share some personal information, you should use your professional judgement about keeping confidentiality, while at the same time never promising confidentiality. Remember that providing details of alternative sources of advice and of treatment does not count as sex education, but nevertheless always be guided by the school policy.

Some areas of the sex education curriculum, particularly how to approach sexual orientation and the issue of children's rights, currently remain rather uncertain for schools. Sex education embraces both the reproductive process and sexuality, and therefore benefits from a positive acknowledgement of all types of relationships including non-heterosexual ones (see Harrison, 1999 for a more detailed discussion of these aspects).

◆ *Previous knowledge and experience*

Pupils may have been given considerable information and understanding about aspects of human reproduction and relationships, but research shows this delivery can be patchy. The pupils' own physical and emotional developments are variable and will partly determine the extent to which they have absorbed or questioned information given earlier on. There will be differences in the provision from different homes, social and cultural backgrounds, different primary schools and different teachers within any school. *Curricular Guidance 5: Health Education* (National Curriculum Council, 1990) promotes the notion of a spiral curriculum from 5 to 16 for all nine components of health, one of which is sex education, in order to offer a coherent series of teaching and learning opportunities in addition to the statutory curricula.

National surveys to find out what young people really want in this area generally find that much information is often provided too late. Targeting younger secondary pupils is therefore important. Boys generally have lower levels of knowledge of reproduction, contraception and contraceptive services than girls, and so schools need to take steps to ensure that boys are not excluded from parts of the sex education curriculum. Girls have indicated that they want more adequate discussion and explanations in order to counterbalance an over-emphasis on biological facts. Clearly boys require this too. Educational videos in this area of the curriculum should be chosen with care for their appropriateness and always be used in such a way that there is time for reflection, clarification and discussion of sexual issues in the classroom.

Child abuse

Be aware of signs of child abuse. Identification is often not easy and, in addition to more obvious physical signs such as bruises, burns, bites and scars, a general indicator is neglect. Other indicators of sexual abuse include sexually transmitted infections, recurrent urinary infections, sexually explicit behaviour, young pupils with a lot of sexual knowledge, sexually abusive behaviour towards other children and unexplained pregnancy. Emotional abuse is indicated by low self-esteem, lethargy or attention-seeking behaviour, and delayed social development. A Child Protection Register is a record of all children within a local authority who are subject to an inter-agency child protection plan; an area child protection committee has full details of the Register.

◆ *A teaching sequence*

Try to assess and then extend your pupils' present knowledge of puberty, anatomy, conception and its prevention, the development of relationships and the medical problems associated with early sexual involvement. An important teaching aim is to allow pupils to rehearse the forms of language (possibly both slang and formal words) and, through this, to get used to the feelings they have about the language with which they will need to communicate effectively with their partners later on.

Pupils may have the technical vocabulary but actual understanding can be poor. They need help in knowing where various anatomical parts are located as well as what the parts actually do. Aim to make your audience feel comfortable about not knowing things, while at the same time making it possible for them to find out. Laughter and joking help to make everyone feel good while at the same time enabling you to address every question seriously and with respect.

Physical and emotional changes that take place during adolescence

An exploration with your pupils of how males and females differ physically can enable you to summarise the key changes at puberty. A useful ice-breaking activity might be to place each key point describing a secondary sexual characteristic on to separate cards, which small groups of pupils can then discuss and arrange under one of the two headings 'males' and 'females'.

Ask pupils to investigate the range of heights amongst males and females within a particular age group (or age groups) for a particular population. This is best done using a spreadsheet for all pupil data, to include height along with many other variables such as eye colour, tongue rolling and handedness. (NB It is best to avoid 'body mass'.) (See also Chapter 8.)

Adolescents can be particularly sensitive about their body image and the position they hold in the peer group and, if badly handled, these activities could lower pupils' self esteem. Carefully handled, they allow pupils to take account of their uniqueness with respect to all the characteristics under scrutiny.

Stress the wide variation in the age of onset of puberty and the generally earlier age of onset for girls. Explore possible reasons for the earlier onset over the last 50 years. This is a feature of genetic predisposition as well as of overall health and individual height/weight ratios. Puberty also extends over some years for an individual, as illustrated by the time taken for a consistent menstrual cycle.

Ask pupils to examine typical growth curves for boys and girls and to describe and interpret each curve.

Figure 6.2

The range of ages for height spurt in boys and girls. (Based on Nuffield Coordinated Biology (1998), Figures 20.2 and 20.3, p. 251. Harlow, Longman.)

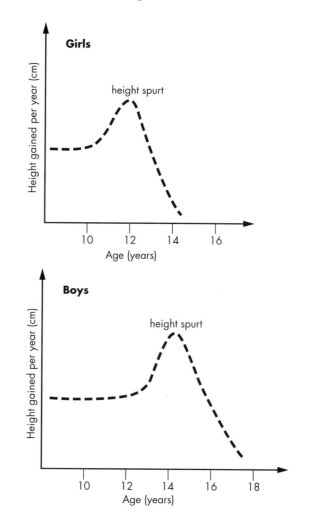

Gamete production, sexual intercourse and fertilisation

From puberty, meiosis in the testis (see Chapter 1) produces immature sperm and these develop into mature sperm in the testes. Statistics are helpful in bringing about a better understanding of male fertility including numbers, size and motility of sperm. A human sperm is about 1.4×10^{-4} mm long and can travel the 15 cm from the vagina to the neck of the cervix in about 3 hours. Sperm production is highest in the early twenties. The relatively large size of the ovum compared with the sperm can be demonstrated with scaled down paper models.

Meiosis in the ovaries produces the immature eggs, which are already present at birth. From puberty the female sex hormones control a cycle that produces one mature egg about once a month. Not all pupils recognise that the two ovaries alternate in this production. The egg develops in a follicle and one of the important jobs of this follicle is to prepare the uterus for pregnancy.

Note that pupils might be confused if you say the egg moves from the ovary to the uterus; the egg is actually propelled indirectly by the action of cilia and mucus, from the oviduct to the uterus.

Use video sequences and other pictures to illustrate and discuss the processes leading to fertilisation, including sexual intercourse. Pupils can devise a flow diagram using ICT to represent the key events leading to fertilisation or, alternatively, ask pupils to produce a pictorial flow chart as a poster to show how the male and female gametes are brought together. The emotional as well as the physical aspects of sexual intercouse should be addressed through discussion, but check that the school sex education policy allows this.

Human reproductive system, including the menstrual cycle

Pupils tend to have muddled ideas about how many urinary, genital and defaecatory orifices people have (girls have three, boys have two) and often both boys and girls do not know from where a girl urinates.

Key vocabulary for the male genital organs includes: scrotum, testis, epididymis (sperm-producing tubes), sperm duct, seminal vesicle, prostate gland, urethra, penis, erectile tissue, foreskin; and for the closely associated urinary organs: kidney, ureter, bladder, urethra; and defaecatory organs:

rectum and anus. Pupils should understand that the urethra has a dual function in the male. The similarity in sound and spelling of some terms such as 'ureter' and 'urethra' can also be confusing for pupils.

Key vocabulary for the female genital organs is: ovary, Fallopian tube (egg tube or oviduct), uterus (womb), cervix, vagina, clitoris and vulva. In the female the urethra has only one function, which is in connection with the urinary system. The vocabulary for the urinary and defaecatory systems are the same as for the male.

The structure and function of the parts of the reproductive system

Older pupils need to know the structure and function of all these parts; younger pupils can be presented with a reduced list of key terms or simplified terminology. It is generally best to provide an accurate, but unlabelled, line diagram that pupils can then label themselves. This activity can be extended into a card-sorting/matching exercise in which pupils are provided with key names on one set of coloured cards, and a further coloured set of cards with the key functions of the parts.

Help pupils to understand that the erectile tissue of the penis becomes firm as it fills with blood when the penis is stimulated either manually or indirectly through specific visual or other stimuli. Some male pupils may need your reassurance about the normality of wet dreams and masturbation. The dual role of the urethra in the male will need some clarification: glands at the base of the bladder produce secretions that wash away the urine in the urethra since urine can destroy sperm. Masturbation for female pupils also needs clarification, particularly as it is rarely discussed openly in school sex education or in school textbooks. Indeed the clitoris is often rendered invisible by being absent from diagrams as well as absent in any discussion about structure and function.

Muscle rings in the sperm duct squeeze the sperm along the passage. You can simulate this action by pushing toothpaste along in its tube, which is similar to peristalsis in the intestinal tract (see Chapter 2). Further glands mix nutrient secretions with the sperm to form semen. Ask pupils why this is necessary. Illustrate the volume of the ejaculate: about one teaspoon of semen is produced at ejaculation. The prostate gland is often incorrectly referred to as 'prostrate'! It is frequently enlarged in older men and pupils can deduce the effect of any enlargement on the frequency of and difficulty in urination.

Since the female reproductive organs are largely invisible, and therefore particularly mysterious, ask pupils to site the position of the ovaries by placing their fingers on their own abdomen. To do this, suggest they feel for the front points of the pelvis and move in towards the navel an inch or so. Ask pupils to feel the tip of their nose with a forefinger. Say that this feels rather like the cervix, the ring of muscle that closes the lower end of the uterus where it joins the vagina. There is a very small hole in the cervix to permit sperm to enter; the cervix dilates during labour; check that they understand why.

Pupils can estimate the size of the adult vagina and the size of the adult non-pregnant uterus. For comparison use a medium-sized inverted pear (about 10 cm long) and tilt it backwards slightly to illustrate the angle of the uterus with respect to the vagina. Point out the need for a good blood supply to the uterus and explore why this is so. Ask pupils to suggest how long the egg takes to be moved from the ovary to the uterus (24–48 hours). The vagina is a muscular tube with sensitive nerve endings and glands that can secrete mucus. Explore with your pupils the reasons for these.

Sperm swim towards the oviducts aided by movements of the female reproductive system. After an hour they no longer swim but they can survive in the uterus for 24 hours and in the oviducts for 48 hours. Explore with your pupils why it is important to be aware of this and how the timing of ovulation can influence the chance of fertilisation (see also page 142 in this chapter).

Most confusing for pupils are the, often dramatic, video shots of the moment of ovulation, or the cartoon pictorial accounts of the subsequent movements of the ovum in the oviduct. Neither give any idea of scale or the relationship of the microscopic structures to the macroscopic organs and their actual positions in the body. Always take steps to use the pause button on the video sequence and check your pupils fully understand the events portrayed.

Sexual intercourse

Textbooks and most teaching materials assume intercourse is heterosexual and that sexual activity is penetrative (vaginal) intercourse. Such texts might be described as sexist since many words describe intercourse from the male rather than female point of view. Ejaculation by the male is frequently mentioned; orgasm in the female is mentioned only rarely. Diagrams almost always show the so-called 'missionary position' with the female underneath the male. Any accounts of the loving relationships, or indeed the passions or pleasures associated with sex, are notable by their absence. It is important to create a balance between an anatomical account and a psychological and emotional account.

Most seriously, there is little to be said in any textbooks and many teaching materials about legal issues and most particularly about the fact that, in Britain, it is illegal to have sexual intercourse with anyone under the age of 16. DfEE *Circular 5/94* has a useful summary of the law on sexual behaviour with regard to incest, rape, indecent assault and other indecent conduct.

Menstrual cycle, ovulation and menstruation

Menstruation remains a taboo subject in our society, which is unhelpful to an adolescent girl for whom it is acutely realistic. The physical, emotional and practical aspects of periods, particularly in the school setting, do very little to reassure girls of the positive experiences of becoming a woman. When pupils are asked 'What is menstruation?' research has shown that over one-third of 13 to 14-year-old pupils do not mention menstrual fluid, and when questioned specifically, the actual source of the menstrual blood is frequently misunderstood. Try to aim for a balance between a purely physiological approach and a more personal account that goes some way to acknowledging the reality of this event for up to half the school population!

Using a 28-day calendar ask pupils to predict when a young woman might expect:

- the day of ovulation
- the day of the start of the menstrual period
- the days when she might be able to conceive.

It is important for pupils to appreciate that the time interval between day one of the menstrual period and the time of ovulation is very variable, both from one individual to another and from one month to another for any woman. Fourteen days after the release of the egg from the follicle the uterine wall breaks down (enable your pupils to appreciate that this time interval between ovulation and the start of the menstrual period is a *fixed* time) (see also Chapter 5).

Medical uses of hormones, including the control and promotion of fertility

The teaching and associated discussion of the natural and artificial methods of preventing pregnancy (i.e. birth control or 'family planning') frequently falls to the science teacher.

Be guided by your school sex education policy and be mindful that the use of contraception is not acceptable to all adults or young people. The health risks, both physical and emotional, of under-age sex should always be explored fully with your pupils. Pupils need both general and local guidance about how to seek information and advice (e.g. 'drop-in sessions' to a school nurse or youth clinic) and how to buy items or to access the particular medical services that can supply them (the diaphragm, intra-uterine device, contraceptive pill and the 'morning after' pill).

Information on its own about a contraceptive method is of little use to pupils; they should be shown the correct ways in which to use a particular item. This applies particularly to the sheath or condom, in both male and female forms, the use of spermicides, withdrawal, and the rhythm method (safe period), which may involve using the calendar or particular detection methods such as a temperature or a hormone detection kit such as Persona. The poorly named emergency 'morning after' pill needs particular clarification since it is possible to use it up to 72 hours after intercourse. Discussion should always include the relative reliability and risk of failure of the item or method, together with its effectiveness in reducing the transmission of sexually transmitted infections. Pupils need to gain an understanding that, at different ages or stages in a relationship, one contraceptive may be more appropriate than another.

The contraceptive pill is a package of hormones that prevents egg release. The fertility pill is a package of hormones that stimulates egg production and release. Ask the pupils to suggest suitable hormones for the contraceptive pill and for a fertility pill and to explain their choice. Why do doctors find it much easier to determine a dose for a contraceptive pill rather than for a fertility pill?

Ask pupils in groups of three to five to make a video or PowerPoint presentation advertising a particular contraceptive. They should consider how the contraceptive works, for whom it would be most useful, and present the chief risks. Alternatively, using DTP, small groups of pupils might produce a leaflet concerned with one type of contraceptive.

Sexually transmitted infections (STIs)

A detailed study of these falls best within the teaching of microbiology (see Chapter 10) and the modes of transmission should be considered for the six commonest STIs: chlamydia (bacterial), genital warts (viral), gonorrhoea (bacterial), genital herpes (viral), hepatitis B (viral) and Human Immunodeficiency Virus – HIV (viral). Other STIs might include syphilis (bacterial), pubic lice (crustacean), urethritis (bacterial), thrush (fungal), thrush (yeast), bacterial vaginosis and trichomoniasis (protozoon).

Reinforcement activities can encourage pupils to consider the routes of infection and importantly, since several of these diseases are life threatening, to consider how they are passed on to another person and how they are best avoided. Offer the reassurance that, with early detection (with the exception of HIV infection) all may be safely treated. Aim to dispel misunderstandings, find out what the pupils do, or do not, know about STIs, and challenge prejudices about those who may catch an STI. They need to know that people infected with HIV do not have to look ill.

Providing accurate and up-to-date information must be one of the early and important teaching objectives. An excellent publication, *Infection Protection: Teaching About Sexually Transmitted Infections* (1997) covers the major infections. One activity that provides information involves the assembly of six jigsaws, one for each STI, and each with four pieces of information covering cause, symptoms, effect on health/complications and treatment.

Since the routes of transmission involve sexual contact, a second and equally important teaching objective is to raise pupils' awareness about the need for safer sex. Pupils must be told about the risks of transmission through the mixing of body fluids, which include semen, vaginal secretions and blood. This is best addressed when teaching about contraception so pupils can weigh up the 'pros' and 'cons' of the various contraceptives in terms of effectiveness in preventing transmission of STIs.

Most teachers and youth workers feel anxious about their legal position when it comes to discussing homosexuality with young people. No current legislation prohibits sensitive and sensible discussion about homosexuality and teachers are within the law to educate against prejudice and discrimination. However, you do need to work within the framework of your school's sex education policy. There is a lack of information about sexual identity in school textbooks and other teaching materials, and what information there is, often presents homosexuality as a second-best option, particularly for young people, that a person might well grow out of. Bisexuality is mentioned even less frequently. In terms of equal opportunities these are serious omissions. Rarely is there mention about the actual expression of non-heterosexual feelings, and in connection with STIs we can see that there are aspects of teaching about safer sex (e.g. during anal intercourse) that might be overlooked.

Finally, pupils need information about testing procedures and local GUM (genito-urinary medicine) clinics. Should you be asked by a pupil about a sexual activity and you do not know what it involves, you can contact the National AIDS Helpline (tel: 0800 567123) for information about what is safe or unsafe and provide the pupil with information at a later time. Inform pupils about the higher incidences of HIV infection in other parts of the world, including France, Italy and Spain, and promote some discussion about safer sex on holiday. Case study scenarios and 'agony aunt' letters make useful classroom resources for increasing dialogue about the issues.

Schools may wish to invite health professionals into the classroom to support the teaching in this area, and local health promotion units and GUM clinics will often provide help. There are good video sequences, too, though it is important to check just how up to date these are, and to plan carefully so pupils have an opportunity to talk about the topics and issues that arise.

◆ *Further activities*

- ◆ Use a three-dimensional model of the human torso with interchangeable male/female/pregnant female parts, together with good quality three-dimensional drawings or illustrations of the male and female urinary–genital tracts. These will allow pupils to understand the relative positions of the key organs and structures. Ask pupils questions about number, shape and size as well as the technical name of the parts. Do not take for granted that knowing the names means a full and accurate understanding of their functions.
- ◆ Let pupils look at the male/female reproductive system of a rat that has been dissected to expose these areas. They can identify the key parts and find out what they do or where they lead to.
- ◆ Examine the microscopic structure of the testis and ovary. Let pupils have a look, under the low power of a microscope, at a prepared, stained slide of a mature mammalian testis (i.e. a thin section which has been cut and mounted on the slide).

Point out the sperm located in the tubules. The testes produce sperm continuously and store them in the epididymis, typically 350 million sperm, at lower than core body temperature. Ask why it is an advantage for the testes to be situated outside the main body cavity, and whether there may be disadvantages too. A prepared microscope slide of a mature ovary of a mammal can reveal, under low power, the immature eggs towards the edge of the ovary.

Figure 6.3
Time chart and information cards to make a diagram showing the hormones involved in the menstrual cycle.

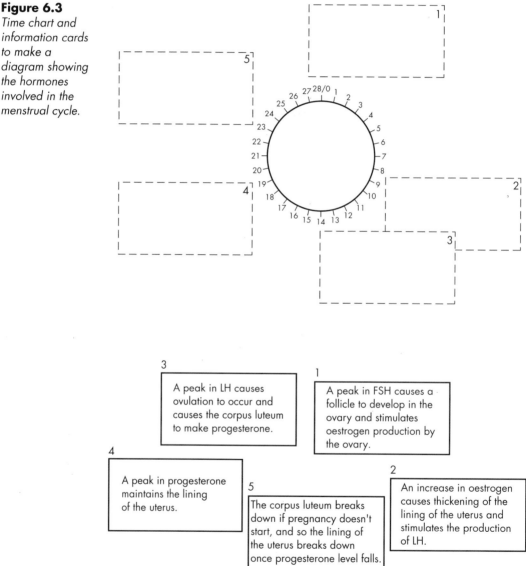

3

A peak in LH causes ovulation to occur and causes the corpus luteum to make progesterone.

1

A peak in FSH causes a follicle to develop in the ovary and stimulates oestrogen production by the ovary.

4

A peak in progesterone maintains the lining of the uterus.

5

The corpus luteum breaks down if pregnancy doesn't start, and so the lining of the uterus breaks down once progesterone level falls.

2

An increase in oestrogen causes thickening of the lining of the uterus and stimulates the production of LH.

- For more able/older pupils, ask them to summarise in a flow diagram the way the pituitary and ovarian hormones interact to produce a regular menstrual cycle. Alternatively, provide pupils with a circular time chart (Figure 6.3) together with five 'cards' containing relevant information about oestrogen, progesterone, luteinising hormone, follicle-stimulating hormone and the corpus luteum. They should stick the cards on the outside of the chart against the part of the cycle they correspond to, and then number them from 1 to 5 in the sequence in which they occur.

◆ *Enhancement ideas*

- Examine the packaging, labelling and instruction sheets of some different types of sanitary wear including tampons. From 1992 the following warning has been placed on tampon boxes:

  Health warning:
  Tampons are associated with toxic shock syndrome (TSS). TSS is a rare but serious disease that may cause death. Read and save the enclosed information.

  Ask pupils how effective they think this warning is, then get them to write a further passage for the tampon consumer leaflet about the exact cause of the disease (see also Chapter 10).
- Issues to do with biodegradability, details of information about absorbency, and the accuracy of diagrams can all be explored from the point of view of the consumer as well as in terms of scientific literacy and accuracy.

6.4 Human pregnancy

♦ *Previous knowledge and experience*

Pupils are likely to have met some of the processes of fetal development; some understanding of the role of the parents and child care will also be present.

♦ *A teaching sequence*

Development of the fetus in the uterus, including the role of the placenta

Explore what happens to the fertilised egg (zygote) in the 6–7-day journey from oviduct to uterine wall. Older pupils will need to know that the hollow ball of cells implants in the uterine wall. Once it is fully implanted, after a further 6–7 days, its cells begin to produce the hormone human chorionic gonadotrophin (HCG). It is this hormone that is detected by most pregnancy tests.

ICT

The development of the human embryo during the 40-week period of gestation lends itself well to some descriptive writing by pupils, and can be reinforced with some high quality videos and photographs. The notion of spontaneous abortion, which is particularly high in the first 2 weeks of gestation (i.e. preimplantation), might be discussed together with the continued risk of miscarriage in the first 3 months of pregnancy.

Many changes take place in a woman's body during pregnancy and hormones play an important role (see Chapter 5). As the implanted embryo grows, the tissues of the uterine lining and of the embryo itself develop into a placenta. At 12 weeks the placenta is fully formed and produces progesterone. The embryo is now referred to as a fetus.

Ask the pupils for which body organs the placenta acts as a substitute. Stress that the fetal and maternal blood supplies are very close but completely separate. Explore with pupils the mechanism by which oxygen, glucose and amino acids can pass from mother to fetus, and by which carbon dioxide and other waste substances, such as urea, can pass from fetus to mother.

Many health related issues can be explored to prepare older pupils as future parents, together with the responsibilities that this entails. Ask pupils which harmful substances or organisms might pass from mother to fetus.

Birth can be summarised by pupils using a flow chart that shows the main stages of labour. The whole topic of pregnancy, birth and neonatal care provides good opportunities for pupils to get to know more about the medical, maternity and welfare services of GPs and the NHS, as well as parenting. A school nurse, local midwife or health visitor may be helpful in providing your class with accurate information and detail about Caesarean section, induction of birth, breech birth, up-to-date monitoring techniques, child-care and so on.

The many excellent videos and photographs should always be used with care, to avoid embarrassing or distressing those pupils who may find that some sequences make them feel squeamish and faint. Always be sensitive, where pregnancy and birth are concerned, to their impact on pupils and their families (e.g. adoption, miscarriage or neonatal death).

Social and ethical issues

Artificial insemination of a woman with her husband's sperm (AIH) allows an infertile couple to have a child without a third party being involved. If the husband cannot produce sperm then sperm from a donor might be used (AID). You can explore with older pupils how this might be similar to, or different from, adoption of a child by the couple. Ask the pupils to make a list of issues that might be of concern with AID.

In vitro fertilisation, or IVF (which used to be called making 'test-tube babies'), provides a particularly useful discussion topic. It is used to treat women whose ovaries are functioning but whose oviducts are blocked, or where sperm motility of the partner is poor. The woman is treated hormonally to superovulate. Ask your pupils, 'What are the risks of IVF?'

Cloning livestock embryos is an important technique in animal breeding (animal clones are genetically identical individuals formed by carefully dividing a 16- or 32-cell stage ball of cells, or by growing a ball of cells from some maternal body cells, as was the case in Dolly the sheep). The ball of cells is planted into the prepared 'pregnant uterus' of the cell donor. Ask your pupils to summarise the advantages of such processes in animal breeding.

◆ *Further activities*

- ◆ Protection of the developing fetus from mechanical, chemical and pathogenic damage can be addressed through questions such as the following.

- Why are young girls offered a vaccination against Rubella (German measles)?
- Why are pregnant women offered additional iron supplements?
- Why are pregnant women advised: not to smoke; to take care and read the advice given with legal or prescribed drugs; to avoid drinking alcohol?

♦ A premature baby aged 28 weeks can survive. Pupils can find out what a baby looks like at this age. Ask them what an incubator has to provide for such a baby.

♦ *Enhancement ideas*

♦ Ask your pupils to find out more about the Human Fertilisation and Embryology Authority's Code of Practice in the UK, which regulates the conduct of infertility treatment and embryo research. Experimental cloning of a human embryo was reported from the USA in 1993 but is banned by the Human Fertilisation and Embryology Authority in the UK. Ethical objections can be raised against some or all of these procedures; allow your pupils to debate these from an informed point of view and to explore the debate about the age limits imposed on embryo research.

♦ With older pupils, explain how chorionic villus sampling, as a procedure to detect genetic abnormalities in the first weeks after implantation, is useful and yet hazardous in terms of fetal loss and inaccuracy. Removal of fetal cells from the amniotic fluid for tissue culture and genetic examination can be done at a later stage; again explore the advantages and disadvantages of this procedure (amniocentesis). You can continue the discussion by exploring the legal situation in the UK with respect to the availability of therapeutic (induced) abortion.

♦ Abortion is a particularly sensitive issue that needs careful handling by you, with due consideration for particular religious and cultural groups. You should endeavour to remain *neutral* at all times when presenting the debate and allow your pupils to work out for themselves the position they may wish to adopt. Be particularly cautious about how you might use the materials and resources produced by some of the key pressure groups.

Equipment notes

Asexual reproduction in plants and animals

Bread mould cultures require moistened pieces of stale bread in dishes exposed to the air for 24 hours. Keep the bread slightly moist to prevent it drying out, and cover with a glass jar to keep it humid.

! *Ensure that pupils do not lift the jar.*

A **cell suspension of actively growing yeast cells** can be made at the bottom of a small flask, using 8 g fresh baker's yeast and 10 g glucose (or cane sugar), made up to 200 cm³ with distilled water. Plug with cottonwool and leave in a warm room (22 °C) for 20 minutes before use with the class. Always pretest culture conditions before the lesson to ensure that cell division is taking place. In a small pipette transfer one drop of the culture to a microscope slide with a small amount of methylene blue stain and cover with a slip. Use methylene blue for staining living cells as follows:

1 g methylene blue; 0.6 g sodium chloride; 100 cm³ distilled water.

! *Methylene blue is harmful.*

Sexual reproduction in plants

A specially selected mutant **rapid-cycling *Brassica*** provides a versatile and easily maintained resource to develop pupils' understanding of the life cycle of a flowering plant in 4–6 weeks when grown under a specially constructed artificial light bank in the school laboratory. Its versatility lies in the opportunity to study its life cycle at any time of the year; it can be 'grown to order' to obtain germinating seedlings, pre-flowering or flowering plants for a particular teaching day. There are numerous investigative ideas available for teachers as part of extensive resource packs. Contact SAPS (Science and Plants for Schools), Homerton College, Hills Road, Cambridge CB2 2PH (tel: 01223 507168; website: www-saps.plantsci.cam.ac.uk). There is a regular SAPS newsletter called *Osmosis*.

Starch agar plates are made up as follows: make a starch suspension with 10 g starch and 1 dm³ distilled water. To do this, mix a little of the starch with cold water; bring the rest of the water to the boil; add the starch mixture to the boiling water. To make up the iodine solution use 3 g iodine crystals and 6 g potassium iodide. Dissolve the potassium iodide in 200 cm³ distilled water, add the iodine crystals and make up to 1 dm³ with distilled water. Make up 24 hours before it is to be used to allow the iodine to dissolve fully.

! *Iodine crystals are harmful; use gloves and eye protection when handling.*

Sexual reproduction in animals

Using a scale of 1:200, pupils can make **scaled two-dimensional models of an egg and a sperm**. To do this for the egg draw a circle with a diameter of 20 cm. For the sperm draw a head diameter of 0.8 cm, and overall length including head of 10 cm. The actual dimensions are indicated on the diagrams below.

Figure 6.4
Actual dimensions of human egg and sperm.
(Based on Nuffield Coordinated Biology (1988), Figure 19.1b, p. 245. Harlow, Longman.)

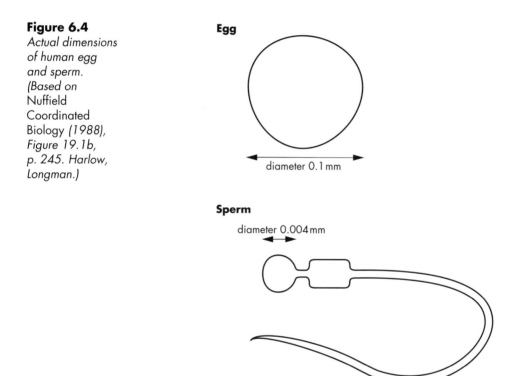

Egg

diameter 0.1 mm

Sperm

diameter 0.004 mm

overall length = 0.05 mm

Human reproductive system

Three-dimensional model of the human torso (Philip Harris). A local Health Promotion Unit/Family Planning Clinic might be willing to loan schools models and other resources.

Other resources

- Family Planning Association *Contraceptive Kit.*
- Brook Publications (1990). *Penis Model Pack: Learning Strategies for Effective Condom Use.*
- Brook Publications (1997). *Two's Company: Everything Young People Want To Know About Relationships.*
- Philip Harris, *Human Torso, Bisexual,* has interchangeable male and female reproductive parts, with an African female version also available. Available from Philip Harris, Lynn Lane, Shenstone, Lichfield, Staffs. WS14 0EE (tel: 01543 480077).
- Philip Harris, *Pelvic Section of Pregnant Human Uterus with 9 Month and 3 Month Fetus.*
- Health Education Authority (1998). *Folic Acid Education Pack.* Folic acid has been shown to have a role in preventing neural tube defects such as spina bifida, and this resource pack for teachers and pupils aims to improve understanding of the importance of folic acid prior to conception and during the first 12 weeks of pregnancy. Available from Health Education Authority, Trevelyan House, 30 Great Peter Street, London SW1P 2HW (tel: 0171 222 5300).

◆ *Videos*

- BBC Videos for Education and Training (1994). *Malice in Wonderland.*
- BBC Videos for Education and Training, *The Private Life of Plants* (1995), episode 1 *Travelling* illustrates the way plants move and colonise.
- Channel 4 Schools, *Scientific Eye, Life and Living Processes 2* (1998), programme 2 on *Cells* has a section on tissue culturing of human skin cells. A study guide suitable for younger secondary pupils is also available.
- Channel 4 Schools, *New Living Body: Skin* (1998), is a good sequence on the dangers of exposure to UV light when sunbathing, with an emphasis on the risks of skin cancer and particularly melanomas in white northern Europeans.
- BBC Videos for Education and Training, *The Big C* (1997), follows four patients' diagnosis and successful treatment of cancer.
- BBC Videos for Education and Training, *Sexual Encounters of the Floral Kind* (1981, archive), has good and exotic examples of a variety of pollination mechanisms in plants.

- BBC Videos for Education and Training, *Trials of Life* (1990), has two episodes *Courting* and *Continuing the Line*, which illustrate a variety of breeding activity.
- Channel 4 Schools, *Science In Focus, Life Science 2 Human Biology: Hormones* (1997), gives information on growth and sex hormones, menstrual cycle and the pill, together with a study guide.
- Channel 4 Schools, *Science In Focus, Life Science 2 Human Biology: Defence Mechanisms* (1997), gives information on bacterial and viral infections, HIV, cold sores and glandular fever; transmission through unprotected sex of sexually transmitted infections. It also explains a genito-urinary clinic and how HIV infection can be detected.
- Channel 4 Schools, *Scientific Eye, Life and Living Processes 2: Reproduction* (1998), explains fertilisation *in vitro*, the development of the fetus and why it is rare for more than three babies to survive being born together.
- Channel 4 Schools, *The New Living Body: Babies* (1995), illustrates fertilisation, prenatal screening methods, *in vitro* fertilisation and raises the ethical, social and moral questions about the new and possible technologies of genetic manipulation.
- BBC Videos for Education and Training, *Birth: An Everyday Miracle* (1981, archive), shows the development of a baby from the earliest days in the womb to the final stages of birth. The microphotography used for sequences showing the ovaries, Fallopian tubes and womb are outstanding.

◆ *CD ROMs*

- Projection Visual Communication Ltd and Interactive Learning Production Ltd, *Sex Education for Tomorrow's Adults: The Facts of Life* (1994), provides personal, religious and biological information on reproduction which can be used in a variety of ways, e.g. as stimulus material for a class discussion, or for independent study outside the lesson. From AVP, School Hill Centre, Chepstow, Gwent NP6 5PH (tel: 01291 625439; website: www.avp.com).

◆ *Websites*

- *InnerBody* (website: www.innerbody.com/) provides views of the human body including the reproductive organs.
- Liverpool John Moore's University, Sci-Centre (website: www.lmu.livjm.ac.uk) has information and multimedia visuals about the human body.

◆ *Books*

Brook Resource Pack (1997). *Infection Protection: Teaching About Sexually Transmitted Infections.* London, Brook Publications.

Harris, R. (1994). *Let's Talk About Sex.* London, Walker Books. This is a charming book with cartoon illustrations designed to inspire confidence in pupils, teachers and parents.

Harrison, J.K. (1999). *Sex Education in Secondary Schools.* Buckingham, Open University Press.

Harvey, I. & Reiss, M. (1992). *AIDS Facts* (4th edition). Dunstable, Folens. This is an interactive resource about AIDS and is suitable for teachers of pupils aged 11+.

◆ *Background reading*

DfEE (1994). *Circular 5/94. Education Act 1993: Sex Education in Schools.* DfEE School Curriculum Branch.

National Curriculum Council (1990). *Curricular Guidance 5: Health Education.* York, National Curriculum Council.

Reiss, M.J. (1998). The representation of human sexuality in some science textbooks for 14–16 year olds. *Science & Technological Education*, **16**, 137–149.

◆ *Useful organisations*

Local organisations to look out for:

- AIDS support services
- Department of Genito-urinary Medicine (GUM)
- Family Planning Clinic and/or Young Person's Clinic
- Health Promotion Centre
- Lesbian and Gay Communities Resource Centre
- Rape Crisis Centre.

◆ *National organisations*

A number of national organisations with extensive books and support materials for use in secondary schools:

Brook Publications, 165 Gray's Inn Road, London WC1X 8UD (tel: 0171 833 8488).

Family Planning Association, Healthwise Bookshop, 27–35 Mortimer Street, London W1N 7RJ (tel: 0171 636 7866).

Sex Education Forum, c/o National Children's Bureau, 8 Wakley Street, London EC1V 7QE (tel: 0171 843 6051; website: www.ncb.org.uk/sexed.htm).

7 *Genetics*

Jenny Lewis

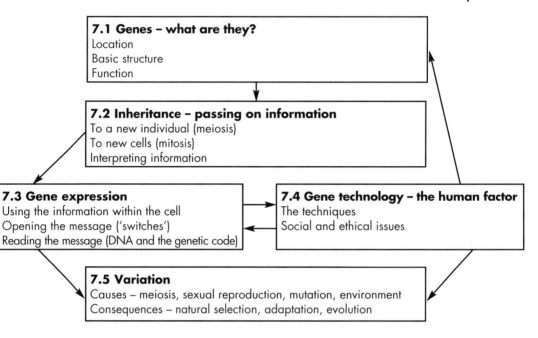

7.1 Genes – what are they?
Location
Basic structure
Function

7.2 Inheritance – passing on information
To a new individual (meiosis)
To new cells (mitosis)
Interpreting information

7.3 Gene expression
Using the information within the cell
Opening the message ('switches')
Reading the message (DNA and the genetic code)

7.4 Gene technology – the human factor
The techniques
Social and ethical issues

7.5 Variation
Causes – meiosis, sexual reproduction, mutation, environment
Consequences – natural selection, adaptation, evolution

◆ *Choosing a route*

Genes, and the DNA of which they are made, are the basis of life itself and central to the study of biology. In addition, the rapid development of gene technology has led to some astonishing scientific advances in recent years, with numerous social implications. As a result, you might expect pupils to find the topic of genetics fascinating. This is not automatically the case – some pupils find genetics difficult and fail to see its relevance to their own lives.

There are a number of possible reasons for this. Genetics can appear very complex. Genes are too small to be seen directly but their effect may be seen in cells, in individuals, in families or even in whole populations. In addition, some effects may be influenced by the environment or by other genes and some may only become apparent over an extended period of time. It is difficult to visualise the processes that can bring such changes about, and the opportunities for practical demonstrations within the school laboratory are limited. In addition, genetics (and especially the study of inheritance) uses a large vocabulary of specialist terms that may overwhelm and confuse. In making the topic accessible to all pupils, these issues need to be taken into account.

When preparing to teach genetics it is tempting to start the topic with a look at human variation, using the class as a sample population. A simple and effective piece of software, called *Variation*, is available for highlighting this (see page 194). Your pupils are likely to enjoy this activity but at this stage their understanding of the concept of a gene is likely to be limited and abstract. You may find that this approach leads too quickly into complex concepts about inheritance for which your pupils are unprepared. However, starting the topic with a discussion of genes – what they are and what they do – is probably not the answer. Genes cannot be seen and cannot be handled. It will be difficult for your pupils to engage with the topic if they have nothing tangible or interesting to relate to it.

One approach that is likely to interest your pupils and need not require much prior knowledge is to start the whole topic with a discussion of gene technology and its uses. Selecting an exciting or topical example, keeping the science content to a minimum, and focusing on social and ethical aspects would enable you to use this approach with most pupils, regardless of age or ability (see *Gene technology*). They enjoy the opportunity to discuss their own ideas, especially when there is no 'right' answer, and may result in them beginning to consider the underlying science and become motivated to find out more. At this point it may be useful to discuss genes. This will help your pupils to develop their concept of a gene as a physical object and provide them with some basic knowledge to build upon when learning about inheritance or gene expression.

Once your pupils have some understanding of inheritance and gene expression it will be possible to reconsider gene technology, this time with the emphasis on the science. Alternatively, you might combine some aspects of gene expression with an example drawn from gene technology.

The concept of variation will run throughout genetics, but a discussion of its causes and consequences is probably best kept until last, as it will need to draw on many other ideas.

The teaching of genetics draws on a number of concepts that are often covered elsewhere in the curriculum – basic cell structure and the process of cell division, for example. While the links between these different topics may seem obvious to you, they may be less obvious to your pupils. It would be helpful to remind them of these ideas and make the links explicit. Where a particular concept includes a large number of specialist terms, it helps if, initially, you discuss the ideas in non-specialist terms. Once they have some understanding of the concept, the scientific terms may become more meaningful to them.

7.1 Genes – what are they?

◆ *Previous knowledge and experience*

At the most basic level, pupils will need some concept of living things, including an awareness that organisms are made up of cells and that all plant and animal cells have the same basic structure – a nucleus surrounded by cytoplasm and contained within a membrane. A prior discussion about some aspect of genetics of interest and relevance to your pupils would give this topic meaning and help to motivate them.

◆ *A teaching sequence*

A scientific understanding of genes is based on a number of related ideas. At a basic level these include the following:

- genes provide the information that living things need in order to function; it follows from this that genetic information is found in all living things
- a gene has a particular structure
- a gene has a specific physical location
- each gene provides the information to make *one* product
- for any gene, a number of different versions (alleles) may exist
- each of these versions will contain slightly different information.

Who has genes?

When teaching genetics there is a tendency for these basic ideas to become embedded in more complex ideas. When this happens the basic ideas seem self-evident and it is easy to assume that your pupils have identified and understood them. This is not necessarily so. It might help your pupils if you make these ideas explicit, if possible presenting them within a context that is familiar.

For example, many pupils seem to be unaware that all living things contain genetic information. They are also confused about the relationship between genes and chromosomes – that genes are grouped together on chromosomes. One way of checking the understanding of these ideas within your class is to ask your pupils about some specific organisms. An example is given in Table 7.1. The organisms used in this example were selected for diversity and represent a vertebrate and an invertebrate animal, a flowering and a non-flowering plant, a fungus, a bacterium and a virus.

Table 7.1 *Probing pupils' ideas on genes and chromosomes. In each box answer yes, no or don't know.*

Organism	Do these organisms contain genes?	Do these organisms contain chromosomes?
Rabbits		
Mushrooms		
Bacteria		
Spiders		
Apple trees		
Viruses		
Bracken		

Using this as a small group activity (one sheet per group; aim for consensus) will enable pupils to exchange ideas and encourage them to justify their views. You will gain most from this activity if you use the feedback session to probe your pupils' reasoning. For example:

- On what basis do they classify some organisms as containing genes and others as not containing genes?
- What was it that made them unsure about some organisms?
- What are their reasons for thinking that some organisms contain chromosomes but not genes (or vice versa)?

This type of questioning will enable you to identify common misunderstandings within the class, which you can then address during your teaching. Remember that the point of this exercise is to probe your pupils' initial understandings about genes. You are not expecting your pupils to know that in plants, animals and fungi genes are organised into chromosomes; in bacteria they are strung together in a circle of DNA; in viruses they are strands of nucleic acids.

Where are genes found?

Most pupils find it difficult to conceptualise a gene as a real, physical structure with a precise location. This may be one of the reasons why they are confused about the relationship between genes and chromosomes. Talking your pupils through a diagram that shows the location of genes within the whole organism might help (see Figure 7.1). A number of points could be made explicit:

- all plants and animals are made up of cells
- all living cells contain a nucleus (exceptions: mature red blood cells and sieve tubes)
- chromosomes are contained within the nucleus (exception: during cell division)
- a gene is a specific region of a chromosome
- a gene has a specific function – it provides information for one particular product
- in any one organism the same chromosomes, carrying the same genes and the same genetic information, will be found in every somatic cell (the body cells: nerve, muscle, bone cells, etc.) but not in the gametes (the sex cells: egg or sperm cells).

The terminology could be adjusted to suit the particular class of pupils. For older or more advanced pupils it might be appropriate to put emphasis on the gene as a section of DNA rather than a site on a chromosome, to discuss gene products in terms of proteins rather than characteristics and to use terms like somatic cells and gametes rather than body cells and sex cells.

Figure 7.1
The relationship between structures.

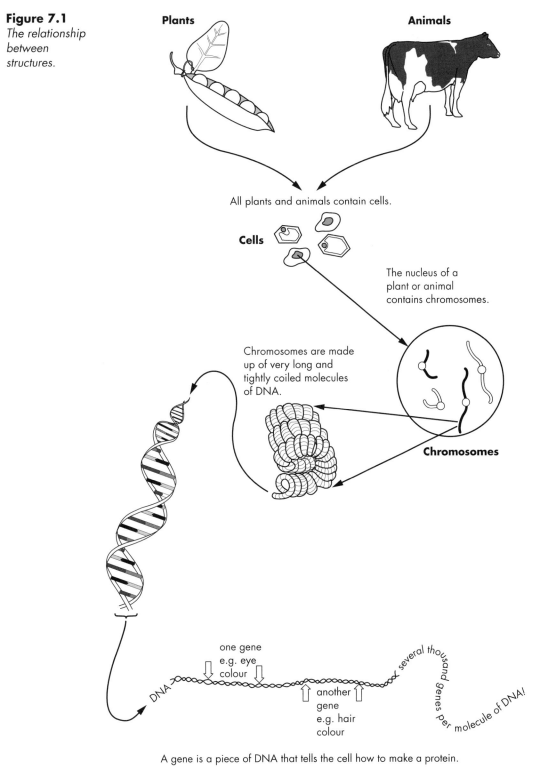

Plants

Animals

All plants and animals contain cells.

Cells

The nucleus of a plant or animal contains chromosomes.

Chromosomes are made up of very long and tightly coiled molecules of DNA.

Chromosomes

one gene e.g. eye colour

another gene e.g. hair colour

several thousand genes per molecule of DNA!

DNA

A gene is a piece of DNA that tells the cell how to make a protein.

Alleles

Many pupils have difficulty in understanding the concept of alleles. Such pupils don't appear to distinguish between a gene (a length of DNA responsible for a particular product) and an allele (the actual information within that gene) and find it difficult to understand what is meant by phrases such as 'alternative forms of a gene'. This difficulty has important implications for their understanding of inheritance. Time spent clarifying the difference now may save time and frustration later on. A simple illustration of the difference between a gene, and the genetic information within that gene, might be useful here. A good example to use is fur colour in rabbits. In some breeds of rabbit the fur can be either black or white. That is, there are two versions (alleles) of the gene for fur colour. One version provides information that results in black fur; the alternative version provides information that results in white fur.

The idea that one gene can exist in several different forms can be reinforced by asking your class to look at some of their own characteristics. Collect data on a number of different discrete characteristics for the whole class. These might include hair colour, hair texture, eye colour and ear lobe attachment. For this activity you will need to avoid continuous characteristics, such as height and weight (see *Continuous versus discontinuous variation* on page 196). Ask your pupils to assume that each characteristic is determined by just *one* gene and to draw up a table of results listing the genes they have looked at and the different version of each that they have found. An example of a results table is given below.

Table 7.2 *Example of a pupil's results sheet for collecting data on class characteristics.*

Characteristic	Variation	Number of pupils (total = 30)	
Hair colour	Black	⊦⊦⊦ ‖	7
	Dark brown	⊦⊦⊦ ⊦⊦⊦ ‖	11
	Golden brown	‖‖‖	4
	Blond	⊦⊦⊦ ‖	6
	Red	‖	2
Eye colour	Brown	⊦⊦⊦ ⊦⊦⊦ ‖‖‖	14
	Blue	⊦⊦⊦ ‖‖	8
	Green	‖‖‖	4

7.2 Inheritance – passing on information

◆ *Previous knowledge and experience*

Explanations of inheritance usually assume knowledge of a number of different concepts. These include:

- the basic ideas outlined in the previous section (*Genes – what are they?*)
- the behaviour of chromosomes during cell division – both mitosis and meiosis
- the idea that chromosomes occur in sets
- the notion that cells may be haploid (contain one set of chromosomes) or diploid (contain two matching sets of chromosomes).

An awareness that gametes are haploid while somatic cells are diploid and an understanding that each gamete contains a unique combination of genetic information would be helpful but cannot be assumed. A substantial minority of pupils up to the age of 16 do not distinguish between somatic cells and gametes.

◆ *A teaching sequence*

The term 'inheritance' refers to the transfer of genetic information from parents to offspring and the interpretation of that information within the offspring, as reflected in its physical characteristics. The mechanisms for transferring genetic information from parents to offspring are meiosis and sexual reproduction. The mechanism for distributing that information within the new individual is mitosis (see Chapter 1).

Genes and chromosomes

When pupils are considering inheritance, the concept of a gene (as discussed in the previous section) needs to be extended. They need to recognise that genes can be accurately copied, allowing information to be passed on to new cells and new individuals. In addition, when considering inheritance in plants and animals, pupils need to be aware that:

- chromosomes occur in sets
- within one set of chromosomes each gene occurs once, at a specific location

- at fertilisation, one set of chromosomes is donated by the female and a matching set (possible exception: the sex chromosome) is donated by the male
- in the new individual each chromosome is paired and so each gene occurs twice (exception: genes occurring on the X chromosome)
- each pair of genes may occur as identical or different versions (same or different alleles).

Although many of these points will have been covered during the teaching of mitosis and meiosis, pupils have a tendency to consider cell division purely in terms of chromosomes. Unless the relationship between chromosomes and genes is made explicit to them and the parallel behaviour of chromosomes and genes during cell division is noted, they are unlikely to recognise the relationship between cell division and inheritance. Because pupils also tend to see sexual reproduction in terms of physical activity rather than fusion of gametes to produce a new individual, they are often unaware that plants reproduce sexually. For this reason it is probably best, when first introducing inheritance, to avoid using plant examples.

It is a good idea to begin by recapping the key points of cell division, noting what this means in terms of genes and genetic information. One approach would be to give an overview of the whole process that emphasises the continuity of information between generations. A possible structure for this is shown in Figure 7.2.

Figure 7.2
A summary of the process of inheritance.

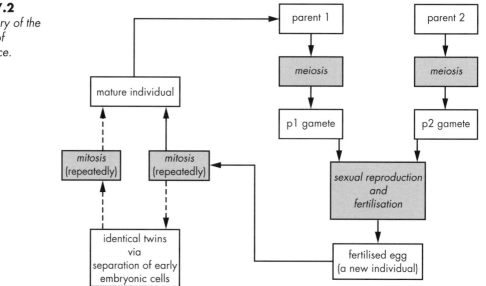

Key points when talking through a diagram like this might include the following.

- Meiosis has two functions – it halves the chromosome number and it increases variation.
- Each gamete is unique; it will have the same number of chromosomes (one set) and the same genes (one for each product) but no two gametes will have exactly the same genetic information. For example, one gamete might contain the blue version of an eye colour gene and the brown version of a hair colour gene while another might contain the blue version of an eye colour gene but the blond version of a hair colour gene.
- Sexual reproduction is the mechanism by which genetic information from two different individuals can be combined to give a new and unique individual.
- Both parents make an equal contribution (matching sets of chromosomes).
- The genetic information in the newly fertilised egg is copied at each mitotic cell division so that each new cell has a complete copy of the information. In this way, every somatic cell in the new individual carries the same genetic information.

Meiosis and mitosis are well illustrated in multimedia encyclopaedias, e.g. pupils can be asked to look these terms up in Microsoft's *Encarta* CD ROM.

Twins

Your pupils will almost certainly be interested in twins. They might like to know that non-identical twins are no more similar to each other, genetically, than to any of their other brothers or sisters. This is because they have developed from two different eggs, each fertilised by a different sperm. The unusual thing is that their mother produced two egg cells at one time, instead of the more usual one. In contrast, identical twins both develop from the same egg, fertilised by a single sperm. In this case, the new embryo splits into two during an early (mitotic) cell division and each half then develops into a new individual. Because identical twins originate from just one cell they are genetically identical.

Having considered the general principles, you can use some specific examples to illustrate the ways in which genetic information will be interpreted within the new individual. This interpretation is at two levels – that of chromosomes and that of genes. Making clear the distinction between these two levels may help your pupils to develop their understanding of the relationship between genes and chromosomes.

Chromosomes and sex determination

It is easiest to start at the chromosome level, where interpretation is simpler and the objects can actually be seen during cell division. You might begin by using photos of human chromosomes (karyotypes) to illustrate the concept of matching sets of chromosomes. When looking at these it is helpful to remind pupils that chromosomes are normally enclosed within the nucleus and cannot be seen. They only become visible under the microscope during cell division, when the chromosomes become shorter and fatter, as they copy themselves, and are released into the cytoplasm as the nucleus breaks down. You can then go on to identify the sex chromosomes as being the odd pair out – they match (are homologous) in the female (XX) but do not match in the male (XY).

The link between inheritance and chromosome behaviour during meiosis can be made explicit by considering sex determination. This also introduces the concepts of chance and probability. Key points that may need to be emphasised include the idea that:

- it is the sperm that determines the sex of the child
- each fertilisation is an independent event; X and Y sperm have an equal chance of fertilising an egg, consequently the probability that any fertilisation will produce a boy (or a girl) will be 0.5.

Pupils find the ideas of probability and chance and independent events counter-intuitive. They feel, for example, that if a couple already have several boys, the next child *should* be a girl. They need to recognise that chance effects can give a distorted impression in a small sample. When large numbers are considered, the random effects of chance are evened out. If all the births for a whole country are considered, then the number of boys born in any one year will roughly equal the number of girls. You can illustrate this within the classroom by asking your pupils to toss a coin and record heads or tails. Continue until time or patience are exhausted then collate the results. Within the class data there may be long sequences of either heads or tails, but in total there should be roughly equal numbers of heads and tails.

Dominant and recessive relationships

Things are a little more complex at the gene level. One reason for this is the need to interpret the conflicting messages when a pair of alleles are not identical. As a starting point here, it might be useful to go back to the example of fur colour in rabbits. Now that your pupils know that the gene for fur colour will be present twice in a rabbit, once in the set of chromosomes received from its father and once in the set received from its mother, do they see a problem? What happens if the rabbit receives one allele for black fur and one allele for white fur? In this case, even though the rabbit has alleles for both colours, it will have black fur. This is because the allele for black fur is dominant to the allele for white fur. The allele for white fur is recessive to the allele for black fur.

At this stage it might be appropriate to introduce the most common terms and conventions that are used when discussing inheritance. Conventionally, the dominant allele is given a capital letter to represent its version of the characteristic (in this case 'B' for black fur) and the recessive allele is denoted by the lower case version of this same letter (in this case 'b' for white fur). It is then possible to describe the information in the genes (the genotype) using these letters as a shorthand. When a pair of genes carry the same information (BB or bb in this case) the organism is said to be *homozygous* for that characteristic. When a pair of genes carry different information an organism is said to be *heterozygous* for that characteristic (Bb in this case; conventionally, upper case come before lower case letters). The physical expression of the genotype (black fur or white fur in this case) is called the phenotype.

Monohybrid inheritance

With some awareness of how genetic information is passed on to the new individual, and some awareness of the relationship between alleles, your pupils may now be ready to consider monohybrid inheritance in more detail and to start using the Punnett square. You could begin by using the rabbit fur example and then move on to consider other examples, including inherited disorders in humans.

When a homozygous black rabbit (BB) is crossed with a homozygous white rabbit (bb), all the offspring are heterozygous black rabbits (Bb) – the white colour appears to have been lost. If this first generation is allowed to interbreed, the white colour will reappear again in their offspring. In this second generation, the genotypes will be present in the ratio of

1 homozygous black (BB) to 2 heterozygous black (Bb) to 1 homozygous white (bb), giving a phenotypic ratio of 3 black to 1 white rabbit. The probability that any one rabbit in the second generation will be black is therefore 0.75. This can be shown using a Punnett square (Figure 7.3).

Figure 7.3
Drawing up a Punnett square.

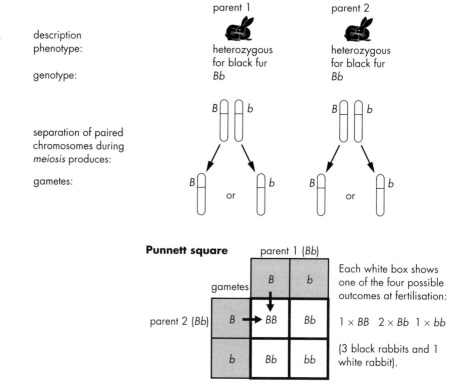

When using Punnett squares your class is likely to divide into those who find it comes easily and those who find they have to struggle. This second group will need support, but you shouldn't feel complacent about the first group. There is ample evidence that many pupils can learn the technique of completing Punnett squares without understanding the processes or outcomes that these squares represent. Although many pupils do not believe that plants are capable of sexual reproduction they are unlikely to question the use of a Punnett square to show the outcome of sexual reproduction between smooth and wrinkled peas. One way of reinforcing the link between the representations in the Punnett square and the actual processes is to list the stages of the process and to represent them diagrammatically, reminding pupils of the relationship between genes and chromosomes.

Human characteristics

Once your pupils have some understanding of monohybrid inheritance you can move on to look at human characteristics. While learning about human genetics is important and is likely to catch the interest of your pupils, it needs to be handled sensitively. It is unwise, for example, to use a human example to introduce monohybrid genetics. The necessary manipulation of matings would be unacceptable in humans.

If you are using eye colour as a human example, with B representing the brown allele and b representing the blue allele, some pupils may apply the lesson to their own family and learn more than you intended. If both parents have blue eyes but your pupil has brown eyes he/she might start asking some difficult questions. The possibility of this happening may be reduced by emphasising that a description of the inheritance of eye colour based only on blue and brown alleles is a simplified explanation. While it is accurate as far as it goes – brown is dominant to blue – there are other colours involved, such as green, and the relationship between all possible colours is more complex. It is also worth remembering that the brown allele might have arisen by chance mutation (see *Variation* on page 194).

A number of human diseases are caused by variations in a single gene, some examples are listed in Table 7.3. Your pupils are likely to be very interested in these conditions. However, many inherited diseases have serious, sometimes fatal consequences. Before going into details about any of these diseases, it is a good idea to probe the prior knowledge or experiences of your pupils. Have they heard of the disease? If so, what do they know about it and how did they come to hear of it? You may also want to consider the whole school situation – does any pupil in your school have that particular illness? You can then adjust your approach, or modify the information you choose to give, accordingly. For example, the continuous respiratory and digestive problems suffered by people with cystic fibrosis puts a strain on their whole body and reduces their life expectancy. While you might want to discuss the basic symptoms of cystic fibrosis, and their treatment, you might prefer to leave out the consequences (reduced life expectancy) – especially if any pupils, or their family or friends, are affected.

Table 7.3 *Examples of inherited single gene human disorders.*

Disorder	Description	Inheritance
Cystic fibrosis	Mucus collects in lungs causing respiratory problems; poor digestion	Recessive
Thalassemia	Accelerated destruction of red blood cells	Recessive
Sickle cell anaemia	Malformed red blood cells lead to reduced uptake of oxygen and excess wear and tear	Recessive (but some effect in the heterozygote)
Huntington's disease	Progressive degeneration of the nervous system; no symptoms until late 30s or 40s	Dominant
Haemophilia	Lack of blood clotting factors leading to excess bleeding from wounds	Recessive and sex linked

Genetic diseases also tend to show racial variation. The most common genetic disease amongst northern Europeans is cystic fibrosis. Thalassemia occurs more commonly in people originating from Mediterranean countries and certain regions of India. Sickle cell anaemia occurs most commonly in people originating from Africa and the West Indies. The persistence of these potentially lethal diseases in a relatively high proportion of these populations suggests that they confer some selective advantage in the heterozygous form (see *Variation* on page 194). This has been shown for sickle cell anaemia, where heterozygotes have an increased resistance to malaria. However, singling out just one disorder for further discussion may give the unintended impression that the affected groups are somehow genetically inferior to other groups. If you only have time to consider one disease it may be best to focus on cystic fibrosis, since one in 27 people in the UK are carriers of this disease. That is, they are heterozygous for a cystic fibrosis allele and can pass the disease on to their children, even though they themselves are unaffected. Because heterozygotes are symptomless they may remain unaware of their carrier status unless their partner is also a carrier and they have an affected child (see *Genetic screening* on page 181).

Discrete versus continuous variation

Each of the inherited characteristics mentioned so far are controlled by a single gene. These represent the minority of characteristics, but they are the easiest to explain. Most characteristics are multifactorial. They arise from a number of genes that influence each other and are in turn influenced by the environment. For example, height is in part inherited and in part determined by environmental factors such as diet.

You can demonstrate the difference between discrete (single gene) characteristics and continuous (multifactorial) characteristics by looking at variation within your class. Collect data on a range of characteristics from the whole class. Ensure that it includes some continuous characteristics such as height. It may be best to avoid weight as many teenagers are particularly sensitive about this. (If you have already collected data on discrete characteristics you will only need to collect data on continuous characteristics now.) Separate the characteristics into those for which there are a discrete number of independent variations, e.g. eye colour, and those that show a continuous range of values, e.g. height. For a discrete characteristic, the frequency of different variations within the population can be shown using a bar chart. For a continuous characteristic, the frequency of different values can be shown using a histogram. The result, if enough data are collected and an appropriate interval selected, will be a bell curve or 'normal distribution'. You can increase the effectiveness of this activity by setting up a database and, each year, asking your pupils to add their measurements to it. As your population size grows, the normal distribution will become clearer.

It is important to remember that some characteristics are caused entirely by the environment, e.g. scarring as a result of injury, or the docked tails of some domestic animals. Such characteristics cannot be inherited. This was shown in a famous experiment in which the tails of mice were cut off over successive generations; in each new generation the mice were born with tails.

 A simple and effective piece of software is available for highlighting variation, called *Variation* (on the *Games for Life* CD ROM). Pupils enter facts such as hair colour, eye colour and type of ear lobes and the program tells them how these characteristics are inherited. It also deftly calculates the frequency of these characteristics based on the people using the program to date.

Social and ethical issues

The extent to which a characteristic is determined by genes rather than the environment can have important social, political, ethical and moral implications. For example:

- if intelligence is determined mainly by genes, then the value of education for all may be questioned
- if there is a gene for criminal behaviour then the responsibility of the criminal for their actions may be questioned
- if obesity is genetic, individuals may feel that they have no personal responsibility to eat healthily
- conversely, if it is the environment that has the greatest effect on a characteristic we may be considered to have a moral responsibility to ensure the best environment for everyone.

The discovery of new genes is reported and discussed in the media on a regular basis. A current example, and the issues it raises, might provide a useful context for discussion within your class (see *Choosing a route* on page 156 and *Gene technology – the human factor* on page 178). Discussion of such issues would also enable you to integrate part of the 'citizenship' curriculum into a specialist subject area. When considering such issues it may be helpful to remember that the majority of characteristics are multifactorial and that as yet, despite extensive efforts in some areas (e.g. intelligence), it has not been possible to quantify the genetic component of such characteristics.

♦ *Enhancement ideas*

Chromosomes

- ♦ Humans normally have 23 pairs of chromosomes (46 chromosomes in total) but occasionally a person has one extra or one less chromosome. For example:

  - Turner's syndrome (XO – a female with only one X chromosome)
  - Kleinfelter's syndrome (XXY – a male with an extra X chromosome)
  - Down's syndrome (usually an extra chromosome 21).

- ♦ Only a few such conditions are known to occur. This is because errors at the chromosome level always involve a large number of genes and usually result in major developmental problems that are incompatible with life.

In most cases the fertilised egg fails to develop. It is interesting to note that too much genetic information may be just as damaging as too little genetic information.

Inheritance

♦ The relationship between pairs of alleles is more complex than a simple dominant and recessive model would suggest. For example, there are three alleles in the ABO blood grouping system. Both A and B are dominant when paired with O but when paired with each other they are both co-dominant. Neither dominates the other and they are both expressed in the phenotype. They are identified as a distinct blood group, AB.

♦ Heterozygous and homozygous dominant individuals are usually indistinguishable, phenotypically. It is possible to identify heterozygotes by a process of back crossing (or 'test' crossing). Using the rabbits as an example, it is possible to identify the heterozygotes by mating the black rabbits (BB or Bb) with white rabbits (homozygous recessive, bb). If the black rabbit is homozygous (BB) then all the offspring will be black. If the black rabbit is heterozygous (Bb) then half the offspring will be black and half the offspring will be white. When back crossing is not possible, e.g. when working with humans, heterozygotes can be identified by pedigree analysis and a process of deduction. For example, if two apparently unaffected people give birth to a child with cystic fibrosis then they must both be heterozygous for cystic fibrosis (see *Genetic screening* on page 181).

♦ Genes that are located on the X chromosome show atypical patterns of expression in males. This is because the X chromosome, and the genes located on it, usually only occur once in male cells. As a result, the alleles remain unpaired and each one will be expressed in the phenotype. Many pupils have difficulty with the concept of sex linkage. This may be because they don't recognise that the terms dominant and recessive apply to a particular relationship, rather than a particular allele. It may also reflect their general uncertainty about the relationship between genes and chromosomes. You can help your pupils to visualise the process by including the chromosomes as well as the alleles when producing a Punnett square. Again, pedigree analysis can be used to deduce the genotype of unaffected family members.

7.3 Gene expression

◆ *Previous knowledge and experience*

In preparation for this section it will be helpful if your pupils:

- are aware that mitotic cell division is the mechanism that enables a single fertilised egg to grow into a multicellular organism
- are aware that the purpose of mitotic cell division is to ensure that each new cell contains an exact copy of all the genetic information contained in that original fertilised egg
- are aware of the relationship between chromosomes, genes and DNA
- understand that genetic information is organised into genes and that each gene contains the information needed to make one product.

More advanced students might also need to know that proteins are made up of amino acids.

◆ *A teaching sequence*

Opening the message

The effect of genes can be seen at a number of different levels. Within the cell, gene action may result in the accumulation of a particular gene product. Within the organism, the effect of genes can be seen in the development of specialised cells, each with a distinctive structure and function. At the whole body level, genes determine the distinguishing features and characteristics of an individual.

Making sense of genetics at all these different levels is quite a challenge for your pupils. Even if they have understood both the basic concept of inheritance (that there has been a physical transfer of information from parent to offspring) and the concept of dominant/recessive relationships between pairs of alleles, they still have a problem. If all somatic cells within an individual contain the same genetic information, then how come different types of cell look so different? Intuitively, they feel that each type of cell must contain just those genes needed for its particular function. You can check the ideas within your class by asking your pupils to compare the genetic information found in different types of cell taken from the same individual (see Table 7.3). As with previous activities, you will learn most about your pupils' thinking if you probe their reasoning.

Table 7.4 *Probing pupils' understanding of gene expression.*

Cells	Same or different genetic information?	Reasons
Two cheek cells from the same individual 		
One cheek cell and one nerve cell from the same individual 		
One cheek cell and one sperm cell from the same individual 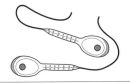		
Two sperm cells from the same individual 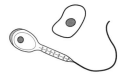		
Two cheek cells from two different individuals		

What most of your pupils will lack is the idea that genes can be switched off. What they need is an awareness that genes may be switched on, as and when their product is required, then switched off again when their product is no longer required. An example that pupils can visualise might help here. Sunshine contains potentially harmful UV light. Skin cells respond to sunlight by producing a pigment, melanin, which protects the underlying cells against the UV light. This is very apparent in people with pale skin – they become suntanned. In the winter months there is little sunshine. In the absence of sunshine the skin cells switch off the genes that produce melanin and the suntan fades.

Reading the message

The details of how the cell reads the message within a gene are potentially complex and the concepts are often seen as abstract and difficult to relate to. As a result you might be tempted to avoid this topic with lower-achieving pupils. This would be a pity as they will need some understanding of this process if they are to understand gene technology – an area of potential interest to them. One possible approach is to link this topic with a discussion of genetic engineering (see *Gene technology – the human factor* on page 178) using whatever example is currently in the news. The underlying concepts on which the process of genetic engineering is based can be made accessible to most pupils if non-essential details are kept to a minimum. The basic ideas can be described using a language analogy in which DNA is a book, genetic information is the text, genes are the sentences and the genetic code is the language. They might include the following:

- genetic information (the text) is organised into genes (sentences) and stored in the DNA (a book)
- each gene contains the instructions (words) needed to make one product (individual words identify the materials to be used and the sequence of words specifies the order in which these materials should be assembled)
- a very simple 'language' (the genetic code) is used – it has just 64 words
- a near infinite number of different messages can be written with a vocabulary of 64 words
- every living thing uses the same language (the same genetic code) but different types of organism use it to produce different sets of instructions, resulting in very different characteristics (a horror story, a love story, an adventure story, etc.)
- because all living things use the same language, genetic engineering is possible – every organism can read and understand the genes of any other organism.

These last two points are very important. Many pupils are confused between the genetic code (the 'language' of genetics) and the message that has been written with that code (the 'text'). Some pupils find it almost impossible to accept that the same code is used by all organisms.

◆ *Enhancement ideas*

Gene expression

◆ The language analogy can be extended to explain that there are only four letters in the 'alphabet' (A, adenine; C, cytosine; G, guanine; and T, thymine) and that all the 'words' are exactly three letters long. This introduces the concept of the triplet code and could lead into a more detailed discussion of what the 'words' mean. This might include a recognition that:

   • some words (triplets) provide punctuation – they identify the beginning and the end of the message
   • each remaining word (triplet) corresponds to one specific amino acid
   • when the message is read, a chain of amino acids is produced and the sequence of these amino acids corresponds to the sequence of words (triplets) in the DNA
   • these amino acid chains (polypeptides) are used to produce proteins.

At this point one of your brighter pupils might notice that there are too many words (64) and too few amino acids (20)! While each 'word' corresponds to just one amino acid, most amino acids are specified by several different words.

◆ Any change in the sequence of DNA bases (the sequence of letters) has the potential to change the sequence of amino acids in the polypeptide chain (the meaning of the sentence). For example, in sickle cell anaemia a small change in the DNA sequence changes just one amino acid in the haemoglobin molecule – a glutamic acid is replaced by a valine. This one change alters the way in which the haemoglobin responds to oxygen and so causes the disease.

7.4 Gene technology – the human factor

♦ *Previous knowledge and experience*

It is possible to consider the social and ethical aspects of gene technology with very little understanding of the underlying science. What will be needed is a specific context and enough background information to enable your pupils to identify and respond to some of the important issues. Understanding the basic principles of the techniques will require a good understanding of the basic genetic concepts introduced in sections *7.1 Genes – what are they?* and *7.3 Gene expression.*

♦ *A teaching sequence*

The techniques

Scientists now know enough about genes and how they work to be able to manipulate them for human advantage. In the last decade this has opened up a rapidly expanding and developing field of science – gene technology. Despite the astonishing pace of these developments, and the resulting media attention, many pupils have a limited awareness of gene technology. The knowledge that they do have is frequently gleaned from TV fiction – *The X-Files, Red Dwarf,* soap operas and crime stories – rather than factual news or science books. Not surprisingly, given the sources of their information and the astonishing nature of some recent technological developments, many pupils find it difficult to distinguish between fact and fiction. In particular they seem to be unaware of the scientific basis of, and limitations on, the use of gene technology. For example, pupils are more likely to believe that it is possible to increase intelligence by genetically modifying the human embryo (scientifically near impossible, intelligence is multifactorial) than to believe that it is possible to produce transgenic animals that contain human genes and can produce human proteins (current practice).

A class discussion focusing on video clips from a popular TV programme, or on newspaper cuttings about some recent technological development, might be a useful way into this topic. You could use this discussion to sound out your pupils' knowledge and understanding of different gene technologies and their ability to evaluate the potential of gene technology – what is, and what is not, scientifically feasible. It might also reveal some of the misunderstanding that your pupils have about the underlying genetics.

Some curricula and syllabuses make specific demands regarding the techniques that must be covered. Simple details of the techniques are given below. In preparing to teach some of the basic principles, you might find it helpful to identify the genetic concepts on which they are based and to consider the extent to which your pupils understand these concepts. You can then help your pupils either by simplifying the basic principles, or by providing additional information about the genetic concepts.

Cloning

- **At the gene level**: this means making exact copies of a particular gene, which can then be used in other techniques, e.g. genetic engineering, or in particular applications, e.g. gene therapy.
- **At the whole organism level**: this means using an existing organism to produce new organisms that are genetically identical to the original. Basic techniques may be based on naturally occurring processes such as asexual reproduction (bacteria, plants) or regeneration – splitting an existing organism and allowing each piece to regenerate (primitive invertebrates, many plants). More complex techniques were needed when Dolly the sheep was cloned from a single somatic cell taken from her 'mother'. This was because developmental genes, which are switched off in the cells of a mature animal, had to be switched back on again.

Genetic engineering

This means adding, deleting or transferring genetic material. It may take place within one organism, between organisms of the same species or between organisms of different species. A CUT–COPY–PASTE technique is used, analogous to word processing. The required gene is identified and restriction enzymes are used to cut it out of the DNA. Once isolated in this way the gene is cloned to produce thousands of copies. Copies are then inserted into the host organism, together with a switching mechanism to ensure that the gene can be turned on. The uses to which genetic engineering can be put are potentially limitless and include:

- the production of transgenic organisms (bacteria, sheep) that can produce human proteins

- gene therapy – to replace a non-functional version of a gene with a functional version, e.g. severe combined immunodeficient disease (SCID), cystic fibrosis
- agriculture, e.g. to increase the yield or improve pest resistance in crops (resulting in genetically modified food).

It is sometimes said that genetic engineering is no different from selective breeding, a process that humans have been engaged in for thousands of years. This is not necessarily true. In selective breeding we select two individuals of the same species who have some desirable characteristic and we breed them in the hope of getting more individuals with the same desirable characteristics. By applying selective pressure in this way over many generations we can produce breeds or varieties with very distinctive characteristics, e.g. lean cattle, high yield crops, fast race horses. Genetic engineering between two organisms of the same species is directly comparable to this process. The advantage is that genetic engineering removes the element of chance associated with sexual reproduction and inheritance. However, genetic engineering between two individuals from different species is not comparable to selective breeding. No amount of selective breeding between cattle would ever produce a cow whose genome included a human gene for insulin. Pupils are sometimes confused between selective breeding and genetic engineering.

DNA fingerprinting

This is a technique used to compare samples of DNA. The sample is copied many times using a cloning technique and then cut, at specific sites, using restriction enzymes. The resulting fragments are separated by size, using gel electrophoresis, and stained to produce a pattern of bands. Because no two individuals have identical DNA (exception: identical twins) the probability of any two individuals producing the same pattern of bands is close to zero. This technique can be used in:

- forensic work – to check DNA from suspects against DNA from the scene of the crime, looking for a match
- paternity cases – to compare the DNA of the child with the DNA of the putative father; the child receives half of its genetic information from its father so half of the bands in the child should match half of the bands in the father
- preservation of wildlife – to confirm the origins of captive birds and identify those taken illegally from the wild.

Pupils are sometimes confused between DNA fingerprinting and traditional fingerprinting.

DNA sequencing

This means identifying the sequence of bases within a piece of DNA – within a single gene for example. The technique is complex but has now been automated. As a result the Human Genome Project, set up to sequence the entire human complement of DNA, is likely to be completed ahead of schedule. Sequencing can be used to identify the mutations within a gene sequence that cause a specific genetic disease.

Genetic screening

This technique can be used to test an individual's DNA for the presence of a specific genetic disease. Probes that are complementary to the disease-causing gene sequence are mixed with a sample of their DNA. If the disease-causing sequence is present in the DNA the probes will stick to it, acting as an identifiable marker. Screening is now available for a rapidly increasing number of genetic diseases including cystic fibrosis and Huntington's disease, and can even be carried out on samples of DNA taken from the developing fetus; but the results are never 100% accurate. There is always a small possibility of a false positive or a false negative result. While a number of regional screening programmes have been set up, there is no national screening programme. Some tests are now available commercially, through mail order. Screening raises a number of issues, including confidentiality – who should, and who should not, have access to the information?

The internet can provide examples, news and background material. Key words to look up include: genetic engineering, Human Genome Project, genetic disease, cloning and DNA fingerprinting. The websites of government environmental agencies and environmental pressure groups can also be a useful first stop.

The social and ethical implications

Gene technology makes use of a number of different techniques and appears to have almost limitless potential. Because it involves the manipulation of DNA, which is the very basis of life, the use of gene technology raises a number of important social and ethical issues. It is likely that all your pupils, at some point in their lives, will be faced with decisions relating to the use of gene technology – for example, whether or not to undergo genetic screening for particular inherited disorders. They may have made some decisions already, e.g. whether or not to eat genetically engineered food. Consequently, a discussion of gene technology and its uses can have real relevance for them and help to stimulate their interest in the underlying science. It will also give them valuable experience of discussing social issues and evaluating information and ideas within a scientific context.

To encourage pupils to come to a view that they can justify, through exploring and evaluating their own ideas and considering the views of others, it is best to focus the discussions on a specific use of gene technology. Your pupils will not need a detailed understanding of the science in order to engage with the issues and come to a view, but they will need a brief outline of the context. You can focus the discussion further by providing a number of questions for your pupils to answer. An example is given in Figure 7.4. If your pupils are unfamiliar with the context they may find it difficult, at this stage, to identify the important issues. This will limit the discussion. You can help by mentioning some of the key issues.

Figure 7.4
Providing a focus for a discussion of gene technology.

!!!STOP PRESS!!!

And You Thought It Was All In Your Jeans!

A London clinic has recently been offering to produce 'Designer Babies' for parents. For just £50 000 the clinic will check and, if necessary, change the parents' genes in order to produce the baby of their choice. Once selected, the baby develops normally inside the mother. The choice at the moment is limited to sex, intelligence, height and hair colour, but a spokesman said that several other features would soon be available. All 'Designer Babies' are guaranteed free from identifiable genetic diseases.

- Do you think that this is a true report – are such 'Designer Babies' available?
- If it is true, what do you think would be good about this use of technology, and what would worry you?
- Do you think that it should be allowed?
- Do you think that you would feel the same if it was some other animal being designed to order? What about a plant?

For each question, remember to say why you think this.

Working in groups of four will give all your pupils an opportunity to express their views, but they will need some ground rules. They should consider each other's views with respect. They may disagree with another view, present alternative views and argue the merits of different views but if they fail to agree they should remember that there may be no definite right answer.

Reaching consensus

Asking each group to try to reach a consensus is a good way of encouraging your pupils to articulate their thinking and to justify their points of view, but don't necessarily expect them to achieve it! As there may be no right or wrong answers in this activity, just a diversity of views which have been justified to a greater or lesser extent, it is unlikely that they will manage to agree completely. Feedback from each group to the whole class at the end of the discussions will allow the full range of views within the class to be shared by everyone, and perhaps widen the debate. Few pupils will have difficulty giving an opinion, so this activity is suited to all ability levels. What they find more difficult, at all levels, is to justify their ideas (to explain why they think what they think) and to evaluate different ideas. Some pupils may need support in doing this.

In some cases a lack of understanding of the science may mean that your pupils do not recognise an important issue. For example, pupils who do not differentiate between gametes and somatic cells will see little difference between somatic gene therapy and germ-line gene therapy and are likely to be equally supportive of both. If you explain the genetic significance of the difference your pupils will become aware of the implications and they may wish to reconsider their views. You will have made the science relevant.

When selecting a context you may want to consider the extent to which your pupils will be familiar with it, the amount of information they will need in order to relate to it and the type and complexity of the issues that it raises. You will also want to consider the directions that the discussion might take and the additional issues that might be considered. There may be some issues that you would wish to avoid. For example, if you choose prenatal screening as the context, the discussion is likely to include a consideration of abortion of an affected fetus. If your class includes a pupil who suffers from a genetic disease you might want to avoid this context.

7.5 Variation

◆ *Previous knowledge and experience*

The concept of variation, both in terms of the diversity of life and the uniqueness of individuals, should be well established. To appreciate the causes and consequences of variation your pupils will need:

- knowledge of the physical processes of meiosis
- an awareness that DNA is the source of genetic information, and
- a basic understanding of inheritance.

It is clear that it is difficult to discuss the causes and consequences of variation without using a number of relatively complex biological concepts. For this reason, this section is best suited to more advanced pupils. Examples of variation are given in Chapter 8.

◆ *A teaching sequence*

Within one species there is a considerable degree of variation between individuals. Even within one family there is variation. Where does this variation come from? One source of variation between individuals is the random mixing of maternal and paternal alleles as chromosomes are reassorted into new sets during meiosis. Alleles that are physically linked together on the same chromosome are mixed up through a different process, crossing over, during which homologous chromosomes exchange pieces. Variation is increased further by the random combination of maternal and paternal genes at fertilisation.

This shuffling of alleles can rearrange existing alleles into new combinations but it cannot change the total amount of variation within the population. A new variation can only arise within a population if the DNA 'text' within the gametes is disrupted or changed by a mutation. This is a relatively rare event. You can illustrate the effect of a mutation using a simple sentence, e.g. 'The mat was wet'. If one letter is substituted (analogous to changing one base pair in the DNA) this becomes 'The man was wet'. The words still make sense but the meaning is quite different (see *Enhancement ideas, Gene expression* on page 177). A number of factors will increase the rate of mutation including carcinogens such as UV light, X-rays and chemicals found in tobacco. Although mutations are just as likely to occur in somatic cells as in gametes, mutations occurring in the somatic cells cannot be passed on to any offspring.

A common misunderstanding about mutations is that they are a bad thing. In practice, mutations are neither bad nor good. They can only be defined in this way by considering the effect they have on the organism in which they occur and this, in turn, will depend on environmental factors. At some time in the past a mutation occurred in the peppered moth (*Biston betularia*), which resulted in the occurrence of two distinct forms – a pale form and a melanic (dark) form. When the countryside was relatively unpolluted, the pale form was the most common. The dark form was very conspicuous against the pale bark of the trees and was quickly eaten by predators. As a result, very few dark moths survived long enough to reproduce and pass the dark allele on to their offspring. With industrialisation the countryside became polluted and the tree bark darkened. The pale moths were now conspicuous and quickly eaten by predators while the dark moths survived and reproduced. The mutation that had once been a disadvantage had become an advantage and the dark form became the more common form of this moth.

In general, any mutation that gives an organism a selective advantage over the rest of the population will increase in frequency within that population, and any mutation that results in a selective disadvantage will decrease in frequency within that population. The consequences of this, in terms of evolution, are discussed in Chapter 8. Occasionally, a mutation that appears to confer a disadvantage is maintained at unexpectedly high levels within a population. In some cases this is because the heterozygote confers some selective advantage, as is the case with sickle cell anaemia (see the section on *Inheritance, Human characteristics* on page 169). In other cases this is because the characteristic that causes the disadvantage only becomes apparent in the mature individual. By this stage reproduction may be complete and the affected gene will already have passed on to the next generation. An example of this is Huntington's disease.

Many mutations confer neither advantage nor disadvantage and are simply maintained within the population as one of the variations.

◆ *Further activities*

- ◆ The Philip Harris catalogue suggests a number of activities using plants.
- ◆ The NCBE have produced a jigsaw model of DNA, which can be used to illustrate the structure and function of DNA. (Instructions are given both for basic and for advanced activities.)
- ◆ The BBSRC suggest a number of activities, including the extraction of DNA from onions using basic household materials such as salt and washing-up liquid (see their free booklet *Discovering DNA 'The Recipe for Life'* for details). In addition, the following organisations and references provide some interesting suggestions.

Other resources

◆ *Teaching resources*

It is sometimes difficult to keep up to date in a field that is changing as rapidly as genetics and gene technology. The following research councils and charities produce written materials and resources that can be invaluable in providing background resource information and highlighting recent developments. Much of this material is free.

Research councils

BBSRC (Biotechnology & Biological Sciences Research Council), Polaris House, North Star Avenue, Swindon SN2 1UH.

MRC (Medical Research Council), 20 Park Crescent, London W1N 4AL.

Charities/trusts

The Genetics Interest Group, 29–35 Farringdon Road, London EC1M 3JB.

The Wellcome Trust, 210 Euston Road, London NW1 2BE.

Other organisations

NCBE (National Centre for Biotechnology Education), The University of Reading, Whiteknights, PO Box 228, Reading RG6 6AJ.

SAPS (Science and Plants for Schools), Homerton College, Cambridge CB2 2PH.

◆ CD ROMs

Variation part of the *Games for Life* CD ROM available from *Games for Life*, The Wellcome Trust, 210 Euston Road, London NW1 2BE.

Microsoft's *Encarta* CD ROM. Details available on website: www.encarta.msn.com.

◆ Background reading

Clough, E.E. & Wood-Robinson, C. (1985). Children's understanding of inheritance. *Journal of Biological Education*, **19**, pp. 304–310.

Dolan, A. (1996). The making of Mandy – introducing alleles. *Journal of Biological Education*, **30**, pp. 94–96.

Garvin, W. & Stefani, L. (1993). Genetics: genetic disorder and diagnosis: a role play exercise. *Journal of Biological Education* **27**, pp. 51–57.

Jones, S. & Van Loon, B. (1993). *Genetics for Beginners.* Cambridge, Icon Books.

Lewis, J. & Wood-Robinson, C. (1997). Genetics for life. *Education in Science* November, No. 175, pp. 12–13.

Lewis, J., Driver, R., Leach, J. & Wood-Robinson, C. (1997). *Understanding Genetics: Materials for Investigating Student's Understanding, with Some Suggestions for their Use in Teaching.* Centre for Studies in Science and Mathematics Education, University of Leeds.

Radford, A. & Baumberg, S. (1987). A glossary of terms for teaching genetics. *Journal of Biological Education*, **21**, pp. 127–135.

Ratcliffe, M. (1998). Discussing socio-scientific issues in science lessons – pupils' actions and teachers' roles. *School Science Review*, **79** (288), pp. 55–59.

Shaw, A. (1996). DNA makes RNA makes protein. *School Science Review*, **78** (283), pp. 103–105.

Shaw, A. (1997). Alien alleles. *School Science Review*, **78** (284), 108–111.

8 *Classification, variation, adaptation and evolution*

Chris Brown

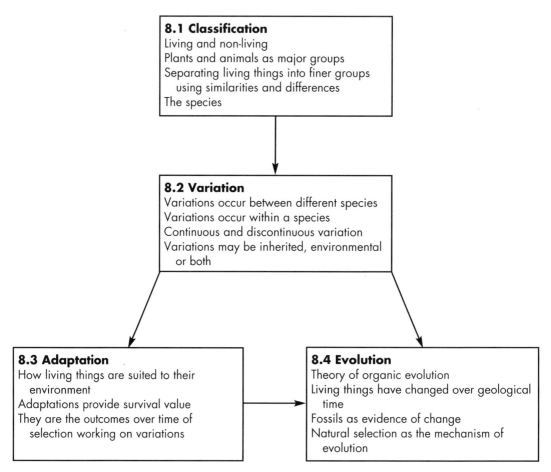

8.1 Classification
Living and non-living
Plants and animals as major groups
Separating living things into finer groups
    using similarities and differences
The species

8.2 Variation
Variations occur between different species
Variations occur within a species
Continuous and discontinuous variation
Variations may be inherited, environmental
    or both

8.3 Adaptation
How living things are suited to their
    environment
Adaptations provide survival value
They are the outcomes over time of
    selection working on variations

8.4 Evolution
Theory of organic evolution
Living things have changed over geological
    time
Fossils as evidence of change
Natural selection as the mechanism of
    evolution

◆ *Choosing a route*

The four content areas of this chapter do not fall into an obvious linear teaching sequence. Classification will be covered early in the secondary school. Adaptation is probably not a 'topic' at all as such but an important idea that will be addressed whilst teaching other topics. Variation will be dealt with in a similar way in the early stages of secondary school, but later will probably be taught as a topic preceding the teaching of genetics and evolution. Teaching of evolution will occur late in the course. All four topics have close links with many other areas of biology.

8.1 Classification

It is possible to deal with the ideas from a number of different starting points, for example from the characteristics of living things (Chapter 1) or ecology (Chapter 9). You may decide to make the topic almost self-contained, dealing with the structure of the classificatory system at an appropriate level and how living things fit into it, introducing pupils to the features used for classifying the various groups, such as insects and arachnids. A perfectly sensible alternative approach is one that delays formalising classification in this way until experience of working with a wide range of living things, e.g. in a local habitat, has been used to introduce some of their characteristic features. Whichever sequence you adopt it is likely that pupils will meet the ideas in the following order: classifying into living and non-living; into plants and animals; and then into the major taxonomic groups of both. Some teachers will wish to introduce pupils to the five-kingdom classification at this point.

◆ *Previous knowledge and experience*

Pupils will have done quite a lot of work on organisms that occur in their school environments. They will have had experience of some of the characteristic features of living things: that they feed, move, grow and reproduce. They will have made collections of plants and animals and used various identification aids, including keys, to classify them. However, you should expect a wide variation both in experience and competence with the ideas as well as some misconceptions. These will need to be tackled in your teaching of the topic. Although classifying will be a familiar activity to pupils (it will have been done on a variety of everyday materials such as rocks and soils and on solids, liquids and gases) it is unlikely that the differences between single and multiple criterion classifications will have been made clear (see later).

◆ *A teaching sequence*

Living and non-living

This is a good starting point because research has shown that a full understanding of the reasons for classifying something as alive or not are unlikely to be fully understood. Early in secondary school pupils meet the characteristic features of living things: they write them down (move, grow, etc.) with their definitions, and some explanatory comment ('breathing and respiration are different . . . all living things respire, only some breathe . . . respiration is . . .'), and then learn them by some mnemonic (MRS GREN, etc.). A moment's thought, however, will reveal some of the problems. Respiration (oxidation of respiratory substrate with associated transfer of energy) will not be taught in those terms until later in the scheme. Until the topic is taught pupils will not have grasped the key concepts, and requiring them to get by with only a formal definition must fail to resolve the problem. Fewer problems exist with 'move', 'feed' (for animals), 'grow' or 'reproduce' because these are directly observable and within everyday experience.

The other key point is that confusion arises in classifying inanimate objects that display one or more of the characteristics of living things, e.g. the movement of a candle flame or of a clockwork toy. Pupils should appreciate that identification of living things is based on the object displaying all of the characteristics, although not necessarily at the same time in its life history, and that closer investigation may be needed to reveal evidence that some of the processes of life are occurring.

The teaching approach should be based on examining collections of living and non-living things. Where possible the displays should be of the actual objects and organisms, perhaps arranged into a 'circus' of exhibits that can be supplemented by a variety of pictures and video clips. It is important to give pupils the time and opportunity to discuss their classifications. The reasons for their decisions should be made explicit and, if necessary, challenged. The display should include some of the 'problem' cases such as an apple fruit, a seed, and a picture of a baby in the womb.

It is useful for this work to be presented in two stages, in the second of which the demands are made greater, e.g. by including a third category 'once alive' and 'never lived' represented by a piece of coral, a fossil, a piece of rock, a skull, a bone, etc. Although only one or two lessons are spent here it is essential that the key ideas are reinforced at every opportunity in subsequent work.

Animal and plant

Research suggests that younger pupils' conceptions of animals are limited to mammals, hence animals are those things that have fur, four legs, make sounds and live on land, usually on farms or in Africa (Driver *et al.*, 1994). Presented with an insect or a picture of one, and asked, 'Do you think that this is an animal?' a likely response is, 'No, it's an insect'. The problem here is failing to appreciate the principle of hierarchy, that an insect is one type of animal, as is a pig or a penguin. This point will be developed later in this section.

Pupils classify living things into animals and plants with ease and the reasons for this can be explored after they have done a grouping exercise based on a series of exhibits. Hence animals move from place to place, have a different method of feeding (ideas about photosynthesis will not be established until later, 'make their own food' will do), respond to changes in their surroundings in different ways, and so on (see Chapter 1). Other problems may be encountered, e.g.:

Teacher: 'Is a girl an animal?'
Pupil: 'No, she's a human being.'
Teacher: 'Is a dandelion a plant?'
Pupil: 'No, it's a weed.'
Teacher: 'What about a carrot?'
Pupil: 'No, it's a vegetable.'

The problem here is we are asking pupils to adopt a scientific categorisation rather than an everyday one. This may involve slightly different meanings, e.g. in everyday speech humans might be excluded from the 'animals' group because of the pejorative flavour of the word. Quick quizzes are useful at this point:

Which of the following are animals? (List given: elephant, fish, snake, fly, boy, bird, cow, lion, slug, whale, etc.)
Which of the following are plants? (List given: carrot, grass, daisy, oak tree, etc.)
Here are some statements . . . are they true or false?
All plants are weeds.
All plants live on land.
A cabbage is a vegetable so it is not a plant.
All trees are plants. A dandelion is not a plant; it is a weed.
An oak tree is too big to be a plant.

Classifying plants and animals

Any process of classifying is based on identifying similarities and differences between things. Younger pupils find it easier to spot differences than similarities, hence some encouragement to use the latter is needed. Pupils' prior experiences in classifying things (rocks, chemicals, materials, etc.) may have involved artificial classifications, artificial in the sense that there are many different ways in which the objects can be classified and the particular one in use is selected for a particular purpose. Such a system is often based on a single criterion, e.g. the ability to conduct electricity allows classification into conductors and insulators. Biological classification is different. Taxonomy, the principles on which this classification is based, involves the use of multiple criteria, the groupings are hierarchical and they have an evolutionary significance.

Living things are grouped into five kingdoms (plants and animals being two of the five). The category 'kingdom' is the highest level grouping in the taxonomy. It is progressively subdivided into the following taxa: phylum, class, order, family, genus and species (see Institute of Biology, 1997). Few of the ideas that underpin the system need to be taught explicitly in the 11–16 age range. Pupils will use the system and understand the principle of grouping similar organisms into the same category and in separating different ones into different categories on the basis of relevant criteria. They will also need to be aware of the principle of hierarchy or subsumption, i.e. that we can say that a housefly is an insect, an arthropod and an animal.

You will have to decide how and where these principles are formalised and consolidated. One idea is to introduce the classification system informally through the pupils having to use it in order to complete a real task. This may well be in the context of some work on ecology. Sorting, identifying and then classifying are much more interesting when a motivating activity is being undertaken. For example, pupils could sort through a collection of leaf litter either *in situ* in a wood or in samples brought into the laboratory. One dustbin bag will do for a whole class. Additionally they can repeat the exercise with pond water samples (on site or brought in) to extend the range of organisms involved. Obviously this can be carried further by work in the school grounds, local park, on the beach, etc. (see Chapter 9).

These activities will produce a very wide range of invertebrates (strictly the term used is non-chordates) and plants. Pupils enjoy identifying the things that they have found. In doing so they will have the opportunity to use a wide range of identification aids. The ultimate aim is for the pupils to be able to use word keys. However, the strategy on which a word key is based will not be immediately obvious to younger pupils. They will have to be taught how to use them. In doing this it is useful to allow pupils to use a range of aids, perhaps starting by matching living organisms against pictures, then using branching keys and flow diagrams, word keys supported by drawings and, finally, word keys alone.

It is sometimes suggested that constructing keys is a useful activity in that it develops understanding of the structure and rules of use. Pupils could make their own keys for identifying cars, laboratory apparatus, members of the class, twigs, leaves, etc. A reservation about these activities is that they are usually based on single criterion decisions at each step and hence differ sharply from true biological keys. Perhaps the time is better spent helping pupils to use keys rather than to construct them.

◆ *Further activities*

- Sorting and grouping collections of pictures of animals and plants.
- Matching exercises, e.g. put in one group all the plants that have roots, stems and leaves and into another the plants that do not have these features.
- Crosswords based on matching names to descriptions.
- Concept circles, e.g. draw a circle and put in it the names of all the animals that have jointed legs, a hard outer skeleton and compound eyes. These are arthropods. Inside this circle draw another in which you put the names of all the animals that have three pairs of legs. These are insects.

◆ *Enhancement ideas*

- Use databases to record, identify, group and sort animals and plants.
- Find out the characteristic features of different groups from a website (e.g. *The Tree of Life*: www.phylogeny.arizona.edu/tree/life.html).

8.2 Variation

Three main strands are covered in studying variation:

- examples of variations between and within species
  (interspecific and intraspecific variation)
- origin of variations and their possible inheritance
- adaptive and evolutionary implications of variation.

This section covers the first of these, the second is mainly covered in Chapter 7 and the third later in this chapter.

Large numbers of examples of intraspecific variation occur in other topics in biology. Pupils will meet the idea in considering the breathing, heart and pulse rates of members of the class. In growth experiments that use plant cuttings, seedlings, duckweed, etc., although other teaching objectives will be pursued, the chance to use the idea of variation should always be taken. Indeed eliminating variation between different batches of experimental material will often be considered as an important aspect of the design of investigations. It is essential that pupils realise that variation is universal in plant and animal species. This idea is best developed by studying living material at first hand. A huge range of possibilities exists, providing material for study at most times of the year. Permanent collections of preserved material can also be made, provided conservation principles are not infringed.

◆ *Previous knowledge and experience*

When classifying living things the idea that variation occurs between different 'sorts' of organisms will have been used. This work will have concentrated on interspecific variation.

◆ *A teaching sequence*

To distinguish between variation within and between species, clearly a working concept of species is necessary. We need not burden pupils with the difficulties and debates that surround the concept. To them a species is a 'sort' or 'type' of living thing. We will want to consolidate this by reminding them that the members of a group of organisms that we call a species are similar and breed among themselves to produce similar, fertile offspring. Some examples are necessary, e.g. lions and tigers belong to different species. Occasionally hybrids can be produced, as in this example, but most hybrids between species are sterile.

It is useful to illustrate that some organisms that may look quite similar can belong to different species or even to different genera. Pupils could study collections (preserved if necessary), photographs or line drawings to identify the differences between organisms classified into different species or genera. Water boatmen (two common genera, *Notonecta* and *Corixa*) and woodlice (examples of four common clearly distinguishable genera are easily found: *Oniscus, Armadillidium, Porcellio* and *Philoscia*) are useful for this work. Specimens of some of the common species of buttercup can also be used (picked not uprooted).

In these examples, the names of the organisms are not important, indeed the different specimens could be given reference letters or numbers instead of names. Pupils should be encouraged to observe and record the different features that could be used for separating the species into different taxa. A difficult idea, which nevertheless should be tackled, is that some characters are of use in classifying but others are not. Pupils should be introduced to the developmental variation that can occur, most obviously in sizes at different ages, but also in form and structure, e.g. the different stages in insect and frog life histories. This is a point to be mentioned only briefly.

Variations within species

A useful starting point is to have pupils consider some examples of the results of artificial selection. There are a number of different possibilities and it is not essential that all pupils consider the same material. Pictures of different breeds of dogs or domestic fowls are easily collected. Seed catalogues are also useful to provide examples and descriptions of different varieties of flowers and vegetables, e.g. potatoes, radish, broad beans, peas, dahlias and roses. Pupils should identify the different characteristics that have been selectively bred and the possible reasons for this (not methods of doing so at this stage). Some of this information, e.g. features of different varieties of potato, could be entered into a database. Ideas worth considering are the shapes, sizes and colours of the tubers, how growth rate varies in first and second 'earlies' and 'main' crop varieties, planting and harvesting recommendations, different yields, the different nature of varieties that are recommended for boiling, roasting and making chips, eelworm resistance, and so on.

Continuous and discontinuous variation

It is usual to distinguish between continuous and discontinuous variation. In the former the characteristic concerned does not fall into discrete categories; in the latter it does and any individual either possesses or does not possess that characteristic or trait. This distinction may be introduced by taking some interesting human examples. Such examples may be taken from the class itself, always being careful to avoid potential embarrassment of pupils who may be sensitive about differences they may possess. Alternatively, the background knowledge of the class can be drawn upon, to be supplemented by examples that you provide, perhaps as a resource collection of photographs.

Discussion with the class should clarify which are examples of continuous, which of discontinuous variation and why. Appropriate human examples of continuous variation are: height and weight, blood pressure, heart rate and cholesterol levels. Examples of discontinuous variation are: blood groups, normal haemoglobin and haemoglobin S (the sickling trait), attached and free ear lobes, the ability to taste phenyl thiocarbamide, and fingerprints (divided into the four basic types). Some of these examples lend themselves to some practical work by the pupils.

At this point in the teaching sequence you could introduce the possibility of inherited or environmental origins of variation or you can return to this later in the topic after doing further work on some non-human examples.

It will be inevitable in studying some of these examples that ideas about the significance of the variations will emerge. The extent to which these are considered to be adaptive will vary from example to example. There is an argument for presenting pupils with some examples of variations to which no obvious adaptive or selective significance can be attached (see *Arum maculatum* on page 199).

There is a huge range of possible non-human examples on which you can draw. Your immediate school environment will provide some excellent opportunities; you may also wish to include material that you have collected previously or even bought in from biological suppliers. Permanent preserved collections can be built up over the years. Whatever you decide to do, the emphasis should be on pupils looking at biological material rather than considering it always at second hand. Here are some possibilities from which you might select.

Buttercup (*Ranunculus*) flowers
Collect a large number of flowers of the same species of
buttercup or lesser celandine. Distribute them among the class
and ask them to find out if all the flowers have the same
number of petals. Several hundred flowers can be examined in
a few minutes by a class. This will lead to the collection of data,
from which a column graph can be drawn.

Pupils will find a wide variation in the number of petals, five
probably being the modal value, depending on the species, with
the possible range being from four to 20. This is an example of a
variation where the character involved, the number of petals, is a
whole number. It is because of this, of course, that the data are
plotted as a column graph rather than as a histogram because no
class intervals are selected. It is important that pupils learn how to
present such data appropriately.

This short exercise can be followed up in a number of ways
and taken to different levels, e.g.:

- Do all the flowers on one plant have the same number of
  petals? In fact this is not so, terminal flowers tend to have
  extra petals more frequently than lateral flowers – a pattern
  that can be 'found' by the class or group concerned.
- Are there variations in the number of stamens and carpels?
  Counting large numbers of small things might be rather
  tedious (buttercup flowers have about 70 stamens on
  average and about 50 carpels) but each pupil only needs to
  examine one flower.

ICT
These data can be entered into a spreadsheet and a scatter
graph produced to introduce the idea of possible correlation
between the data.

Each of these activities could be extended by taking samples
from different locations and the results used to speculate about
genetic and environmental causes for variation (see later in this
section).

Ranunculus ficaria (lesser celandine) can be used for a
number of other activities. The plant is widely distributed, has
a long flowering time and flowers at a 'convenient' time, early
spring, for school work. The leaves of these plants can be used
to illustrate the following aspects of variation.

- Samples of the leaves are taken from different plants (or even better from populations growing in different places). Pupils measure the length and breadth of the leaves, plot these data as scatter graphs and compare differences.
- A portion of the lower epidermis of the leaf is easily stripped off after tearing the leaf. This is mounted in a drop of water on a microscope slide. Under high power, chloroplasts can be seen clearly enough in the guard cells to be counted. Samples of about 20 guard cells taken from different leaves show wide variations in chloroplast numbers.

In fact two chromosome races of this plant occur, one diploid ($2n = 16$), the other tetraploid ($4n = 32$), another example of variation. Tetraploids can be distinguished by the fact that later in the year they produce small bulbs in the axils of the leaves; these are absent in diploid plants. Comparison of diploid and tetraploid plants could form a useful extension exercise.

Fruit flies

Pupils can sort through a collection of freshly killed or preserved (in 50% ethanol) fruit flies that comprises wild type flies and examples of clear cut mutations, such as vestigial wing, curled wing, white eye and ebony body. Pupils should be told that this is an artificial population: all the variations might be seen in wild populations but at much lower frequencies! You may wish to teach the pupils how to sex the flies at this point if they are going to undertake some experimental genetics with this material.

Primroses

In spring a small bagful of primrose flowers can be collected in a few minutes. Pupils can 'dissect' the flower and discover the different arrangement of stamens and stigmas constituting pin and thrum flowers (see Figure 8.1). Pupils in the final 2 years of the 11–16 curriculum should be able to identify the structures as those favouring cross-pollination by insects. Cowslips can also be used for this exercise.

Red campion flowers at the same time as primrose, the flowers are dioecious (either male or female) and provide an additional example of variation in arrangement of parts of a flower.

Figure 8.1
Pin (left) and thrum (right) flowers of Primula.

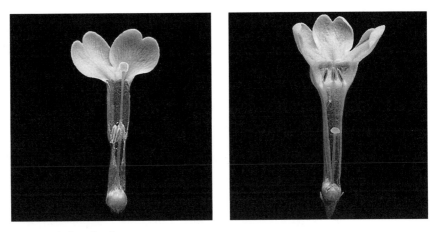

◆ *Further activities*

Arum maculatum (Cuckoo pint, Lords and ladies)

If this plant is to provide the basis for some work by pupils they should be warned that all parts of the plant are poisonous.

This is a common hedgerow and woodland plant, widely distributed in England and Wales. It is immediately identifiable. It produces leaves early in Spring and flowers soon after, producing the well known, but odd, inflorescence from which bright red berries subsequently develop. The plant shows some spectacular examples of variation. The leaves of some plants carry obvious purple/black spots; on other plants the leaves lack these. Leaves can be either spotted or not on any one plant. The frequency of spotted leaves varies considerably from place to place, occurring more frequently as one goes from north to south.

In some plants the curious poker-like inflorescence is yellow; in others it is purple. The flowers are surrounded by a pale green ensheathing leaf rolled to the right or to the left (see Figure 8.2). The botanical niceties of the structure are not important to pupils but they can tackle some interesting questions.

- Is the spotting characteristic associated with particular inflorescence colour or curling of the 'flower-leaf'?
- Are these two characteristics themselves associated?

If one or two pupils become particularly interested in the idea of geographical factors in variation they could be encouraged to communicate with other students via the internet and e-mail in order to compare different populations.

Figure 8.2
Left and right coiling of the flower-leaf of Arum. Examples of spotted and unspotted leaves are shown.

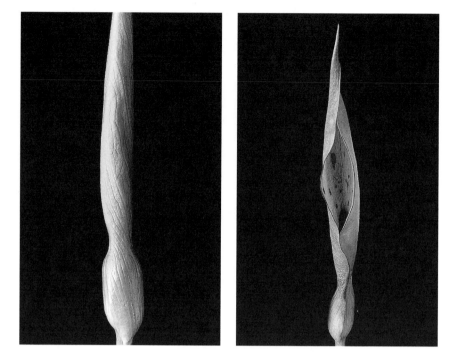

Cepaea nemoralis (the brown-lipped, banded snail)

The extensive polymorphism of this animal is well known. Snails differ in the background shell colour – pink, yellow or brown – and in the number and distribution of the prominent dark brown bands that occur. The number varies from 0 to 5. Differences in the width of the bands as well as their positions allow grouping into a very large number of categories (e.g. if a snail has a single band it can occur in the 1, 2, 3, 4 or 5 position, on a background that is either pink, yellow or brown). Collections of empty shells can be made from a variety of habitats. They keep well in screw-top jars and will retain their colour for years, especially if given a coat of nail varnish. Clearly this work can be greatly extended by comparing the frequency of various types found in different habitats (see later). Living snails may also be collected. They are easily maintained in the laboratory. They breed very easily and there is the possibility of using them for genetics experiments.

Are variations inherited or environmental?

There is of course no single answer to this. Some characteristics are inherited, others are environmental and yet others involve a combination of the two.

Family trees
The usual way into this area of work is by considering human family trees. A wide selection is available to draw on, e.g. the royal haemophilia, the Habsburgs' lip and the occurrence of marked scientific ability in the family to which Josiah Wedgwood, Charles Darwin and Francis Galton belonged (see the Nuffield texts mentioned under *Books* on page 212). Pupils' own family trees may be collected but they must be screened by the teacher before class use and an explanation prepared in advance for any apparent anomalies. Essentially this part of the work is used to set up the idea that characteristics can be inherited, and some work on practical genetics (or its second hand equivalent) usually follows (see Chapter 7).

The effect of the environment
Pupils will be aware, with a little prompting, of some interesting effects of the environment on humans. Suntanning, dieting, the effects of weight training and other health-related activities will be familiar examples. Some practical work may also be attempted with non-human material as follows.

- **Sun and shade leaves:** Some plants show significant differences in the leaves that grow in deep shade and in full sunlight. Such effects are best demonstrated in a single individual plant, allowing any genetic cause of variation to be ruled out; this is a good discussion point for the class. Collect samples of leaves of beech, *Fagus sylvatica*, growing on the exposed, preferably south, side of a hedge or tree and from the shady area within the canopy or hedge. Measure the surface area of the leaves, either by drawing the outline on to squared paper and subsequently counting squares or by calculating the product of the length and breadth of each leaf (this gives a rough correlate of area).

  Pupils can then calculate and compare the mean areas of the sun and shade leaves. Sun and shade leaves of beech show interesting anatomical differences. Sun leaves are much thicker than shade, a difference that is easily detectable by hand and eye. As an extension exercise, sections taken of the leaf lamina (either hand cut or bought prepared slides) could be examined. They show that the palisade mesophylls are dramatically different – a single layer of cells with relatively small numbers of chloroplasts in shade leaves, whereas sun leaves have two or three layers of palisade cells packed with chloroplasts. Pupils could consider the significance of these features and their relationship to environmental variables.

- **Plantains:** If you examine members of the same species of plantain (*Plantago major* or *P. lanceolata*) you will find that considerable differences occur between the plants growing in heavily trampled or extensively mown areas (goal areas of the school field or lawns) and those plants growing in less trampled places or longer grass. Pupils can identify the main differences in these plants (height of leaves above ground, size of leaves, length of flower stalk, etc.). They can speculate about possible causes of the differences they identify and how they would test whether those differences were environmental or genetic. If time and enthusiasm allowed, some pupils could test their ideas by digging up young plants from different locations, planting them in compost in pots and maintaining them under similar water and light regimes. This is a long-term investigation requiring several months for results to be gained. Permanent records of the results should be made, for instance by taking photographs, making pressed specimens and keeping any relevant data, in case next year's class are not as enthusiastic!

Interaction between genetic and environmental factors

In order to provide a convincing demonstration of the interaction between genetic and environmental factors it is necessary to show that a characteristic that is known to be genetically controlled requires an environmental factor to be expressed, i.e. the two factors act in tandem. An excellent demonstration of this is available using chlorophyll-deficient seedlings.

In tobacco a recessive allele for chlorophyll deficiency results in albino seedlings that survive for a few days only. Seeds from F_1 heterozygotes (from Philip Harris) are sown on black agar in Petri dishes. After 10 days the seedlings produce cotyledons and the plants, when scored, will be found to occur in the ratio 3 green:1 albino. If they have covered work on genetic ratios, pupils will see that the results provide evidence that cotyledon colour is an inherited characteristic. The pupils are then presented with further seedlings that were sown at the same time as the first batches but were subsequently maintained in the dark (e.g. in a cupboard). All the seedlings will be seen to be albino. These seedlings, when placed in the light for several days, will produce a pattern of results similar to the earlier ones, i.e. 3 green:1 albino. This illustrates that an allele for chlorophyll production has to be present to produce green cotyledons but that its expression depends on the presence of light.

8.3 Adaptation

♦ *Previous knowledge and experience*

Pupils will have met the idea of adaptation, if not the term, in the context of animals and plants being adapted to their environments, e.g. fish being adapted to swim in water and plants adapted to catch light.

♦ *A teaching sequence*

It is necessary to say a little about the meaning and use of the concept 'adaptation' before considering details of teaching it. Here are some examples of the use of the word in biology.

- Mammals are adapted to live on land.
- The leaves of desert plants are adapted to reduce water loss by evaporation; some of these adaptations are. . . .
- People visiting high altitudes for several weeks adapt to the lower oxygen content in the air by producing more red blood cells.
- On entering a dark room, human eyes take a few moments to adapt to the lower light intensity there.

These examples show that two quite different meanings are given to adaptation: the first is a process that involves a change of some sort taking place and the second is a state that represents the results of a process of some sort. There is another difference between these statements. Adaptation to lower oxygen content or adaptation of the eye when someone enters a dark room are short-term changes that are reversible and involve the individual; adaptation to life on land is long term and reversible only in the sense that some land-living mammals have secondarily returned to the water. Adaptation to life on land also involves the species not the individual, and such adaptations are the result of the process of natural selection. Natural selection has nothing to do with the other sort of changes apart from having brought about the development, over time, of systems that can make these types of short-term physiological adjustments.

At this stage you will realise that it is possible for pupils to become extremely confused about the different meanings that they hear attached to the word 'adaptation'. Their confusion is potentially dangerous because inability to distinguish between these nuances of meaning leads to misconceptions. Pupils should be alerted to the different ways in which the term is used.

There are other issues too, e.g. when is a particular feature of a living organism actually an adaptation? It is unscientific to assume that because an organism living in a particular environment shows some structural feature that is different to that of another organism in a different environment the feature must be an adaptation. Some of the so-called xeromorphic (protecting against excessive water loss) features of desert plants are often given in texts as good examples of adaptations, e.g. the (apparently) reduced leaf surface area. If we read that surface area reduction leads to a 30% reduction in the rate of water loss compared with that of a related plant that grows in temperate woodland, then we have evidence that this is an adaptive feature. The key point is that, unless such evidence is available, we can only hypothesise that a feature is adaptive.

In another sense, all adaptations are relative. If an organism is adapted to a particular environment, it must also be less well adapted to a different one. It is also better adapted to that environment than is another organism that does not live there. This type of thinking is useful in that it illustrates the need for experimentation and also some of the different experimental designs that may be involved.

Teleology

The word 'adaptation' also crops up in everyday language, e.g.:

- some Jane Austen novels have been adapted for television
- an old chimney pot can be adapted for use as a plant container.

In both of these examples there is a sense of purpose involved, a deliberate intention to make something to achieve an objective. When similar statements are used about aspects of biology they are said to be teleological. Such statements are very common particularly when structure and function relationships are involved. They usually include the words 'design' or 'need' or the phrase 'in order to'. Here are some examples:

- the coat of the mountain hare turns white in winter in order for the animal to be camouflaged in snow-covered country
- the leaf of a plant is designed to bring about efficient gaseous exchange
- the walls of the alveoli need to be thin so that diffusion of gases is efficient
- arteries have thick walls in order to be able to carry blood at high pressure.

Many biology teachers not only see nothing wrong with using expressions of this sort, but also deliberately use teaching techniques based on such thinking: 'Design an animal that lives in ... and feeds on ... Say why you gave it the features you did'. However, some of these statements, like the first one above, are potentially misleading in that they may support a Lamarckian interpretation of evolution (see later), so be careful. It suggests that the organism showed some purpose in developing the adaptation so that it could achieve the outcome. It needs to be made clear that the feature came about by random mutation and by chance it conferred some advantage.

   The other objection to all these statements and to this teaching approach is that they suggest that if something is designed there must be a designer. As Richard Dawkins has famously argued in *The Blind Watchmaker*, there is no designer; the watchmaker is natural selection and that is blind.

Anthropomorphisms

A current concern is that microbes 'have learnt to become resistant to modern antibiotics'. We could easily hear in a television natural history programme that the hare 'knowing that winter approaches grows a white coat' or read that a virus 'tricks the cell into copying its genetic code'. All these are examples of anthropomorphisms, where human emotions, needs or competencies are attributed to other living things. Whilst such expressions are used for popular effect perhaps they are best avoided in your teaching. Or, if you do use them, make sure that your pupils do not take them literally.

Teaching adaptation

Opportunities to consider adaptation will occur throughout your teaching in the 11–16 range. It is unlikely that your school scheme of work will include a specific topic on it. In ecology work you will use the ideas when considering the unequal distribution of organisms in a habitat. When comparing the different living things found in, say, running and standing water there will be a range of ideas to develop. The effect of abiotic (physical) factors on distributions is bound to involve a consideration of adaptation. Interactions between organisms, particularly when considering what eats what and why, will provide additional ideas.

   Most topics involving the flowering plant and the mammal will allow you to discuss examples of adaptations. There are large numbers of potential examples in other chapters of this book. The points mentioned earlier can be drawn on to inform your teaching approach.

8.4 Evolution

Typically, coverage of this topic will occur in the last year of compulsory secondary education. Here pupils will be able to draw on the wide range of ideas they will have gained from their work on variation, adaptation and genetics. They will be required to examine evidence that some species of plants and animals died out in the distant past and that modern species are their descendants. This will usually take the form of considering aspects of the fossil evidence and how they support the theory of evolution. Most courses require a treatment of the mechanism of evolution, that is by natural selection. This gives you a good opportunity to consider with pupils the nature of evidence and the role of theory in sciences in the context of what is, arguably, the most important integrative idea in biology. You can also introduce pupils to the writing of one of the most famous scientists of all time, Charles Darwin.

For some pupils, evolutionary ideas may pose problems because of religious views that they hold and hence this topic may be a controversial one. This is an additional reason for you to think very carefully about how you present the ideas, particularly emphasising that it is quite possible for the theory of evolution and belief in a Creator to co-exist. The thought that in some ways these ideas are mutually exclusive should be dispelled strongly.

◆ *Previous knowledge and experience*

Many youngsters are intensely interested in and remarkably knowledgeable about fossils in general and dinosaurs in particular. They will also bring to the class their own ideas about evolution (Deadman & Kelly, 1978). These are an obvious starting point for this work. On the negative side, however, having seen *Jurassic Park* and other similar films, some pupils will have acquired some erroneous ideas that will need to be tackled. Among these will be that *Jurassic Park* is a real place!

In addition, some pupils' views about the mechanism of evolution will be rooted firmly in Lamarckian ideas: features acquired during the life history of the organism can be transmitted to the next generation. Research studies have revealed that these ideas may be developed long before pupils are formally taught this topic and that they are resistant to replacement by Darwinian interpretations. They may survive secondary school teaching and even early undergraduate teaching. Such thinking requires consistent and sensitive challenge (Brumby, 1979 and Engel Clough & Wood-Robinson, 1985).

◆ *A teaching sequence*

A possible teaching sequence at an introductory level is as follows.

1. Outline the main ideas involved in the theory of organic evolution: animals and plants alive today are descended from simpler ancestors. Point out that the theory (although having a tentative status) has enormous explanatory power in accounting for the history of life on Earth.
2. Present evidence to support that theory. This will mainly be based on the fossil record. Extension work for able pupils might take in the evidence from geographical distribution, classification and comparative anatomy.
3. Look at some examples of selection in action.
4. Explain how natural selection provides a mechanism for evolution.

Studying fossils

Ideas about extinction and the fact and rate of change are particularly important. Evidence for both can be shown by examining the fossil record.

- Examine a collection of fossils (real and pictures) that includes examples of organisms very similar to surviving ones (e.g. sea urchins, *Ginkgo biloba*) and very different from today's (e.g. *Archaeopteryx*). The well known horse fossils probably provide the best example of a sequence of change over time (see Figure 8.3). Pupils should be told that the sequence presented to them is a simplified version of the record.
- Construct, to scale, a timeline (using string or a roll of paper) or a clock face that gives the history of the Earth in geological time. Get the pupils to place on the diagram the periods when the various organisms first appear in the fossil record. Work with major taxa of plants and animals. Talk about the significance of the sequence of increasing complexity that is shown.

Figure 8.3
The evolution of the horse.

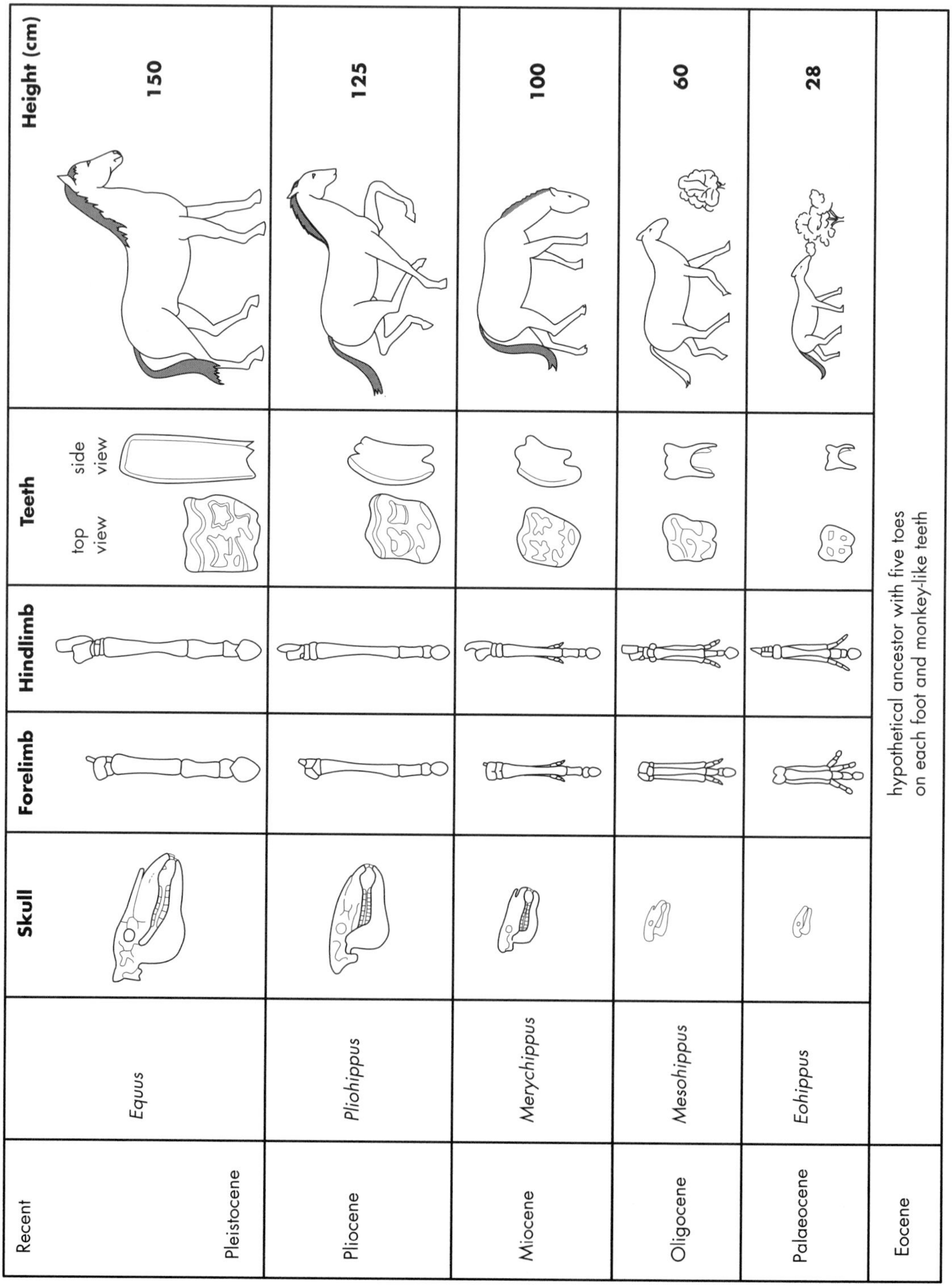

	Height (cm)	Teeth	Hindlimb	Forelimb	Skull		
Recent Pleistocene	150	side view top view				Equus	
Pliocene	125					Pliohippus	
Miocene	100					Merychippus	
Oligocene	60					Mesohippus	
Palaeocene	28					Eohippus	
Eocene		hypothetical ancestor with five toes on each foot and monkey-like teeth					

Selection

Selection provides part of the explanation for the mechanism of evolution (variation and its origins another part). It is important that pupils understand that natural selection is an ongoing, widespread and rapid phenomenon that occurs in the present day, as well as having shaped past events. It is also important to stress that selection does not automatically lead to speciation (the formation of new species). This point is dealt with later.

A simulation

A useful practical starting point is to do a simulation of selection using red and green cocktail sticks (plastic or dyed wooden ones). A hundred of each colour are needed. A square of grass (e.g. 15 × 15 m) is marked out using string and pegs and the cocktail sticks are randomly distributed by the teacher within the square beforehand. A group of six pupils act as 'birds' feeding on the red and green 'insects'. They are allowed to feed for a 30-second period and to collect as many 'insects' as possible in this period. The results of their predation are scored individually. The process is repeated several times and the total number of prey items is totalled for the different 'birds'. Analysis of the results usually shows:

- the selective advantage that the green insects have in this environment
- that predators vary in their ability to detect prey (red/green colour blindness is particularly disadvantageous) and so on.

Pupils should be asked to think about the possible outcome if a similar situation occurred in the wild over a longer period time. The idea can be extended to think about different kinds of backgrounds and the effect on geographically isolated populations.

Modern examples

Useful and well-known examples are melanism in Lepidoptera (e.g. the moth *Biston betularia*) and predation by song thrushes on *Cepaea* (second-hand data about shells collected at anvils compared with frequency of different banding patterns in living populations of different habitats). Note that these are not instances of the formation of new species, but of selection leading to changes in the frequencies of different colour forms in populations of one species in each case. Such events are sometimes described as 'microevolution'.

The appearance and spread of the rice grass *Spartina townsendii* is another useful example (see *Revised Nuffield Biology Text 4*, 1975), although the selective pressure is less obvious. In this instance the formation of a new species (macroevolution) was involved. Modern work on Darwin's finches is also useful to provide evidence of rapid selection (see below) as well as some additional historical interest.

Natural selection and evolution

One way to present the sequence of ideas is to use some chapter headings from the *Origin of Species*. Pupils could be provided with some selected quotations (see below) that can be discussed and interpreted from their earlier work on variation, genetics and selection.

The Origin of the Species by means of Natural Selection (1859)

Chapter 1   Variation under domestication
'Any variation which is not inherited is unimportant . . . but the number and diversity of inheritable deviations of structure . . . are endless.'
[Darwin's examples were dogs, fowls, domestic pigeons.]

Chapter 2   Variation under nature
'The many slight differences which appear in the offspring from the same parents . . . may be called individual differences. . . . These individual differences are of the highest importance for us for they are often inherited . . . and they thus afford materials for natural selection to act on. . . .'

Chapter 3   Struggle for existence
'A struggle for existence inevitably follows from the high rate at which all organic beings tend to increase. . . . Hence as more individuals are produced than can possibly survive, there must be a struggle for existence. . . .'

Chapter 4   Natural Selection; or the survival of the fittest
'This preservation of favourable individual differences and variations and the destruction of those that are injurious, I have called Natural Selection or the Survival of the Fittest. . . . If variations useful to any organic being ever do occur . . . individuals so characterised will have the best chance of being preserved and . . . will tend to produce offspring similarly characterised.'

◆ *Further activities*

- ◆ Visit the Natural History Museum website (www.nhm.ac.uk) and research the database on dinosaurs. This can be downloaded to an Excel file and used to classify the animals in various ways; to consider possible adaptations; to work out some possible food webs, etc.
- ◆ Research the possible reasons for the extinction of dinosaurs.
- ◆ Use an internet search engine and read about the discovery of modern coelacanths and discuss the significance of the coelacanth.
- ◆ Show relevant clips from the film *Jurassic Park* and ask pupils for their thoughts about whether it is fact or fiction. If they are unable to accept your assurances about technical issues they can research this for themselves by contacting the Natural History Museum website. Sequences in the film when the main characters first visit *Jurassic Park* and when they are lectured on the cloning techniques are particularly useful.
- ◆ Look at the reconstructions of some of the animals of the Burgess Shale in British Columbia (see *Books*; there is also a website: www.geo.ucalgary.Ca/~macrae/Burgess_Shale). The University of California's website (www.ucmp.berkeley.edu/) includes details of other fossils. The trilobite section is interesting. All these provide vivid examples of animals that no longer occur on Earth and raise the question, 'Where did they go?'
- ◆ Read about Darwin's voyage on the *Beagle*.
- ◆ The reception that the publication of the *Origin* received, the debate which followed and the reasons for the debate make this an obvious example to take to deal with the historical impact of a scientific idea. You might try some role play.

  Consider the present day status of the ideas and how modern genetics provides additional information to support them.

◆ *Enhancement ideas*

- ◆ Consolidation is required by giving pupils some further examples to discuss that are open to both Lamarckian and Darwinian interpretations. You might start with the legendary giraffe's neck or weightlifter's biceps. Other possible ideas are to return to melanism (Did the industrial revolution and the increased soot production cause the melanic mutations?) or a host of other examples drawn from the literature or your own imagination.

Other resources

♦ *Books*

Darwin, Charles. (1859). *The Origin of Species.* A number of facsimile editions and reprints are available.

Dawkins, R. (1986). *The Blind Watchmaker.* Harlow, Longman. See Chapters 10, 'Classification' and 11 'Lamarck, Darwin'.

Gould, S.J. (1980). *The Panda's Thumb.* Harmondsworth, Penguin. See pages 65–71 for an account of Lamarck, Darwin and adaptation.

Gould, S.J. (1989). *Wonderful Life. The Burgess Shale and the Nature of History.* Harmondsworth, Penguin.

Maynard Smith, J. (1993). *The Theory of Evolution.* Cambridge, Cambridge University Press.

Nuffield Secondary Science 2, Continuity of life. (1971). Harlow, The Nuffield Foundation and Longman.

Poole, M. (1995). *Beliefs and Values in Science Education.* Buckingham, Open University Press. See Chapter 7, 'Darwin in context'.

Revised Nuffield Biology Text 4, The Perpetuation of Life. (1975). Harlow, The Nuffield Foundation and Longman.

Ridley, Mark (1993). *Evolution.* Oxford, Blackwell Scientific Publications.

Ruse, Michael (1982). *Darwinism Defended. A Guide to the Evolution Controversies.* Reading, Addison-Wesley. An account of Darwin's ideas and the Creationist positions.

Weiner, Jonathon (1995). *The Beak of the Finch.* London, Vintage.

♦ *Articles*

Brumby, M. (1979). Problems in learning the concept of natural selection. *Journal of Biological Education,* **13**, pp. 119–122.

Conway Morris, S. & Whittington, H.B. (1979). The animals of the Burgess Shale. *Scientific American,* **240** (Jan), pp. 122–133.

Deadman, J.A. & Kelly, P.J. (1978). What do secondary school boys understand about evolution and heredity before they are taught the topics? *Journal of Biological Education,* **12**, pp. 7–15.

Scientific American, September 1978 issue (Vol. 239. No. 3) was devoted to articles on the modern interpretation of the theory of evolution – excellent articles by Mayr, Ayala,

Valentine, Maynard Smith and Lewontin (adaptation) in particular. This was also published as a book.

◆ *Internet*

A number of resources are available starting from the ASE's website: www.ase.org.uk. A good summary of evolution is given by Chris Colby. Locate this under General Biology Resources: Introduction to Evolutionary Biology.

◆ *CD ROMs*

- *The IT in Secondary Science Book* and *Software for Science Teaching* by Roger Frost (1998, ASE Booksales) lists a large number of databases and CD ROMs for this topic.
- The BECTa internet site has reviews of over 1000 CD ROMs with a search facility (website: www.becta.org.uk).
- *Games for Life* (1996) is an inexpensive CD ROM with a programme that surveys human characteristics, provides data about the numbers of people with the features and their inheritance. It can be obtained from The Wellcome Trust, Wellcome Centre for Medical Sciences, 210 Euston Road, London NW1 2BE (website: www.wellcome.ac.uk).

◆ *Background reading*

Berry, R.G. (1977). *Inheritance and Natural History*. London, Collins.

Briggs, D. & Walters, S.M. (1997). *Plant Variation and Evolution*, 3rd edition. Cambridge, Cambridge University Press.

Driver, R., Squires, A., Rushworth, P. & Wood-Robinson, V. (1994). *Making Sense of Secondary Science Support Materials for Teachers* and *Research into Children's Ideas*. London, Routledge.

Engel Clough, E. & Wood-Robinson, C. (1985). How secondary students interpret instances of biological adaptation, *Journal of Biological Education*, **19** (2), pp. 125–130.

Institute of Biology (1997). *Biological Nomenclature, Recommendations on Terms, Units and Symbols*, Second Edition. London, Institute of Biology.

Lucas, A.M. (1971). The teaching of 'Adaptation'. *Journal of Biological Education*, **5**, pp. 86–90. An old reference, but still of value.

Osborne, R. & Freyburg, P. (1985). *Learning in Science: the Implications of Children's Science*. London, Heinemann.

9 *Ecology*

Susan Barker and David Slingsby

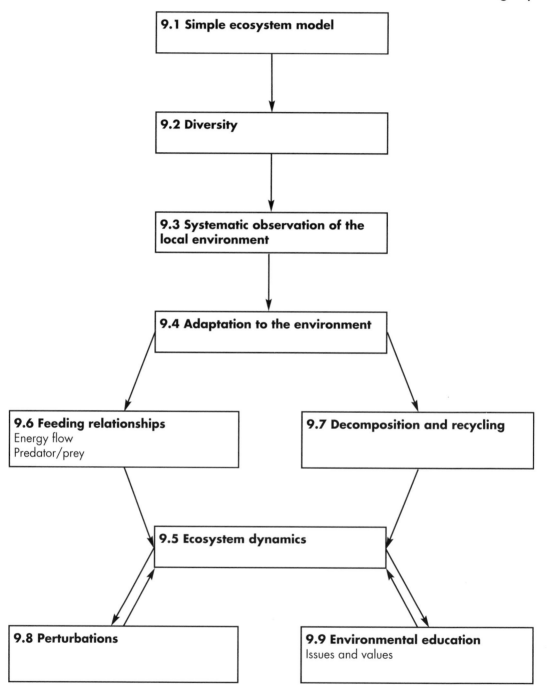

◆ *Choosing a route*

Ecology is a branch of science that emphasises the inter-relationships between living organisms and their environments. It is a fascinating discipline and becomes really exciting when it pervades the whole of the Science curriculum. Ecology when taught as a purely theoretical subject with a mass of technical terms and flow diagrams can be a real turn-off to pupils. The subject becomes much more meaningful and motivating when it is taught by making observations of real life examples, by recognising interactions and then by using these as a basis from which to explore the more abstract concepts. For instance, for many pupils the nitrogen cycle is all too often a diagram from hell with little to do with reality. The reason they find it difficult is often because each word on the diagram is the tip of a biological iceberg and there are too many difficult concepts per square centimetre on a single page to be taken in in one lesson.

Ecosystems are a central concept in ecology, but knowledge and understanding of ecosystems is gained by studying the component parts. We therefore consider it important not to have a separate entry for ecosystems because ecosystems appear in all the other sections.

The best way to start is through a simple introduction to the ecosystem concept followed by an emphasis on the animals and plants in the local environment and to the adaptations that enable them to survive. After this there are several ways one may proceed, but we recommend that each feeds into developing the concept of the ecosystem. Whichever route you choose do cover all the topics and explore the inter-relationships between them. An understanding of ecosystems provides the means to appreciate what happens when an ecosystem is disrupted by, for example, a form of pollution. A realisation of how far reaching the effects of such pollution can go may, in turn, feed back to develop a deeper appreciation of the ecosystem concept itself.

9.1 Simple ecosystem model

In its simplest form an ecosystem is a group of living organisms that interact with each other and the non-living environment to form a self-sustaining system. It is the fundamental concept at the heart of ecology, but one that can be too challenging if introduced too early or as a sophisticated definition presented out of context. It is important to introduce the ecosystem idea early on but only as a *simple* model. A deeper understanding develops by frequently revisiting the concept during consideration of its individual components.

◆ *A teaching sequence*

The transparency ecosystem model

A simple way to put the ecosystem idea across is through a set of three overhead transparencies used as overlays. These can be prepared by photocopying cut-out pictures or stickers on to an acetate sheet. For a woodland ecosystem:

- Transparency 1: 'The ecosystem is composed of: non-living factors', plus drawings or cut-out pictures of the non-living environment components, e.g. Sun, clouds, rocks, soil.
- Transparency 2: 'and plants', arranged to line up under the term 'non-living factors'. On this overlay draw on or stick on copies of trees, shrubs, ferns, etc.
- Transparency 3: 'and animals' to line up under plants and here you draw on or add pictures of woodland animals. You can buy stickers of animals in any toy shop; it raises a chuckle from the class if bears are found precariously balanced astride a branch high up in a tree!

You can also demonstrate the likely sequence if you interfere with any of the components – 'if you chop down all the trees' – remove Transparency 2 – 'then there will be no habitat for the animals' – remove Transparency 3 – 'and the non-living environment will be affected' – 'the climate will change with less rain, the soil will be lost through erosion and all that will be left will be the Sun and the rocks!'

The brine shrimp model ecosystem

The Bottle Planet (Figure 9.1) offers a very concrete, 'hands-on' introduction to the ecosystem because each pupil can have their own ecosystem to look at! The brine shrimps feed on algae but the algae never run out because as fast as they are eaten new ones are formed. Oxygen never gets all used up because the algae recycle it and when things die there are bacteria in the system that decompose them and liberate the elements they contain for reuse. All the system needs to sustain it is light energy. The Bottle Planet is described in the *Brine Shrimp Ecology* book by Dockery & Tomkins (1999). The book provides all the instructions for setting up your own Bottle Planet. It also contains a range of suggested investigations in which the Bottle Planet can be used to study ecosystems at various levels of complexity.

Figure 9.1
The Bottle Planet ecosystem. (Based on Dockery & Tomkins, 1999.)

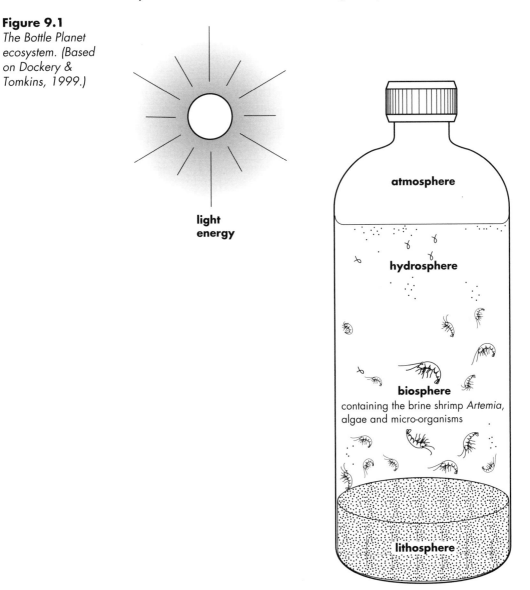

light
energy

atmosphere

hydrosphere

biosphere
containing the brine shrimp *Artemia*,
algae and micro-organisms

lithosphere

9.2 Diversity

♦ *A teaching sequence*

Diversity is something to be *seen* rather than defined in words and it is important to build on (rather than stifle) the natural curiosity and fascination of the pupils. Observation is very much an element in primary science education but it can become an intellectually challenging technique for secondary science teaching through:

- applying it in unfamiliar situations
- using it with predictions
- moving towards systematic and more sophisticated observational techniques
- integrating it with other areas of the science curriculum
- linking it to data analysis.

Making observations

Observation of diversity within any ecosystem is a worthwhile activity and there are many ways to achieve this through examining ecosystems where diversity is obvious, e.g. in a pond, *and* through examination of systems where diversity requires searching, e.g. in soil or grass turf. A useful starting point is to pose the following questions and to get children to make predictions:

- How many species live in a tropical rain forest?
- How many organisms live in the school grounds?

ICT

The pupils could use secondary sources (library, internet, CD ROM, etc.) to find answers to the first question, then be invited to find out how many different organisms actually live in the school grounds. At its simplest this could be a class walk around the grounds listing conspicuous species, progressing towards more specialised sampling to get a more complete picture, e.g. setting pitfall traps to find species that are active only at night or those that hide when a class of 33 pupils descends!

Pupils are often surprised to find how long the list of species can be following some searching of a habitat:

- bring samples of fresh soil into the classroom and examine with a magnifier
- look closely at a patch of grass
- look at pond water under a microscope.

! *Good hygiene is essential when handling soil and pond water.*

Naming and classifying organisms is a natural progression from this activity and pupils are usually keen to do this. When a pupil realises that there are two or three types of beetle they tend to want to know what to call them. Names give pupils pegs to hang things on and can lead to them realising that there are not two or three types of beetle but five or six! This simply means that the teacher is succeeding in opening the pupil's eyes to the fascination offered by biodiversity. Concerns about identification need not and should not put teachers off taking children into the field but it is important to consider how to overcome the problem.

Identification and the beginner: strengths and limitations

Some systems are much simpler to work with than others. An example of such a simple system involves only common soil invertebrates (such as spiders, beetles and centipedes) found using pitfall traps (Figure 9.2 on page 222) and identified using the easy-to-use Field Studies Council key with pictures of soil invertebrates (Bebbington *et al.*, 1994). The keys, available for a range of habitats, are on laminated card, are inexpensive to buy and thus a class set is not an unreasonable proposition. They are so good that the class can use them themselves with a little help and encouragement. The teacher does not need to pretend that he/she is an expert on invertebrate identification (it can be very liberating to discover that the pupils did not expect you to be anyway). The teacher can work with the pupils, teach study skills and share his/her own fascination and curiosity. Perhaps the most important thing is to enjoy it yourself and let your enjoyment be infectious. Wherever contact with living organisms or their habitats is made it is worth mentioning at the outset that respect for life is paramount and that any specimens collected should be returned to their original source (alive and well!).

 There are useful CD ROMs available about animals and habitats; many include data that can be analysed, e.g. *The Wide World of Animals* from AVP is very good and it is very animal and habitat friendly!

Identification and the expert: the advantages and the pitfalls

Inexperience in identification need not be a barrier to teaching good biology out-of-doors but there is no disputing the fact that expertise can be useful. There are, however, pitfalls for the 'expert'. If the ecological story is mainly about trees, brambles, nettles, ivy, grass and bare ground it may be simply irrelevant and confusing to encourage pupils to record obscure species as part of the teacher's ego trip. Also, it is not necessarily a good thing to tell the pupils everything when they can work things out for themselves. It is, as with all teaching, a question of sensitivity to the pupils. When a pupil says, 'I think there are two sorts of these things with blue flowers – both look like Speedwell', if you are there at the time and can say, 'Well done – the big hairy ones are Germander Speedwell and the one with smaller leaves is called Slender Speedwell' you will reinforce some fine discrimination skills. If you then add, 'And do you think they grow in the same sort of place or not?' then you are more than likely teaching good ecology.

9.3 Systematic observation of the local environment

A more systematic approach to observation is essential to allow predictions and hypotheses to be made. This moves us away from 'What is this?' to 'Why is there more of this here than over there?' and thus starts to explain why the distribution of organisms is not random – a key aim of ecology. Try to encourage pupils to:

- be curious
- notice interesting patterns
- describe patterns more carefully
- make hypotheses
- make predictions
- test them.

Collection of data in a systematic fashion is often remembered for its repetitive nature rather than the purpose of the exercise, thus it is *vital* that a purpose is identified and made explicit. However, collection of good scientific data does have an element of repetitiveness in it. Pupils quite like doing it as long as it is:

- clearly focused
- satisfyingly accurate – they can see that it is scientifically valid rather than crudely subjective
- a lot of data are collected quickly.

Good practice in fieldwork

Your school or local education authority will have a safety policy that covers working outdoors with pupils. It will give you guidelines on staff/pupil ratios, first aid certification requirements, etc. (There are also some useful texts on this area, see Institute of Biology, 1999.) Do not underestimate the importance of such information as you are legally responsible for the safety of pupils in your care. Being outdoors can be a very motivating factor, and class management needs careful thought with such excited pupils. Think about issues such as:

• What if a pupil needs toilet facilities?
• What if the weather is bad?
• What are the contingency plans in case of an accident, e.g. mobile phone?
• What if a pupil wanders off?

Many such issues can be circumvented by careful management and planning, particularly preparatory site visits, so do not let the bureaucracy put you off.

Fieldwork also needs to be environmentally responsible, especially with regard to sensitivity to ethical and conservation issues and of course the Wildlife and Countryside Act (HMSO, 1981). Make sure you gain permission from the landowner and keep to paths where possible. If you as a teacher demonstrate that you care for, appreciate and value the environment, then you are likely to instil these qualities in your pupils.

Pitfall traps

These are very easy to set up and can enable pupils to collect quantitative data as well as beetles! (See Figure 9.2.) At one level, pitfall traps can be used simply to find out what is there. A grid of (say) 25 traps set by a class might be set in a wood and then another 25 in a different habitat, such as an open field. The class might have predicted that there would be more woodlice in the wood than in the field because there are more dead leaves for them to eat and the study should enable this prediction to be tested. For a more quantitative survey try the mark–recapture method (described in all three books in the *Background reading* section) to estimate population sizes in different habitats and/or at different times of year.

Figure 9.2
A correctly set up pitfall trap.

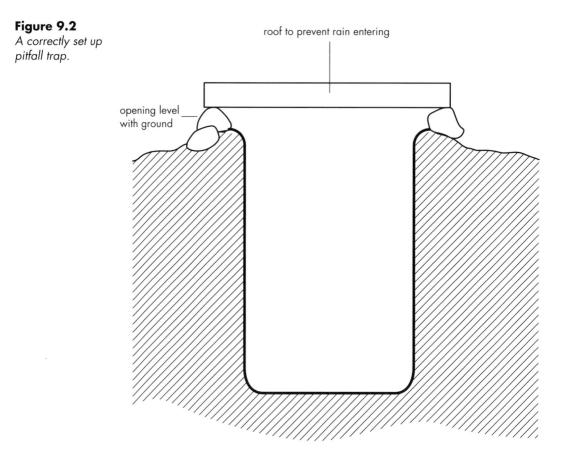

roof to prevent rain entering

opening level with ground

Quadrats

Technically a quadrat is a sample area and is defined by a quadrat frame; in practice most people refer to quadrat frames as quadrats. You cannot possibly look at every square centimetre of a study area so a quadrat is a method of obtaining representative samples. Recording such representative samples is a means of *estimating* what the whole area is like. This offers a way of introducing the principles of statistical sampling to a science course. There are all sorts of different levels and approaches to the use of quadrats and thus subsequent data analysis can be tailor-made to meet the needs of your class's level and ability. It is important that *you* as a teacher select the appropriate method and present it to the pupils for them to apply in their own individual investigations or class exercise. Choice of method by pupils at this age range often leads to confusion and to a shift of emphasis away from the hypothesis to the methodology.

What shall I record?

You can decide to record frequency, density or cover. It is best if the teacher introduces the exercise having already selected the method and shown the pupils how to carry it out before inviting them to apply it. To be truly objective, quadrats should be placed randomly, either using random numbers as co-ordinates or throwing them *carefully* without looking.

Frequency

This is the probability of a species occurring in a randomly placed quadrat (see page 226). Essentially you record whether a species is present or absent in a large number of rather small quadrats, e.g. 10 cm × 10 cm, and each species is expressed in terms of the number of quadrats in which it was recorded as a percentage of the total number of quadrats used.

Density

This is the number of individuals per unit area and could be used, for example, to estimate the number of barnacles per square metre on rocks on a sea shore. It could also be used for estimating the number of species of plants in a pasture although it can be unsuitable where it is difficult to determine where one plant stops and another starts, e.g. grass. In such situations it is probably better to use percentage cover.

Percentage cover

This is the proportion of the quadrat covered by a species and is expressed as percentage cover. There are two methods:

1. Cover estimation – here you make a subjective assessment (by eye) of the proportion of the quadrat covered by each species. The recorder has to imagine that all the individuals have been moved into one corner of the quadrat before giving it a percentage cover value (Figure 9.3). Where the vegetation is layered with large plants such as trees and shrubs overhanging smaller plants, the total cover can be well over 100%. In woodlands one needs to look upwards and record tree cover before completing the recording of a quadrat.

Figure 9.3
*Recording cover
using quadrats –
subjective cover
estimate.*

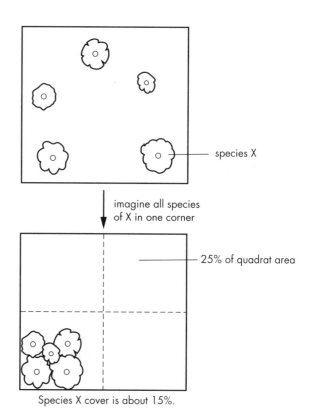

imagine all species
of X in one corner

25% of quadrat area

species X

Species X cover is about 15%.

2. Using a point quadrat – instead of a square frame lying on the ground, a point quadrat frame stands upright and has a row of evenly spaced holes through which a knitting needle can be inserted and allowed to fall (see Figure 9.4). Each species hit by the point of the needle as it falls is recorded in a tally. It may, for example, hit a blade of grass first and then a dandelion leaf at ground level. Both species would be recorded. The point quadrat frame can be placed randomly (although it's not usually a good idea to throw it!) or regularly (say every metre along a measuring tape). A score of ten hits on grass would thus be 100% grass cover, whereas dandelion, hit only four times, would score 40%. If the point hits the ground without touching a plant then it is recorded as a hit on 'bare ground'.

Point quadrats are particularly suitable for investigations in short vegetation, such as the closely mown grassland of the school playing field. However, there are two disadvantages. Firstly, to get enough point quadrat data is more time-consuming than cover estimation. Secondly, point quadrats are unsuitable for use in tall vegetation.

Figure 9.4
Using a point quadrat.

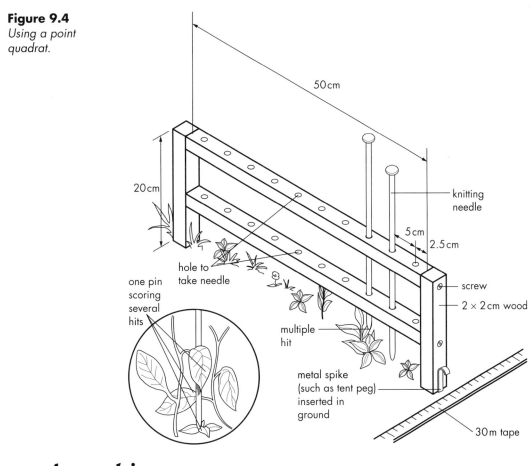

50 cm

20 cm

knitting
needle

5 cm

2.5 cm

hole to
take needle

one pin
scoring
several
hits

screw

2 × 2 cm wood

multiple
hit

metal spike
(such as tent peg)
inserted in
ground

30 m tape

◆ *A teaching sequence*

When and where do I teach quadrat techniques?
The most effective way of doing this is usually in the field when the pupils are motivated and keen to get going. A theoretical lesson on quadrat techniques is about as interesting as watching paint dry on a Friday afternoon, with equal learning outcomes!

Key points in using quadrats are:

- the focus of the investigation is the hypothesis rather than the methodology
- have a prediction that is to be tested – a clear focus that the pupils understand
- use quadrats to collect relevant data
- collect sufficient data but not too much
- be consistent in sampling and recording techniques so that comparisons between studies can be made.

Deciding on what are sufficient data can form part of the pupils' evaluation of the exercise and is a useful discriminating factor for assessment.

Making comparisons in grassland

Any grassland habitat would be suitable, e.g. a football pitch, lawn or meadows. At first sight pupils might consider this habitat to be all rather boring and 'just grass'. It will not take long for them to realise that it isn't all the same. There are likely to be numerous microhabitats at the site, e.g.

- football pitch: trampling in goal mouths
- cricket square: closely mown – weed-killer, extra fertiliser?
- shaded areas under trees
- close to path: low species diversity – recently disturbed?
- by river bank: high species diversity – moist soil and/or old established turf?
- long, straight narrow strip with daisies – over buried pipeline?
- sloping area: better drained – drier?
- rough area: longer grass – mowed less frequently than the rest?

Working individually or as a group, suggest that the pupils select two places on the grassland that they feel are different, make a prediction and then test it by quadrating. (They of course have to think of reasons for their predictions.) Remember to show the pupils the quadrat methodology. In this example, a frequency procedure would be most appropriate. Frequency in this context means 'the probability of a species occurring in a randomly placed quadrat'.

A 10 × 10 cm quadrat is thrown in each area 50 times (randomly and carefully!). Each time just the species present are recorded as a tally.

$$\text{frequency for each species} = \frac{\text{number of quadrats with species}}{\text{total number of quadrats recorded}} \times 100$$

An example of a completed record sheet for this method is presented in Table 9.1. Encouraging pupils to emphasise the key features of the data by means of a summary table or chart will help them to acquire the important skill of seeing the wood for the trees.

Table 9.1 *Recording sheet for using frequency to compare species composition of two contrasting habitats.*

	Shaded grassland			Unshaded grassland		
	Tally	Total records	Frequency (%)	Tally	Total records	Frequency (%)
Daisy	|||	3	6	₸₸₸₸₸ ₸₸₸	15	30
Grass	₸₸₸ ₸₸₸ ₸₸₸ ₸₸₸	20	40	₸₸₸ ₸₸₸ ₸₸₸	15	30
Dandelion	₸₸₸ ₸₸₸	10	20	||||	4	8
Rough hawkbit		0	0	₸₸₸ ₸₸₸ |||	13	26
Bare ground	₸₸₸ ₸₸₸	10	20	|||	3	6

The hypothesis was that some species are more common in the shade and others in the open because some plants have adaptations that allow them to manage with less light than others.

The prediction was that some species will be more common in the shade whilst other species will be more common in the open.

Transect: changes and patterns from place to place

A transect is a line along which recordings are made in a systematic way in order to describe patterns and relationships. Across a woodland margin is just one of many places to record a transect as the habitat changes significantly over a very short distance. It will be very clear to the class that, as one passes into the wood, the vegetation and microhabitats change. There will be less grass but more brambles, possibly ivy and bare ground, and most obviously, the cover of trees overhanging the ground will increase. In the middle of the transect you will find typical woodland herbs but maybe also more common generalist plants like nettles. As woodland communities are strongly influenced by seasons you may find relics of the previous season, e.g. if your fieldwork is in the summer you may find bluebell leaves and seed pods but not flowers. This is an excellent teaching opportunity to point out seasonality. Concentrating on only a few species focuses the mind on the *changes* across the transect rather than *names* of large numbers of species.

Deciding what to do as a group activity: hypothesising and predicting

A class discussion is a good way to start. Prompt the class to think about differences in light intensity and that this might be a critical factor in influencing the vegetation. This will possibly lead to a suggestion that it would be worth measuring the light intensity at ground level along the transect. Other things they might measure are: soil pH, soil and/or air temperature, humidity, etc. You as a teacher may not know if any of these factors will influence the change in vegetation across the transect but this is all part of an investigation. You could suggest a few hypotheses and encourage the pupils to think of more, both as predictions as the group plans the investigation and as possible explanations to the results.

There are gadgets you can use, some expensive, such as an electronic humidity meter, and others cheap, such as soil thermometers or an old-fashioned whirling hygrometer. If you intend to return the following day, the class could set up pitfall traps along the transect – perhaps there are more or different creepy crawlies in the humid and shady woodland than out in the open. A group of pupils thrust into the alien environment of a woodland soon warms to a transect and enjoys measuring things along it. The teacher need not discourage such enthusiasm but it can be channelled along scientific lines within a hypothesis-generating and prediction-making culture. The role of the teacher is not to have all the answers but to have a few good ideas to get the pupils coming up with their own.

Getting on with the job

Once the pupils know:

- where to set out the transect
- how and what they intend to measure
- why they intend to measure it

they are ready to start. Remember to guide them as to how to measure vegetation cover, e.g. recording plants by percentage cover every 1 m using a 0.5 × 0.5 m quadrat. Results can be recorded in a pre-prepared table (see Table 9.1). In 1 hour you could reasonably expect pupils to record percentage cover and abiotic data in about ten quadrats. If a whole class have worked together on a single transect, collate the data either before leaving the site or back in the lab (time and weather dependent!), so that everyone has a full set of results.

Collating data and analysing it by computer

There are things the pupils need to learn about how a team collects and collates data so that it is internally consistent and reliable. It may sound rather quaint but some teacher direction can speed it up. 'Who did quadrat number 5?' elicits 'I did: bare ground 50%, grass 20%, nettles 10%, brambles 20%, light 550 lux, pH 6.5, humidity 80%, soil temperature 19 °C'. All the class can then enter the data on their own record sheets. Using a computer to analyse their data adds to their satisfaction and provides an excellent opportunity to introduce some ICT. A spreadsheet system can be used to handle and work with the data, but the options are almost infinite. Using software designed for field data can be tremendously advantageous. With the *Fieldworks* program you can plot kite diagrams (see Figure 9.5) and histograms very easily. For mathematically minded pupils there are facilities for statistical analyses, such as correlation coefficients, diversity indices, etc. and it also has a database about common plant species. The *Warwick Spreadsheet System* is a little more difficult to use, especially for the beginner, but it is more versatile and will enable you to do more with the data. It also has the advantage of providing demonstrations of real ecological models.

Discussing transect data

This can be done by gathering the group around *Fieldworks* on the computer screen and pointing out, for example, how light intensity goes down as tree cover goes up. Perhaps soil temperature goes down and humidity goes up on entering the wood. And why does the pH change (if it does) along the transect? Why do some plant species grow at particular places along the transect?

Transects rarely prove anything; they demonstrate patterns and relationships that lead to new hypotheses. Often there are several alternative hypotheses invited by the relationship and these need evaluating. A written account of a transect can provide good opportunities for teaching and assessing data analysis and evaluation skills to various levels. Figure 9.5 presents sample data of a woodland transect using *Fieldworks*. Species are presented as kite diagrams and physical (abiotic) factors by means of bar charts. A transect like this provides excellent opportunities for analysis of data and evaluation with scope for assessment.

Figure 9.5
Woodland transect data, presented using Fieldworks.

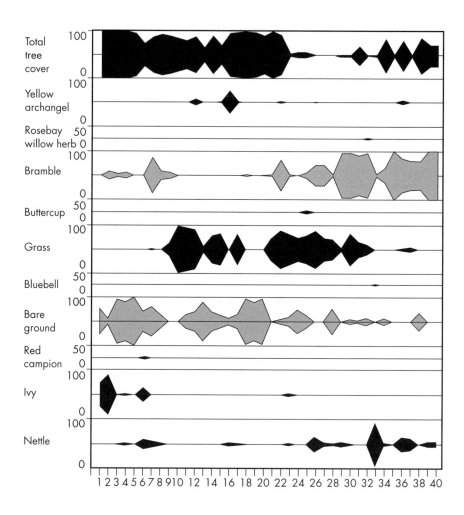

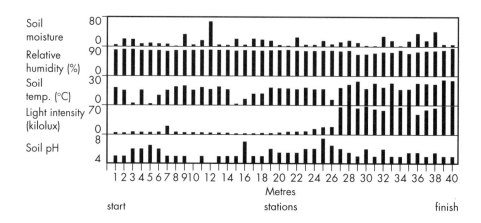

The key ecological trends shown are as follows.

- There is a clear pattern of light intensity. Tree cover at the beginning of the transect casts a deep shade whilst at the other end of the transect, where there is less canopy, light intensity is higher.
- There is a pattern in soil pH and moisture. The variation in the data for soil pH suggests some experimental error – perhaps pupils did not insert the probe to the same depth?
- The data suggest that ivy could be shade tolerant whilst bramble is more shade tolerant than grass but less than ivy.
- The temperature is cooler in the shaded part of the transect, but variations suggest recording errors. Was there a standard technique? For instance, was care taken always to insert the probe to the same depth every time a measurement was made?
- Humidity – this is highest in the shade, falling at the woodland margin, but rising at the end of the transect owing to the close proximity of a river.

Humidity was measured using an electronic humidity meter but it can be measured in the field more cheaply using cobalt chloride paper carried in a boiling tube containing anhydrous calcium chloride (Figure 9.6). The time taken for the exposed paper to change from blue to pink can be an indicator of humidity useful for comparative purposes.

Figure 9.6
A simple method for measurement of humidity.

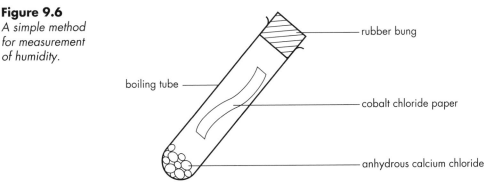

rubber bung

boiling tube

cobalt chloride paper

anhydrous calcium chloride

◆ *Further activities*

- ◆ Individual investigations: pupils learn a lot from group work but once they have had some experience they will be ready to work more independently. A transect or study involving a comparison of two sites or microhabitats is a reliable winner, but the best predictions come not so much from you as from your pupils!

9.4 Adaptation to the environment

Ecology is very much concerned with interactions between one species and another and between species and the environment. Adaptation to the environment is a key biological principle that is important from an ecological point of view and is dealt with elsewhere (Chapter 8). However, the influence of the environment on a variety of plant and animal characteristics is often one of the easiest and simplest ecological investigations to perform.

◆ *A teaching sequence*

Light intensity and leaf width in bluebells

- **Prediction:** As the light intensity falls along a transect the width of the bluebell leaves increases. Scientific explanation: wider leaves have a larger surface area and this is an advantage because this increases the opportunity to absorb light energy.
- **Method:** Select 100 bluebell leaves in the shade and 100 in the open at random. Use a 15 cm ruler to measure the width of the leaves. Plot the results as overlapping histograms on a single sheet of graph paper.
- **Results:** There is likely to be some variation with overlap but certainly you will find a general difference between the two sites. The prediction is likely to be right in most cases. The pupils will look to you as the teacher for a clever explanation! It doesn't have to be correct but it does have to be plausible and it may stimulate your class to come up with a better explanation. The key point is that bluebells do most of their growth in spring before there are leaves on the deciduous trees. From a bluebell's point of view, what seems to be shady in May and June is actually well illuminated in March and early April, when it matters. In very shaded environments, e.g. under evergreens, photosynthetic capability is likely to be very much reduced anyway; in these situations leaves may be considerably smaller overall.

This exercise can be carried out along a path without damaging the bluebell plants and without destructive sampling. It is a great opportunity to discuss with your class their own potentially destructive effects on the habitat. Working in a beautiful and interesting place appeals to a combination of emotional, aesthetic and intellectual responses and makes the need to treat it with respect seem self-evident. This is far more effective than six 'boil-in-the-bag' reasons why we should conserve a rainforest and provides a basis for a real discussion about conservation of exotic ecosystems.

◆ *Further activities*

◆ Light intensity and leaf size in brambles: on the basis of preliminary field observations similar to those in the previous example, a pupil predicted that the leaves on the shaded side of a bramble bush would have a larger surface area than those on the open side. The graph presented in Figure 9.7 confirms that bramble leaves in the shade have a larger surface area. Remember to point out that size of an organism or parts of it are only partially determined by environmental factors and that heredity is important too. Note that in this investigation genetic diversity as a factor was eliminated by using shaded and open aspects of the same plant.

Figure 9.7
Size of blackberry leaves in open and shaded aspects, presented using the Warwick Spreadsheet System.

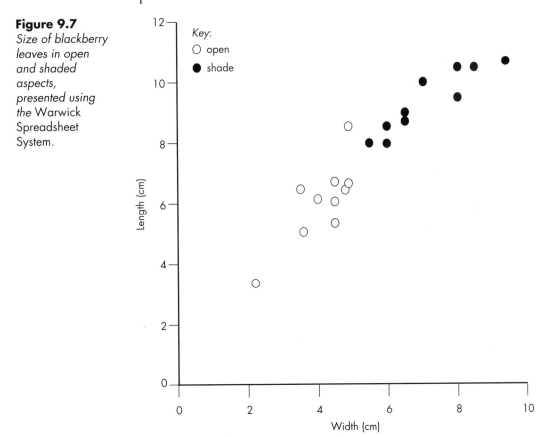

9.5 Ecosystem dynamics

Ecology is about studying animals, plants and microbes interacting with their physical environment as systems – ecosystems. These systems sometimes remain remarkably the same for a surprisingly long time whilst others undergo change before your very eyes. These changes (and sometimes the lack of them) constitute ecosystem dynamics.

◆ *A teaching sequence*

Seasonality

The fact that the biological world around us changes with the seasons has long fascinated not only natural historians but also artists and poets. The traditional primary school 'nature table' has still much to commend it as have wall posters about nature and the seasons. The bluebell examples on page 132 illustrate how the seasonal component can be brought into more systematic investigations. It is possible to make observations in school grounds with the seasons although time to do this is usually limited within the constraints of the school timetable except through project work. Videos and 35 mm slides of familiar habitats at different times of the year can be very useful.

Succession

Succession is an ecological process occurring before your very eyes and, since it is more concrete than concepts like nutrient recycling, energy flow and ecosystems, it offers a key progressional link between reality and abstraction. Succession is a concept not often emphasised in the secondary curriculum but it is worth incorporating into a teaching scheme because it helps to ensure that a lot of the rest of ecology makes sense. A good way to study succession is to clear a plot in the school grounds so that there is a patch of bare soil; records about this can be kept over months and years and a database including quadrat data and photographs built up by successive classes. If sufficient space is available a new plot may be cleared each year and successional progress compared with older plots. The pace of change will be rapid to start with but will probably slow down as the ecosystem tends towards stability.

The progression from bare soil to forest will take more than the lifetime of a pupil but they can observe parts of the process within a year. They can extend their experience by looking at last year's quadrat data (long-term monitoring is an important ecological process) and they can relate what they see happening to what you tell them about the theory. It is also worth saying that rain forest destruction does not always lead to desertification. In many places succession leads to regeneration of woodland both in the UK and in the tropics. This humble plot can be the focus for a lot of good thinking. Ecosystems can be destroyed by humans, yet they can also recover by natural ecological processes. Many human activities threaten ecosystems and may upset balances but we can predict the outcomes if we understand how ecosystems work.

9.6 Feeding relationships

◆ *A teaching sequence*

Food chains and food webs

A good starting point is for pupils to describe feeding interactions in habitats from situations with which they are already familiar. In the school grounds – a nibbled leaf, worm cast, even an empty crisp packet all provide evidence of something feeding on something else. Animal behaviour also provides clues to feeding relationships, e.g. pecking for seeds, soaring/circling birds of prey and web making to catch insects. Examination of mouthparts of specimens caught in pitfall traps also offers evidence of feeding behaviours, e.g. chewing, sucking, piercing, and appendages for digging, grabbing, hooking and collecting. From this type of information, food chains and ultimately a food web can be constructed for the school grounds but it will only be a very small part of the actual complexity.

Getting pupils to construct food chains that explain the origin of a meal they have eaten can be a useful activity for them to use secondary sources to link themselves with the global ecosystem. What, for example, do tuna fish eat and what are the conservation issues of commercial tuna fishing? What kind of food is fed to the animals that many people eat as food and what are the ethical issues that this knowledge raises? This links to nutrition (Chapter 2).

Ecological pyramids and energy flow

One of the reasons why food chains are quantified and represented as pyramids (numbers, biomass and energy) is to demonstrate that the amount of energy transferred at each successive stage in the food chain decreases with increasing trophic level. Hints on teaching energy flow:

- energy in biology is the same as energy in physics and chemistry
- the Sun is the ultimate source of energy for most food chains
- energy is not recycled in an ecosystem – a continuous input is required to sustain it
- some energy is 'lost' at each trophic level as heat to the environment
- food chains rarely have more than five links.

Constructing pyramids of numbers

It is possible for pupils to count producers, herbivores and carnivores in a sample from pitfall traps, from leaf litter or from a pond and thus construct a pyramid of numbers. This usually only demonstrates the principle of pyramid of numbers very crudely. In pitfall traps the carnivores may eat the herbivores before they can be counted! In leaf litter many of the herbivores, such as springtails, are very small and easily overlooked. In pond water the countless millions of microscopic algae on which most of the food chains rely for energy are not normally noticed at all. It is, however, well worth carrying out such an exercise because it makes the theoretical treatment, which must inevitably follow, much easier to understand by making some difficult concepts more concrete. In a sample from a lake there may be hundreds or thousands of water fleas. The pyramid of biomass diagram in the textbook asks pupils to believe that the total biomass of water fleas in the lake far exceeds that of all the other animals put together. It also expects them to believe that the total biomass of algae far exceeds that of the water fleas.

Good hygiene is essential when handling leaf litter and pond water.

Grazing: algal populations fluctuate before your very eyes

When setting up a Brine Shrimp tank (see page 216) or bottle planet one starts from having a large volume of water with few brine shrimps. In the absence of shrimps to eat the algae, the algal population rises and the water becomes green. The abundant food supply leads to a population explosion of brine shrimps. These eat the algae until the water stops being green but then the brine shrimp population falls. The fluctuations may continue for months but a tendency towards an increasingly stable equilibrium can be observed without even having to be measured quantitatively.

◆ *Enhancement ideas*

◆ Simulating predation: the natural predators of brine shrimps include flamingos. The *Brine Shrimp Ecology* book includes an exercise where pupils can simulate flamingo predation using tea-strainers as model flamingo filter-feeding beaks. It is possible to show practically that there is a critical level of predation at which brine shrimps reproduce at the rate they are eaten and so an equilibrium can be demonstrated. This also illustrates how a brine shrimp ecosystem can be manipulated to produce brine shrimps in a sustainable fashion, serving as a model of ecosystem management. Apart from the use of brine shrimp model ecosystems, opportunities to treat predator–prey interactions as a practical subject in secondary education are limited. Computer modelling, using, for example, the *Warwick Spreadsheet System*, offers interesting possibilities.

9.7 Decomposition and recycling

The reasons why pupils often find this aspect of ecology difficult include:

- microbes are too small to see
- lack of understanding that plants need carbon dioxide and mineral salts from the soil and that continued plant growth depends on recycling of these substances.

It is thus important that pupils have already been introduced to plant nutrition (Chapter 2) and to microbiology (Chapter 10). Substances such as carbon dioxide and mineral salts needed by plants rarely run out because they are continually recycled owing to microbial action with the help of detritivores such as earthworms and woodlice. Animals depend on plants to recycle oxygen and to produce food by photosynthesis.

◆ *A teaching sequence*

Decomposer investigations

Cellulase activity due to soil microbes can be demonstrated and measured simply by placing samples of moist soil in Petri dishes in incubators at 25–30 °C and recording how many days it takes small pieces of thin unglazed paper to disappear. (Most will go in a week!) Burying dead leaves in plastic mesh bags may be useful in specific projects but this procedure usually takes too long for class practical exercises.

Detritivores are animals, such as earthworms and woodlice, that play a part in decomposition. When dead plant material passes through a detritivore it is partly digested and absorbed but what remains comes out in the droppings. Digestion of the remains is then completed by soil microbes. Pupils find this interesting and most investigations can be completed in 3 days.

The investigations can be set up to examine food preferences in woodlice and earthworms. Essentially you collect leaf litter and identify the species (works well with oak, sycamore, ash, holly, beech). Cut 2 cm squares of each type of litter and place in an alternating sequence in a Petri dish (line with moist filter paper); mark the position of the fragments (they sometimes get moved around by the woodlice but for the most part remain in their original location); place two woodlice in the Petri dish; put in a cool dark cupboard and leave for 2–3 days. Remove the woodlice and return them to their natural home. Stick the fragments of leaf litter on to graph paper. By counting squares on the graph paper you can work out how much of each type of litter has been eaten and so work out woodlice food preferences. In most cases the woodlice will select the most palatable fragments first, usually well-rotted leaves, those with a high nitrogen, moisture and sugar content and will only consider drier, tougher leaves last. If you leave the experiment too long the woodlice will eat everything, so timing is quite important.

Most nutrient cycles contain some very difficult concepts; be careful not to teach more theory than necessary. You do not have to teach every nutrient cycle for pupils to get the idea of cycling. The overriding challenge is to find exciting and motivating ways to teach nutrient cycling. A visual representation of each component is a good start, e.g. a piece of coal, an inflated balloon, a plant, an animal and some leaf litter could all be suitably ordered to make a representation of the carbon cycle.

◆ *Further activities*

- ◆ Variations on the theme of decomposition are tremendous; as well as different types of litter, different stages of decomposition can be used, other vegetable material (if woodlice are only fed on carrots they produce orange faeces – always goes down well!), paper fragments, cardboard, etc. The same theme can be used with earthworms – two earthworms in a large flower pot full of soil. Place the leaf fragments on the surface and see which ones are taken first and how many over a period of time.

9.8 Perturbations

The notion that natural ecosystems tend towards stability as a result of the establishment of equilibria can be very useful at secondary school level even if it can sometimes be an over-simplification. A perturbation is something that upsets this relatively stable system. Perturbations can happen naturally but human activity can often be the cause of them. This section examines the way in which the science of ecology helps not only to explain ecological events but also to predict the consequences of environmental change.

◆ *A teaching sequence*

Food chains and food webs – bioaccumulation of persistent substances

Knowledge of food webs helps to explain why persistent substances introduced to the environment at low levels turn up at a high, and often lethal level in top consumers. Examples of persistent substances include: persistent pesticides such as DDT; radionuclides, e.g. caesium 137; and heavy metals, e.g. mercury.

Ecological knock-on effects in a food web

A food web diagram can be used to predict:

- the effect of the removal of a single species from a web, e.g. through hunting
- the effect of the introduction of an alien species, e.g. mink
- the impact of management regimes, e.g. grazing, burning.

Nutrient cycles

Global warming – a perturbation of the carbon cycle?

Global warming is a context that makes the carbon cycle interesting because it illustrates how a stable system can be influenced by humans with potentially enormous consequences – it's real life stuff! There are facts, hypotheses, predictions and falsities involved; thus it is an interesting scientific case study to educate pupils in critical analysis and consideration of a variety of scientific approaches. It also offers a scientific basis for speculation on other environmental issues, such as climate change where global warming is used as a predictive model. One of the points of teaching global warming has to be to encourage your pupils to appreciate that what they hear about or read in the papers or are taught is not all certainty: they need to evaluate information to distinguish between facts and speculation.

Some hints for teaching global warming are listed below.

- The greenhouse effect is a natural phenomenon essential for life on Earth, without which the Earth would be too cold to support life.
- The carbon cycle shows how burning fossil fuels could lead to an increase in atmospheric carbon dioxide concentration. This has led to predictions of an enhanced greenhouse effect likely to cause global warming. There is evidence of an increase in atmospheric carbon dioxide and of increases in global temperatures but the link between them is not proven.
- When tropical rain forests are chopped down it is true that in the short term there is a sudden pulse of carbon dioxide released into the air from the processes of decay and burning. However, in the longer term less photosynthesis means there is less organic matter to be broken down into carbon dioxide. Thus in the long term a rain forest is a balanced ecosystem and it is not a net absorber of carbon dioxide. Basically, what goes up must come down.
- Ozone depletion and global warming are both global issues but the two are quite separate and must be treated as such.
- Whilst there is evidence that there is melting of ice at the poles there is, as yet, little evidence of sea-level changes linked to this.

Eutrophication – a perturbation of the nitrogen cycle?
In a normal freshwater habitat the reason why accumulation of algae does not take place is because algal growth is limited by inorganic nutrient supply (either nitrate or phosphate) and by grazing – small animals in the pond feed on the algae as fast as the algae reproduce. In the nitrogen cycle, biomass, such as that of algae, can be at equilibrium – the rate of production of new biomass is limited by the rate of decay of dead organisms (releasing available nitrogen). When a large amount of nitrate enters a lake or river from fertiliser effluent or effluent from sewage treatment plants, the algal population, whose growth has until now been limited by nitrate supply, increases very rapidly, much faster than animals can eat the algae. This leads to an accumulation of biomass that, after death, is decayed by bacteria. The normally low numbers of bacteria in an unpolluted stream now increase rapidly and use up much more oxygen than usual, causing the death of fish and other animals, such as stonefly nymphs, which need a lot of oxygen.

A final point to note about equilibria in ecosystems is that it is a balance of many different factors all pushing in different directions. If we reduce the pressure from one direction the *whole* equilibrium shifts.

9.9 Environmental education

The relationship between teaching about environmental issues and ecology as science can sometimes appear confused. It is first important to distinguish the two before going on to explore the important overlap between them.

Ecology is:

- a branch of science with its roots in biology
- objective, experimental and predictive
- interdisciplinary: with links to biology, chemistry, physics, earth sciences and geography
- includes content usually specified in science curricula.

Environmental education is:

- helping people to understand, to appreciate, to care for and to enjoy the environment
- about aesthetics, issues and values as well as knowledge
- often cross-curricular: it brings together elements of science, geography, art, aesthetics, language, mathematics, ethics, religious knowledge, sport and outdoor pursuits
- often not part of the statutory curricula.

◆ *A teaching sequence*

Teaching environmental issues: coping with values and bias

This is an important life skill for a scientifically literate person. The 'unbiased person' probably does not exist however hard he/she may try to be impartial. In considering an ecological issue it is therefore important to:

- realise that nobody is completely free of bias – recognise your own bias
- identify the aspects of the material that you consider the most credible
- identify the aspects that might be true
- ask yourself which factual information looks most suspect
- consider what important information has been left out
- debate what was the perspective of the person who wrote the article.

A science teacher's job is first and foremost to teach the science curriculum in a creative and inspiring way. A good teacher, however, always delivers a teaching programme beyond the bare bones of the examination syllabus. Often as good teachers we are hardly aware of our 'hidden agenda' for the extra we are offering is part of ourselves.

Conservation and sustainability

Section 9.8 showed how we can apply knowledge of ecology to understand what happens when ecosystems appear to go wrong, all too often as a result of human interference. Ecological knowledge can also be used to work with nature. A well-managed ecosystem can provide the human race with resources year after year in what is called a sustainable fashion. Here are some examples:

- commercial sea-fishing populations use knowledge of population dynamics to calculate the maximum sustainable catch from an area of sea
- use of biological control as an alternative to chemical pesticides, e.g. parasitic wasps to control whitefly in greenhouses
- growing wood as a renewable resource of biomass to use as an alternative to fossil fuel. In Sweden, using a modern version of coppicing, fast-growing willows are used to provide fuel for generating electricity as an alternative to nuclear energy
- managing forests for sustainable timber supply
- managing reserves for wildlife and landscape quality for tourism
- conserving habitats and biodiversity for scientific and medical reasons
- organic farming for sustainable agriculture.

A very useful account of how human practices can push an ecosystem beyond the point of no return is *Cod* by Mark Kurlanksy (1998). *The Future Eaters* by Tim Flannery (1996) describes how some people have social customs that lead to sustainable practices, but often they do not.

One final point for emphasis about teaching ecology: this subject is about living things in their natural environment. Sensitive use of living organisms in the field and laboratory in your teaching can increase the sense of awe and wonder at biodiversity and also cultivate respect for living organisms. Wherever possible, within constraints of health and safety and animal welfare issues, do try it!

Other resources

◆ *Background reading*

Books that will really help you with teaching ecology are:

Chapman, J.L. & Reiss, M.J. (1999). *Ecology: Principles and Applications* (2nd edition). Cambridge, Cambridge University Press.

Gilbertson, D.D., Kent, M. & Pyatt, F.B. (1985). *Practical Ecology for Biology and Geography*. London, Hutchinson.

Slingsby, D.R. & Cook, C. (1986). *Practical Ecology*. London, Macmillan.

References

Bebbington, A., Bebbington, B. & Tilling, S. (1994). *The Mini-Beast Name Trail: A Key to Invertebrates in Soil and Leaf Litter*. Preston Montford, Field Studies Council.

Dockery, M. & Tomkins, S. (1999). *Brine Shrimp Ecology*. London, British Ecological Society. Available from the Biology Department, Homerton College, Cambridge CB2 2PH.

Fieldworks (1997) produced by Hallsannery Field Centre, Bideford, Devon EX39 5HE. (Runs on PC.)

Flannery, T. (1996). *The Future Eaters: An Ecological History of the Australasian Lands and People*. London, Secker and Warburg.

HMSO (1981). *Wildlife and Countryside Act*. Norwich, HMSO.

Institute of Biology (1999). *Safety in Biology Fieldwork*. London, Institute of Biology.

Kurlansky, M. (1998). *Cod: A Biography of the Fish that Changed the World*. London, Jonathan Cape.

The Wide World of Animals CD ROM. AVP, School Hill Centre, Chepstow, Gwent NP6 5PH.

Warwick Spreadsheet System produced by Aberdare Publishing, 6 Nuthurst Grove, Bentley Heath, Solihull B93 8PD. (PC and Mac versions.)

10 *Microbiology and biotechnology*

Roger Lock and Sheila Turner

10.1 What are microbes?
Using the media
Classification
Microbe gardens

↓

10.2 What do microbes look like?
Drawings on acetate squares
Size concepts

↓

10.3 Where do you find microbes?
Taping and labelling plates
Incubating plates
Macroscopic differences between fungi and bacteria

↓

10.4 How do you handle microbes safely?
Pouring plates
Inoculating plates

↓

10.5 What do microbes need to grow?
Broth experiment
Food preservation

↓

10.6 How are microbes involved in a healthy life?
Hygiene and food preparation
Investigation of the effect of disinfectants and bacteria
Clean water
Digestion
Microbes and disease
Antibiotics

↓

10.7 How are microbes involved in biotechnology industries?
Microbes and food
Outside visits
Industrial processes
Microbes and genetic engineering

◆ *Choosing a route*

Finding out what microbes are, what they look like and where they are found is basic work accessible to 11 to 12 year olds of all abilities. Understanding these basic ideas is also a prerequisite to the content of other boxes in the flow chart and should determine pupils' first experiences of microbes and biotechnology in a spiral curriculum.

Safe handling of microbes by teachers and pupils is essential for all practical work that involves using cultures of fungi or bacteria. Work demanding a significant level of manual dexterity is perhaps best tackled with older pupils, say 13 to 16 year olds. Work outlined in boxes 10.1 to 10.3 provides a framework for further study, such as conditions that promote and inhibit microbe growth.

The principles involved in personal and domestic hygiene arise from an understanding of the control of microbe growth, e.g. keeping food in the fridge slows down their growth but does not kill them. In addition, when exploring applied aspects of microbiology it is most effective to start with applications closest to pupils' experiences, as they will more readily relate to them, before going on to study the biotechnology industries and genetic engineering.

The importance of microbes pervades work at all levels and has a place in many of the other boxes. For this reason it is best addressed at a range of levels, in different sub topics, as and when appropriate, but it also provides a convenient heading under which work from all other boxes can be drawn together and summarised. In a spiral curriculum, topics 10.4 to 10.8 could represent one or two revolutions of the spiral. In the latter case, topics 10.4 and 10.5 would be studied on a first visit.

There are many reasons why microbiology should be given a prominent place in the biology curriculum (Lock, 1996). Microbes:

- are socially, economically and medically important
- are central to research and new developments in biotechnology
- play a key role in personal, public and domestic hygiene
- are important in food production
- cause diseases and help control them
- are essential in cyclical changes (e.g. carbon cycle, nitrogen cycle)
- help herbivores to digest their food.

A final point in favour of microbes is that they can be used to demonstrate a wide range of biological principles and processes and to illustrate the properties of living organisms.

10.1 What are microbes?

◆ *Previous knowledge and experience*

Microbes and biotechnology are in the media a great deal but the exposure they get is rarely positive when headlines refer to fungi, bacteria and viruses (see Figure 10.1). Such publicity has possibly contributed to some of the concern pupils and teachers have about work with microbes (Lock, 1996); all the more reason for including such work in our teaching in order to redress the balance. Microbes that pupils might have seen or heard about could include yeast, mould, mildew and rust on plant leaves or diseases linked to microbes, such as meningitis, AIDS or flu. With such a legacy of ideas brought to lessons, the importance of a positive approach is readily apparent. Pupils may need reassurance that the majority of microbes are not harmful.

Figure 10.1
Microbes in the media.

The majority of pupils will have had experience of microbes in their primary schools, e.g. when studying food decay and preservation.

◆ *A teaching sequence*

Using the media

This lesson could be started with a brainstorm to find out what pupils already know, or it could be preceded by homework that gets them to look at newspapers and television and to report back on what they can find out. A further approach could be to collect pages from papers with cuttings, such as those illustrated in Figure 10.1, and to set an information-finding activity.

The outcomes from such activities could include noting the balance between positive and negative associations, the use of common terms such as bug, germ and their scientific equivalents and the knowledge that microbes (a convenient shorthand term for 'micro-organisms') are a diverse group, including:

- algae (e.g. *Chlorella*)
- fungi (e.g. yeast, mould)
- bacteria (e.g. *Escherichia coli*)
- protozoa (e.g. the malaria parasite)
- viruses (e.g. influenza virus).

The production of such a list enables elements that pupils already know or have heard about to be drawn together, e.g. where do BSE (caused by a prion) and AIDS (caused by the retrovirus HIV) fit? The development of a spidergram (or concept map) could also achieve the same purpose of helping to organise the information they already know into the scientific diversity of the group.

Classification
If the class have previously studied the classification of living things using the five-kingdom system then it would be appropriate to remind the group that microbes are represented in more than one kingdom and that some kingdoms are exclusively microbes! Now might be the time to raise the issue of viruses/retroviruses and whether they are living things, but some teachers prefer to avoid such complications with younger pupils.

Microbe gardens
Microbe gardens can be a popular feature of work at this stage and can provide a convenient link to what microbes look like. Algae on bark, a block of yeast or yeast tablets, Quorn, mouldy bread and rotting fruit can be used in a small exhibition or circus of activities. The bread and rotting fruit should be in a closed glass or plastic container, a sealed plastic bag would do. The container should be small enough to permit autoclaving without opening before disposal. The reason for enclosure is that it is not known which microbes are growing, although it is unlikely they would be pathogenic (disease causing). In addition, release of spores could trigger an allergic reaction in sensitive individuals if they inhaled enough of them. The bread and fruit should be autoclaved before disposal (see *Equipment notes* on page 265).

10.2 What do microbes look like?

◆ *A teaching sequence*

Microbe gardens provide an initial perspective on variety, but what are microbes like down a microscope? Pupils need the skills of making wet mount slides and using microscopes that magnify up to ×200. It is good to look at algae (use the green stuff that grows on tree bark, usually a species of *Pleurococcus,* yeast and mould (both fungi) and a bacterium (*Bacillus subtilis* is fine). For the mould use a pure culture of *Mucor* and *Rhizopus* and expose the culture to methanal vapour (a filter paper soaked with 40% methanal (formalin) solution in the Petri dish) for 24 hours to kill the culture and the spores. To protect against allergic reaction to spores, which are killed but can still be released, samples of mould should be removed in the fume cupboard. For convenience, slides of mould could be made up beforehand. With the bacterium a single drop from a broth culture diluted in water on a slide is adequate. Used slides should be collected in a beaker of freshly prepared 1% sodium chlorate(I) (hypochlorite) solution and left for at least 15 minutes.

Kill the bacteria before viewing by the addition of methanal solution.

Methanal solution is toxic and corrosive. Use gloves, eye protection and a fume cupboard.

Drawings on acetate squares

A good approach is to challenge pupils to make up slides and then to draw what they can see. They can do their drawings on small squares of acetate (say 10×10 cm^2) using overhead projector (OHP) pens as this provides a convenient way of subsequently sharing everybody's observations using an OHP. Helping pupils to locate areas of the slide to observe ensures that they make drawings of what you are looking for. When sharing observations start with the algae or the yeast because these are biggest and most pupils will have made relevant observations. With the algae pupils may draw isolated cells, groups of two, four and big groups (there will also be other sized groups). A good question to ask pupils is, 'How can we explain one, two, four?' This links to asexual reproduction where organisms successively divide into two. Pupils should now be able to explain the threes! Sharing the acetate drawings ensures that all stages are found. If pupils have been taught about cell structure in plants, then in algae many common features can be quite clearly seen, e.g. cell walls and chloroplasts.

With yeast they see mostly individual cells, but, depending on the species you use, they could see budding or binary fission. The mould will show spores (little round things are common to all the microbes observed so far) and threads from the cottonwool-like bits (mycelium/hyphae).
'Hands up those who've drawn a bacterium. What nobody? Well, I definitely put some in there, so how do we explain this?' This is a great way into the idea that microbes are different sizes and that these bacteria are so small that you can't even see them down your microscope. A demonstration with a more powerful microscope and perhaps with a TV-linked camera will show small rod-shaped objects.

Size concepts

Pupils find it difficult to understand the relative size of microbes and a variety of approaches may help. Using the microscopes to look at familiar objects, such as lines on graph paper or a hair, gives a clue. A chart that shows the 'p' on a one pence piece magnified ×40 and ×200 (depending on the lenses of the microscopes that you have) and the relative size of a yeast cell is good too. An activity in *Nuffield Science 11–13* gives, on Worksheet 33, the challenge of making a microbe poster (Lyth, 1987) that shows protozoa, fungi, bacteria and viruses and their relative sizes. Able pupils could tackle this for homework or it is a good detention activity!

An idea used by a school in Oxfordshire is shown in Table 10.1. Each statement in the table was accompanied by a picture showing the object in question and it formed a frieze that went half way round the lab. Another approach is to produce a model that pupils are familiar with and to show microbes on a relative scale. For example, a model pin with a head 20 cm across with onion seeds stuck on to it.

Table 10.1 *An approach to the concept of size.*

The following was taken from a laboratory wall in Gosford Hill School, Kidlington.

Anna is holding a metre rule.	Anna's hand is 10 centimetres across (0.1 metres).
Her garden is 10 metres wide.	One of her fingers is 1 centimetre across (0.01 metres).
She lives 100 metres from the bottom of her street.	Each of her eyelids is 1 millimetre thick (0.001 metres).
It's 1 kilometre to the Tesco Superstore.	Hairs on her head are 0.0001 metres thick.
It's 10 kilometres across her town.	Her red blood cells are 0.000 001 metres thick.
Her town is 100 kilometres from London.	Some bacteria are 0.000 000 1 metres long.
Her country is 1000 kilometres long.	Small bacteria are 0.000 000 01 metres thick.
The axis of the Earth is more than 10 000 kilometres long.	Some viruses are 0.000 000 001 metres across.
100 000 kilometres is a quarter of the distance to the Moon.	

10.3 Where do you find microbes?

The simple answer is everywhere, with some microbes resistant to high temperatures, long periods of drought and a wide range of pH; some bacteria even live in jet fuel, geysers and rocks. Experimental work at a simple level can involve exposing agar in Petri dishes (plates) to the air in labs and outside for varying lengths of time (30 seconds to 1 hour), or inoculating with water from different sources (tap, river, pond, bottled), soil solutions, finger dabs from washed and unwashed hands, hair, leaves, etc. The general rule here is not to set out to culture potential pathogens by, for example, culturing from raw meat or using nasal swabs. In addition, the upper limit for incubation should be 30 °C in order to avoid selecting for organisms that are adapted to human body temperature (DfEE, 1996). However, yoghurt cultures can be incubated above 30 °C.

◆ *A teaching sequence*

Taping and labelling plates

Any plates used in investigations such as those mentioned in the previous paragraph should be taped and labelled as shown in Figure 10.2. Ideally, label the base rather than the lid (in case the lid gets separated from the base) and do this just before the inoculation is set up, rather than afterwards. Some textbooks show tape going right across the base or lid of the Petri dish. This strategy should not be followed as discoloured tape could prevent quality observation at a later point. Worse still, some suggest taping around the rim of the plate. Petri dishes are designed with, usually, three small lips inside the rim of the lid which raises the lid above the base. This permits diffusion of gases into/out of the dish (but spores remain inside). Taping around the rim would lead to the oxygen inside the plate being depleted so encouraging organisms that grow without oxygen (anaerobically), many of which are pathogens. If your risk assessment suggests that some pupils will attempt to open plates sealed with four strips, then taping around the circumference *after incubation* may give a clearer message.

Figure 10.2
Taping and labelling Petri dishes.

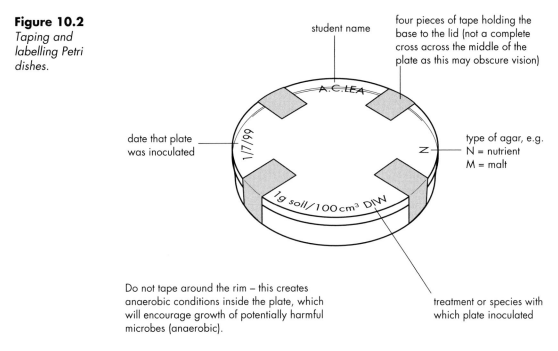

- student name
- four pieces of tape holding the base to the lid (not a complete cross across the middle of the plate as this may obscure vision)
- date that plate was inoculated
- type of agar, e.g. N = nutrient M = malt
- Do not tape around the rim – this creates anaerobic conditions inside the plate, which will encourage growth of potentially harmful microbes (anaerobic).
- treatment or species with which plate inoculated

A.C.LEA

1/7/99

1g soil/100 cm³ DIW

N

Incubating plates

Plates should be incubated upside down (to prevent water dripping on the cultures) and at *no more than* 30 °C. Incubation at 37 °C is not acceptable as you would be selecting for organisms that thrive at human body temperature.

Macroscopic differences between fungi and bacteria

By using malt and nutrient agars it is possible to investigate what type of microbes grow best on each. To do this investigation pupils need to recognise the differences between fungal and bacterial colonies. The first step is to appreciate that a circular colony has developed from a single cell landing on the agar. This introduces the issue of reproduction too. A single bacterium, under ideal conditions, will divide into two once every 20 minutes. Pupils could be encouraged to estimate how many cells there are in a colony that is 24 hours old. Calculators and/or a computer spreadsheet can be used to demonstrate the rate of growth.

The main differences between bacterial and fungal colonies are shown in Table 10.2, although not all features are shown by all colonies. Examination of colonies, using hand lenses, is possible through the lids of Petri dishes. Pupils should easily see the mycelium and spore containers (sporangia) in fungal colonies.

Table 10.2 *Macroscopic differences between fungi and bacteria.*

	Fungi	Bacteria
Colony size	Large	Smaller
(seen from above)
may fill the whole dish
1 mm to 10 mm diameter
Colony profile	Tall	Flat
(seen from the side)		
Appearance of colony surface	Surface is dull	Surface is shiny
Texture	Like cottonwool	Like a drop of liquid
Colour	Grey, white (spores are sometimes coloured, e.g. black, blue–green)	Yellow, pink, white, a range of colours
Growth medium	Grow best on malt agar (more alkaline)	Grow best on nutrient agar (more acidic)

Now pupils can estimate how many microbes sediment from the air on to a Petri dish in 1 minute, how many live in 1 gram of soil or on the pad of one washed finger? This whole area lends itself to a wide range of investigations and questions that pupils can explore. Some ideas are suggested in the *Further activities* section on page 263.

10.4 How do you handle microbes safely?

Figure 10.3
Pupil rules for working safely with microbes. (After an original idea by Lindsay Hudson.)

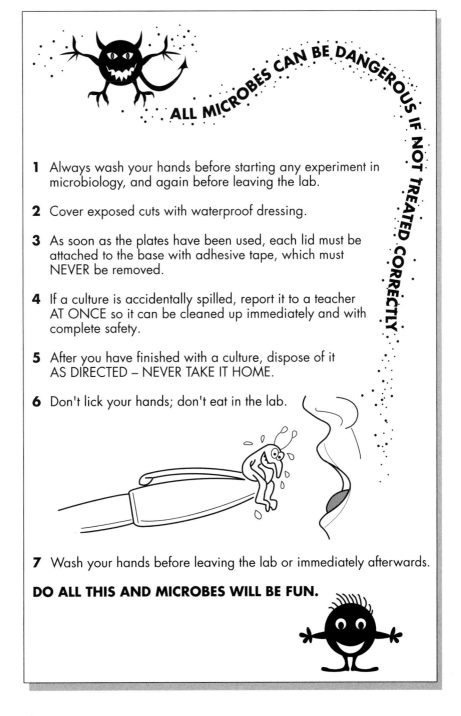

ALL MICROBES CAN BE DANGEROUS IF NOT TREATED CORRECTLY

1 Always wash your hands before starting any experiment in microbiology, and again before leaving the lab.

2 Cover exposed cuts with waterproof dressing.

3 As soon as the plates have been used, each lid must be attached to the base with adhesive tape, which must NEVER be removed.

4 If a culture is accidentally spilled, report it to a teacher AT ONCE so it can be cleaned up immediately and with complete safety.

5 After you have finished with a culture, dispose of it AS DIRECTED – NEVER TAKE IT HOME.

6 Don't lick your hands; don't eat in the lab.

7 Wash your hands before leaving the lab or immediately afterwards.

DO ALL THIS AND MICROBES WILL BE FUN.

It is important for pupils to see and develop good practice and respect for handling microbes in the lab. Most of these procedures have links to food hygiene in the home. See, for example, items 1 and 2 of the pupil rules for working safely with microbes illustrated in Figure 10.3.

◆ *A teaching sequence*

Pouring plates

Pupils should understand how agar plates are produced. Start by showing pupils Petri dishes as supplied by the manufacturer in sealed packs that have been irradiated with gamma radiation, say, a cobalt 60 source, which kills all microbes and leaves the dishes sterile. You can demonstrate the pouring of plates and/or pupils can pour their own. The plates poured by pupils should be taped until it is clear that the agar is still sterile (i.e. no colonies develop within 48 hours). The sterile plates can then be used for inoculation.

Labs should be draft-free to minimise lateral mass flows of air and all work should be carried out close to a Bunsen burner on a non-luminous flame where air, and any suspended spores, will be moving upwards.

Inoculating plates

Pupils can practise inoculation of plates using yeast suspensions, wire loops and spreaders but plates should be taped following inoculation and remain unopened unless the cultures have been killed. A more detailed consideration of safety can be found in DfEE (1996) *Safety in Science Education*, pp. 133–135. Elements of safety specific to teachers are included in the *Equipment notes* section on page 265.

An understanding of how agar is made in a sterile manner can be gained through experimentation using broth culture; this links appropriately with the next element of the teaching sequence.

10.5 What do microbes need to grow?

◆ *A teaching sequence*

Broth experiment

Work in this section can provide opportunities to introduce important work carried out on microbes by Pasteur. The diagram in Figure 10.4 shows an experiment with nutrient broth in the test-tubes; the cloudiness of the broth is an indicator of the extent of bacterial growth. Pupils can set up these experiments. Tubes 1 and 3 (and others if pupils' sterile technique is poor) would need 1 cm³ of 40% methanal solution added before handing the tubes back to pupils to examine.

Figure 10.4
*Broth experiment.
(Based on* Revised
Nuffield Biology,
1974.)

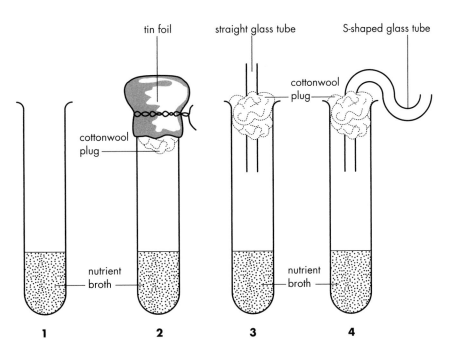

Tube 2 should illustrate that microbes are destroyed by boiling and that 'spontaneous generation' of living organisms does not occur. Tube 4 replicates the experiments that Pasteur did with swan-necked flasks (see *Further activities* on page 263) and has clear links to the shape of air locks used in home brewing activities. Tubes 1 and 3 show that bacterial contamination is by direct sedimentation of spores from the atmosphere, which relates back nicely to the pouring and inoculating plates activities as well as having clear links to food hygiene.

Food preservation

There is a range of experiments where factors influencing growth or growth rates of microbes can be explored. Growth can be measured by turbidity of liquid media or colorimetry, measurement of mycelium diameter (for fungi) or directly by counting cells on a micrometer slide, although this latter method is mainly appropriate for 16 to 19 year olds. With an organism like yeast, indirect measures of activity can be made by measuring the evolution of carbon dioxide. Temperature is an obvious factor to investigate. Pupils could investigate whether refrigeration slows growth but does not stop it; whether freezing and boiling both stop growth and whether the microbes start to grow again when removed from the freezer and whether boiling kills them. Table 10.3 shows a range of factors that influence microbe growth and illustrates how this can be used to our advantage in food production and preservation. Such work makes a clear link with the involvement of microbes in a healthy life.

Table 10.3 *Microbial growth and food preservation.*

Method	How bacterial growth is affected	Example
Ultra-heat treatment (UHT) (135 °C for 2 seconds)	Microbes and resistant spores killed	UHT Longlife milk
Sterilised by boiling (100–115 °C for 15 minutes)	Microbes killed	Sterilised milk
Pasteurised (70 °C for about 15 seconds)	Many microbes killed	Pasteurised milk
Canning (boiling and sealing to exclude oxygen)	Microbes killed and no oxygen available	Tinned beans
Sterilise by irradiation (e.g. from cobalt 60 source)	Microbes killed by gamma radiation	Salmon
Freeze drying	No water for microbial growth	Instant potato
Preserving by adding sugar or salt	Microbes plasmolysed, water moves out of cells	Jams (sugar), fish (salt)
Pickling	pH too acidic for microbes to grow	Pickled onions
Fridge (4 °C)	Microbe growth slowed down	Yoghurt
Freezer (−5 to −10 °C)	Microbe growth stopped	Frozen vegetables

10.6 How are microbes involved in a healthy life?

Headlines and news stories about 'bugs' that affect humans, such as those listed in Figure 10.1, intrigue and interest pupils and therefore provide an excellent starting point for work on microbes and health, as well as a stimulus for individual investigative projects by older pupils. These headlines also provide a context for developing an understanding about fundamental microbiological principles and the ways in which microbes affect the lives of all animals and plants. Earlier work on the topic will have highlighted the need for hygienic laboratory practice and pupils will be aware of the effect of factors such as temperature on the growth of microbes.

◆ *A teaching sequence*

Hygiene and food preparation

Brother and sister fight E. coli

Killer food bugs hits tots

Despite greater public awareness about the need for food hygiene and legislation about the storage and preparation of food in commercial organisations and industry, outbreaks of food poisoning are still common – and most are preventable. Outbreaks of food poisoning are usually caused by people handling food with dirty hands, insufficient cooking or storing food incorrectly, e.g. at the wrong temperature or leaving food uncovered. Pupils could be asked to find out the reasons for the advice given in Table 10.4 about the safe handling of food.

Table 10.4 *Advice on healthy eating. (Health Education Authority, 1993.)*

Remember: whatever food you choose to eat . . .

- Take chilled or frozen food home as quickly as possible, if possible in an insulated bag.
- Keep your fridge at the correct temperature (below 5 °C) – buy a fridge thermometer.
- Cook food thoroughly.
- Do not eat raw eggs or products containing them.
- Observe microwave standing times.
- Store raw and cooked foods separately.
- Check dates on goods – use food within the recommended period.
- Where possible do not re-heat food. If you do have to re-heat food then do not do so more than once.
- Keep pets out of the kitchen. Wash your hands after handling them.
- Keep your kitchen clean and dry. Wash and dry utensils between preparation stages.
- Always wash your hands with hot, soapy water before and after preparing food.

Pupils will by now be aware of the number of microbes that grow on agar plates after they have been inoculated by finger dabs from washed/unwashed hands. They can observe what happens to foods such as bread, fruit and cheese that are left at room temperature over a period of days; care needs to be taken to ensure that the foods are kept in appropriate containers and disposed of safely (see also *Microbe gardens* on page 247). Pupils can also investigate a range of different packaged foods to work out how long different foods can be stored and what 'sell by' dates mean. These investigations can be linked to work on food preservation.

Investigation of the effect of disinfectants on bacteria

Advertisers make much of the ability of disinfectants to 'kill all known germs'. Pupils can investigate the truth of such claims by using household disinfectants at different dilutions. One method involves adding 10 cm^3 of the disinfectant solutions to 10 cm^3 of sterile nutrient broth in test-tubes. The tubes are plugged with cottonwool and left at room temperature for 3 to 5 days. Pupils can observe changes in colour and turbidity of the solutions, which indicate the growth of bacteria.

Care needs to be taken to ensure that pupils do not remove the cottonwool plugs and that tubes and their contents are sterilised before the broth is disposed of.

Clean water

What do pupils think is meant by 'clean' water? Water from a spring, a well or a tap, that looks 'clean', may contain disease-causing microbes. Untreated water supplies are still a major source of ill-health, infant mortality and epidemics in many parts of the world. The story of how the spread of cholera was halted in London in the middle of the 19th century as a result of careful 'detective' work can provide a starting point for pupils to investigate other disease-causing microbes. There are also opportunities for drama as well as for data collection and analysis allied to investigative journalism where pupils prepare questions (and answers) for experts. Pupils might use the internet to find out more about pressure groups concerned about water, e.g. Surfers Against Sewage.

The presence of bacteria in water can be shown by inoculating agar plates with samples of water from different sources, as described earlier in this chapter. Water can also be drawn through filters that are then stained with a dye to show the presence of bacteria. Pupils may need reassurance that the large numbers of bacteria demonstrated by this method are not all 'harmful' to humans.

Pupils can find out about the principles of the first stages of water treatment and purification by filtering muddy water samples: this activity can be done as a problem-solving activity. Chemical purification of filtered samples can be demonstrated and the treated samples tested for bacterial content. Information and posters about water treatment are available from water companies; pupils can also create their own posters and provide advice for consumers on the importance of 'clean' water.

Good hygiene is essential when handling muddy water.

Digestion

Microbes play an important role in digestion in many animals. They are particularly important in the digestion of plant material, such as cellulose and wood, which is not readily broken down in the guts of animals. The guts of herbivorous mammals, such as cows and sheep, contain very large numbers of bacteria that produce cellulase, an enzyme that breaks down (digests) cellulose and that mammals cannot produce themselves. The simpler molecules produced after the breakdown of cellulose by cellulase can be metabolised (used) by the bacteria, which subsequently release chemicals into the gut of the mammal that can be absorbed and used.

Microbes also play a key role in the breakdown of waste material produced by animals and plants that is linked to the nitrogen cycle, as described in Chapter 9.

Pupils can observe how microbes break down or 'digest' plant material by leaving fruit, such as apples, in a container for some days. It is important to ensure that the container has a lid to prevent the dispersal of fungal spores and that the pupils do not handle the rotting fruit. The container should be small enough to permit autoclaving without opening before disposal.

Microbes and disease

'Black death ''offers clue to AIDS'' ' (Source: *Guardian* 9.5.98)

Section 10.1 introduced pupils to the range of different microbes, including examples of those that cause diseases in humans, such as the common cold and influenza. Microbes cause disease in plants and other animals – mice and rats can suffer from malaria as well as humans!

Research into the history and epidemiology of diseases, such as bubonic plague, smallpox, influenza and cholera, can be used to provide insights into how widespread diseases are and how they affect populations in different parts of the world. Pupils can be encouraged to report their findings in a variety of ways, including drama or the use of databases and spreadsheets. This work leads naturally into a study of the development of vaccines and, for older pupils, a study of the functioning of the immune system.

Antibiotics

Most pupils will have been prescribed antibiotics at some time in their lives; however, many will be confused about what sorts of infections are treatable by antibiotics. A brainstorm provides a good starting point to identify what antibiotics are and what they can do. Pupils could undertake library research to find out the causes of different types of infection such as viral, bacterial and fungal and how these are treated. Follow-up work can include the story of the development of penicillin and practical demonstrations to illustrate the effect of antibiotics on bacterial growth.

10.7 How are microbes involved in biotechnology industries?

Microbes are involved in the production of many different things including:

- food and alcohol
- antibiotics
- insulin
- fuels (gasohol).

♦ *A teaching sequence*

Microbes and food

The importance of microbes in industrial processes is best introduced by starting with familiar food products, such as yoghurt, that can be made readily in the laboratory. Other activities could include the making of bread, ginger beer (Monger, 1992) and the fermentation of fruit juices to produce alcohol. Sensors linked to a computer can be used to show the rate of microbial activity. For example, a position sensor can show how a bread dough rises – starting off slowly, rapidly rising and then slowing down. Activities of this type can be undertaken by pupils of all ages.

Pupils will need to be reminded not to taste any of the products made in the laboratory.

Outside visits

Visits to places such as dairies or breweries can provide insights into a number of microbiological principles and applications, including the conditions needed for the growth of microbes and the need for hygiene practices to ensure that contamination of, for example, foodstuffs does not occur. The processes involved in industrial biotechnology are summarised in Figure 10.5. The size and complexity of the equipment used in the production of such things as beer is a revelation for most pupils; identifying the problems faced by industrialists in 'scaling up' processes helps to raise issues about sterilisation of equipment as well as the biology of fermentation. Asking pupils to estimate how many yeast cells are present in a fermentation vat reinforces ideas of size and replication encountered earlier. Videos can provide a useful alternative where industrial visits are not possible.

Figure 10.5
The biotechnology process. (Based on Satelle, 1988.)

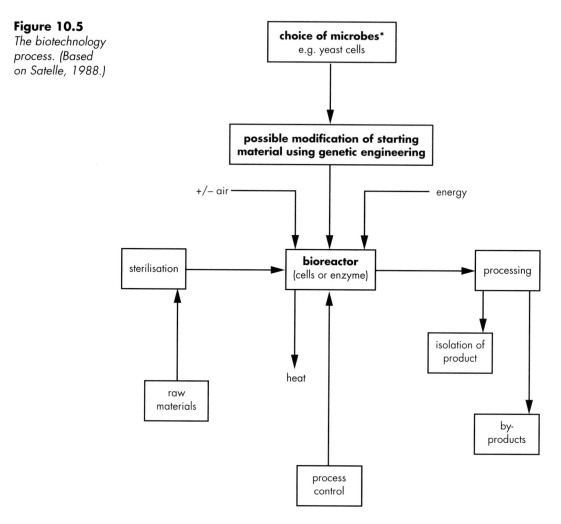

* The same principles apply where animal or plant cells are used instead of microbes.

Industrial processes

Microbes are becoming increasingly important in a range of other industrial processes, including the pharmaceutical industry. Some of these processes can be replicated by older pupils on a small scale in the laboratory, e.g.:

- the breakdown of cellulose waste from plants by bacteria
- the production of plastic from bacteria
- glucoamylase production by yeast.

These activities can form the basis of practical investigations and projects by pupils from 14 to 18 years (NCBE, 1993).

Microbes and genetic engineering

'Top chefs ban GM foods' (Source: *Guardian* 22.4.99)
'Schools fear over "Frankenstein Food"' (Source: *Evening Mail* 16.2.99)

The implications of introducing genetically modified food plants into the human food chain, for example tomatoes and soya, have been the subject of considerable debate and public concern in some countries, including the UK.

The basic principles of genetic engineering are relatively easy to understand if pupils have some understanding of cell structure and DNA. For this reason this topic is better suited to pupils from 14 years upwards. Physical models can be useful in demonstrating how sections of plasmids in bacteria can be modified to incorporate new genetic material. Pupils can extract DNA from onion cells (NCBE, 1993).

Examples of genetic engineering include the production of insulin for use by diabetics from genetically engineered bacteria or yeast (Kjeldsen & Andersen, 1997 and Reiss & Straughan, 1996). Yeast has advantages over other methods of production as it does not produce compounds that are toxic to human beings; it is also cheap and easy to grow in culture on an industrial scale.

◆ *Further activities*

- ◆ Ideas for investigations include the following:

  - How effective are different disinfectants at killing bacteria?
  - How does dilution influence the actions of disinfectants? (You can ask the same question about toothpaste, deodorant, anti-perspirant, antiseptics, Milton, etc.)
  - Is it best to let dinner plates drain, dry them with a tea-towel or use a dishwasher? (The surface of plates can be sampled for spores using sticky tape.)
  - Can bacteria get through loo paper?
  - Which loo paper gives the best protection against bacterial contamination of the hands?
  - What are live yoghurts?

- ◆ Ideas for information seeking and presentation activities using written sources or the internet can involve the role of these scientists in the study of microbes:

  - Louis Pasteur
  - Alexander Fleming
  - Joseph Lister
  - Edward Jenner.

There are no women in this list but you might like to explore the role that Pasteur's wife played in his research and the observations of Lady Mary Wortley Montagu on inoculation against smallpox.

♦ *Enhancement ideas*

This is a list of further issues and questions that pupils can be invited to research, possibly as a homework activity using library resources, e.g. the internet.

- ♦ Very few organisms other than microbes can digest cellulose. For this reason most animals feeding on plants are dependent on microbes for digestion.
- ♦ Many herbivores have special gut structures where microbes live, e.g. cows with four stomachs, rabbits with a caecum.
- ♦ Rabbits refaecate; they eat their own faeces. Because the caecum, where the bacteria are, is near the end of the gut, few of the digested nutrients are absorbed into the blood during the first passage of food through the gut. Rabbits produce soft green faeces, usually at night. They eat these and during the second passage of food through the gut absorption is more effective and the familiar dry, roundish faecal pellets are produced.
- ♦ Where do young herbivores get their gut flora from?
- ♦ Antibiotics destroy gut flora as well as the disease-causing microbes. Why do some people become constipated when taking antibiotics?
- ♦ Why don't doctors prescribe antibiotics for a viral infection?
- ♦ Body odours are caused by microbes breeding in the sweat. What is the difference between an anti-perspirant and a deodorant?
- ♦ Why do cows produce pats? Is it because digestion of the cellulose is so effective that there is no fibre to hold the faeces together?
- ♦ Why is horse dung so full of fibre? Is it because it is not very efficient at digesting cellulose. If so, why?

Figure 10.6
Why use microbes? (After an original idea by Debbie Niblock.)

Do you know that microbes:

breed more rapidly than rabbits?

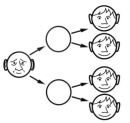

can be killed off without emotional outcry?

do not need to be fed and watered at weekends?

But...
can be harmful, therefore treat with care!

◆ *Equipment notes*

Early planning/advance organisation

Two months before work with microbes you should order safe species from reputable suppliers (see DfEE, 1996). Three weeks before work liaise with technicians. Plates and media can be made up and kept in the fridge, but problems with condensation may result. Unlike some biology topics, work with microbes can be done at any time of the year.

Autoclave/pressure cooker

This is an essential item both for sterilising agars, broth and any other recyclable equipment and for destroying cultures before disposal. Roasting bags are a cheap means of containing plates/cultures during autoclaving and for later disposal with refuse. Autoclaving at 100 kN m^{-2} (or 15 lb/square inch) for 15 minutes destroys all microbes and spores.

Inoculation chamber

It is not essential to have an inoculation chamber for most microbiology work in school – working in an area close to a Bunsen burner on a non-luminous flame that creates an updraft is adequate. However, transfer chambers are not prohibitively expensive and can be used for a range of other activities such as tissue culturing.

Other resources

♦ *Useful addresses*

Association for Science Education, College Lane, Hatfield, Hertfordshire AL10 9AA.

CLEAPSS, School Science Service, Brunel University, Uxbridge UB8 3PH.

National Centre for School Biotechnology, Department of Microbiology, University of Reading, Reading RG6 2AJ.

The Institute of Biology, 20 Queensbury Place, London SW7 2DZ.

♦ *Background reading*

Association for Science Education (1988). Biotechnology. *Education in Science*, **126**, pp. 12–16.

Department of Education and Science (1993). *Microbiology: An HMI Guide for Schools and Further Education* (2nd impression). London, HMSO.

Department for Education (1990). *Animals and Plants in Schools: Legal Aspects*. AM 3/90.

Dunkerton, J. & Lock, R. (1989). *Biotechnology: A Resource Book for Teachers*. Hatfield, Association for Science Education.

Henderson, J. & Knutton, S. (1990). *Biotechnology in Schools: A Handbook for Teachers*. Buckinghamshire, Open University Press. This book is a rich source of reference to other sources.

Katz, J. & Satelle, D.B. (1988). *Biotechnology in Focus*. Cambridge, Hobsons Scientific.

Lock, R. (1993). Use of Living Organisms. In Hull, R. (ed.) *ASE Secondary Science Teachers' Handbook*, pp. 179–205. London, Simon and Schuster.

Olejnikowna, I. (1986). *Biotechnology: Resources for Secondary and Tertiary Education*. Hatfield, Association for Science Education.

Smith, J.R. (1987). *The Speckled Monster: Smallpox in England, 1670–1970, with Particular Reference to Essex*. Chelmsford, Essex Record Office.

Tomkins, S., Reiss, M. & Morris, C. (1992). *Biology at Work*. Cambridge, Cambridge University Press.

Walgate, R. (1990). *Miracle or Menace? Biotechnology and the Third World*. London, The Panos Institute.

Wymer, P. (1987). *Practical Microbiology and Biotechnology for Schools*. London, Macdonald Educational.

References

DfEE (1996). *Safety in Science Education*. London, HMSO.

Health Education Authority (1993). *Enjoy Healthy Eating*. London, Health Education Authority.

Kjeldsen, T. & Andersen, A.S. (1997). 'Insulin from yeast'. *Biological Sciences Review*, **10** (2), pp. 30–32.

Lock, R. (1996). Educating the 'New Pasteur'. *School Science Review*, **78** (283), pp. 63–72.

Lyth, M. (1987). *Nuffield Science 11–13: Worksheet Pack*. Harlow, Longman.

Monger, G. (ed.) (1992). *Nuffield Co-ordinated Sciences: Biology*. London, Longman Group for Nuffield-Chelsea Curriculum Trust.

National Centre for Biotechnology Education (1993). *Practical Biotechnology: A Guide for Schools and Colleges*. Reading, National Centre for Biotechnology Education.

Reiss, M. & Straughan, R. (1996). *Improving Nature? The Science and Genetics of Genetic Engineering*. Cambridge, Cambridge University Press.

Revised Nuffield Biology (1994). *Text 1: Introducing Living Things*. London, Longman.

Satelle, D.B. (1988). *Biotechnology in Perspective*. Cambridge, Hobsons Ltd.

Appendix

A book of this sort cannot contain everything. Many readers will want to use it in conjunction with one or more good pupil texts. We also particularly recommend the following books and organisations.

◆ *Books*

Association for Science Education (1996). *Safeguards in the School Laboratory* (10th edition). Hatfield, Association for Science Education.

Brown, C.R. (1995). *The Effective Teaching of Biology*. London, Longman.

Department for Education and Employment (1996). *Safety in Science Education*. London, Department for Education and Employment.

National Association of Field Studies Officers (1998). *Field Studies Centres: A Code of Practice – Quality, Safety and Sustainability*. Peterborough, National Association of Field Studies Officers.

Ratcliffe, M. (ed.) (1998). *ASE Guide to Secondary Science Education*. Hatfield, Association for Science Education and Cheltenham, Stanley Thornes.

Reiss, M. (ed.) (1996). *Living Biology in Schools*. London, Institute of Biology.

◆ *Organisations*

Association for Science Education, College Lane, Hatfield AL10 9AA (tel: 01707 267411).

CLEAPSS, School Science Service, Brunel University, Uxbridge UB8 3PH (tel: 01895 251496).

Institute of Biology, 20 Queensberry Place, London SW7 2DZ (tel: 0171 581 8333).

Index

INDEX